China's Administrative Divisions

DYNASTIES IN CHINESE HISTORY

Start date	Period
2700 BC	Five Kings
2100	Xia
1600	Shang
1100	Zhou
770	Spring & Autumn
476	Warring States
221	Qin
206 BC	Han
220 AD	Three Kingdoms
265	Jin
420	Northern & Southern
581	Sui
618	Tang
907	Five Dynasties
960	Song
1279	Yuan
1368	Ming
1644	Qing
1911	Republic of China
1949	People's Republic of China

A TREASURY OF CHINA'S WISDOM
—A STORY BOOK FOR EVERYONE

CHINGHUA TANG

FOREIGN LANGUAGES PRESS BEIJING

First Edition 1996

Illustrations by
Dai Dunbang, Chen Huiguan, Ding Cong, Lan Renjie, Gao Yonghui

Hardcover: ISBN 7-119-01860-4
Paperback: ISBN 7-119-01861-2

Published by Foreign Languages Press
24 Baiwanzhuang Road, Beijing 100037, China

Distributed by China International Book Trading Corporation
35 Chegongzhuang Xilu, Beijing 100044, China
P.O. Box 399, Beijing, China

Printed in the People's Republic of China

DEDICATED

to my dear mother and father,
Ge Huiming and Tang Chingan,
and
to my dear aunt and uncle,
Yuan Shiyun and Yang Renjin,
of Shanghai, China,
and
to the loving memory of
my grandfather and grandmother on my father's side,
Tang Heng (1887-1977) and Kang Jingtao (1893-1970),
and
my grandfather and grandmother on my mother's side,
Ge Liting (1899-1981) and Gu Jingren (1903-1978),
and
Professor Zhou Zanwu (1905-1992)
of East China Teachers University

CONTENTS

INTRODUCTION

Upon learning that his mentor, Chang Tsung, was seriously ill, Lao Tzu went to see him. It was obvious that Chang Tsung was approaching the end of his days.

"Master, do you have any last words of wisdom for me?" said Lao Tzu to his mentor.

"Even if you didn't ask, I would have to tell you something," replied Chang Tsung.

"What is it?"

"You should get down from your carriage when you pass through your hometown."

"Yes, Master. This means one should not forget one's origin."

"When you see a tall tree, you should go forward and look up to it."

"Yes, Master. This tells me that I should respect the elderly."

"Now, look and tell me if you can see my tongue," said Chang Tsung, dropping his chin in an obvious effort.

"Yes."

"Do you see my teeth?"

"No. There're none left."

"Do you know why?" Chang Tsung asked.

"I think," said Lao Tzu after a little pause, "the tongue is preserved because it is soft. The teeth fall out because they are hard. Is that so?"

"Yes, my son," Chang Tsung nodded. "That is all the wisdom in the world. I have nothing else to teach you."

Later Lao Tzu remarked: "Nothing in the world is as soft as water. Yet nothing is superior to it in overcoming the hard. The soft overcomes the hard, and the gentle overcomes the powerful. Everybody knows it, but few can put it into practice."

When I graduated from high school in 1968, the notorious "cultural revolution" was in full swing, a so-called revolution which Mao Zedong had started and which the Chinese government later denounced as a catastrophe.

Schools and colleges were closed. Millions of homes were ransacked by the Red Guards. Vast numbers of innocent people were interrogated, imprisoned, tortured or killed. Unable to endure these horrors, many committed suicide.

I was utterly disillusioned. I felt that I had seen the game. I found myself living in an alien and hostile environment in which almost everything was turned upside down. My first instinct was to protect myself and survive.

Mao soon claimed that all the education the young people had received in the past was bourgeois and students needed to be re-educated through hard labor. He decreed that all high school graduates go to the countryside to work as farmhands. I was fully aware what kind of life would be in store for me if re-education was to be my lot. I would be tilling the field from dawn to dusk with primitive tools, carrying loads of manure on my shoulder, living in crowded dormitories without running water and electricity, and having to attend, after a hard day in the field, endless indoctrination sessions on Maoism. I would work without pay except for a meager ration of rice. It would be worse than unemployment. But, worst of all, I would be deprived of my books.

The scenario was clear to me, and I resolved to adamantly resist any attempt to make me go to the countryside, notwithstanding the fact that most of my fellow students had resigned themselves to their fate.

I remained in Shanghai. The local authorities first exerted pressure on my parents as both of them were teachers, teachers being the most vulnerable target of Mao's "cultural revolution." My parents told them that although they supported me to go to the countryside, the decision had to be my own since I was already seventeen years old.

The heat was then turned on me. A team of three party functionaries was dispatched to my home.

They would call on me, at intervals of four or five days, and each time spend two or three hours haranguing me with lectures and urging me to follow Mao's dictate and settle in the countryside. On my part, I would politely ask them to sit down and offer them each a cup of tea. Then I would maintain my silence throughout. I was never provocative, though.

I knew they could not physically move me to the countryside. As long as I was not provocative, it would be difficult for them to find fault with me and thus have an excuse to force me to obey. Their visits invariably met with my passive defiance but I was meticulously polite at the same time. This ritual was repeated for more than a month.

Finally their patience gave way. The head of the team explained to me that they realized they had failed in their task and that they were calling it quits. In a matter-of-fact tone, he said that they needed something to report back to their superior.

For the first time I took him seriously. I asked him what it was that he needed. "A doctor's statement," he said, "to the effect that you are not fit for farm labor."

"What health conditions would be considered acceptable?" I was interested.

"Heart trouble, high blood pressure, and kidney problems are the most common examples," was the reply.

At that point I made him promise never to come to bother me again if I gave him what he wanted.

Three days later, I gave him a signed statement from the local hospital certifying that I had high blood pressure. After that he kept his word and left me alone.

With that nuisance off my back, I began my self-education regime. Besides English, mathematics and the sciences, I studied Confucius' *Analects* and other Chinese classics under the knowing eye of my grandfather, a classical scholar. I read as many books as I could lay my hands on.

In the dark absurdity and hysterical insanity of the "cultural revolution," books became my best friends. The knowledge and wisdom I gained from them inspired me, above all else, with hope.

This volume contains gleanings from years of reading Chinese classics ranging from the *Intrigues of the Warring States* to the *Tales of the Song Dynasty*, from the *Chronicles of Three Kingdoms* to the *History of the Ming Empire*, traversing the vast panoply of China's history. In my daily life, the practical value of the wisdom embedded in those classics often comes back to me as fresh and relevant as I first discovered it. I wish to share the delight and inspiration with my readers.

Together let's embark on a journey to explore, discover and rediscover the untold treasures of the wisdom of China. Wisdom is not one-dimensional or singly focused; wisdom is rich in variety and kaleidoscopic in manifestation. Just as it is impossible to cover every great place in America on one trip, so it is impossible to examine all the treasures of wisdom in Chinese history in a single volume. But, in the following pages, I will call your attention to the gems in the treasure trove and will share with you my thoughts as well as give you some background information as we go along.

PART I
WISDOM IN ACTION

1. JADE SCULPTURE

Pure is he who does not seek power and wealth. Purer is he who is associated with power and wealth but uncorrupted. High is he who does not know how to play tricks. Higher is he who understands tricks but refuses to use them.

—Vegetable Roots (16th Century)

Wisdom is hard to define, for it manifests itself in many ways. To some people, it means a sound philosophy of living. To others, it means effective management of a difficult situation. In any case, I believe wisdom is not an abstract idea, but an applied science that can be studied within a real life context. And the best way to see it is to see it in action.

The following are ten famous stories, each, in its own way, contributing to our understanding of what we call worldly wisdom.

One day there came to Hongren Pawnshop in the city of Shaoxing a customer who wanted to pawn a jade sculpture, an exquisite piece of work to all appearances. The customer said that it was a precious relic of the Han Dynasty, some 2,000 years ago, and that he had inherited it from his father and his father from his father and so on and so forth. He asked for 1,000 ounces of silver. The pawnbroker being out of town, the shop assistant accepted the deal and gave him the amount he had asked for.

When the pawnbroker returned, he examined the piece carefully only to find that it was not an antique but an imitation worth no more than 100 ounces of silver. He got so exasperated that he wanted the shop assistant to compensate for the loss if the owner did not come back to redeem the phony piece of jade sculpture.

Grief overwhelmed the shop clerk for he was a poor man. Not knowing what to do, he went to see a friend named Xu Wenchang who was well-known for his wisdom and resourcefulness. After giving the matter some thought, Xu began to help his friend draw up a plan for immediate action.

A few days later, the pawnbroker sent out invitations to all his friends and relatives to a party in his house. The invitation read:

"The undersigned humbly seeks the pleasure of your company to a party at his residence to share the joy with him of viewing a rare piece of jade sculpture of the Han Dynasty that happens to be in his temporary possession."

Guests came in a stream and food and drinks were served. Halfway through the party, the host announced that he was very pleased that they could come because the jadework had been authenticated as a rare relic of the Han Dynasty. As the owner would come to redeem it pretty soon, he wanted to take the opportunity of showing it round to them before it got back to the hands of its owner. Then he went inside to fetch the treasure.

Minutes later he came out with the jade sculpture. The guests held their breath in silent expectancy. Holding the sculpture in both hands, he passed through the crowd slowly until at last when he was just about to put the sculpture on the table in the middle of the hall, he suddenly tripped and fell. The sculpture slipped out of his hand, fell to the ground and was broken into pieces.

"Oh!" all those present were aghast at the disaster. The pawnbroker was dumbstruck and turned very pale. He wanted his servants to take him to his bed for he felt very sick. The guests were obliged to leave the house, disappointed and very sorry for their host. The next day what happened at the party became the talk of the town.

A few days later, the man who pawned the jade sculpture came to Hongren Pawnshop. Putting 1,000 ounces of silver on the counter, he said that he would like to have the sculpture back. The shop assistant counted the silver without a word, went in and came out again with the jade sculpture. The man was flabbergasted. He gazed at it for a while, speechless. No mistake. It was his phony jade sculpture, intact, unbroken. His face fell, but he had to take back his pawn.

He did not know that the broken sculpture was a fake, too. But it was a fake of his original fake. It was Xu Wenchang's idea that the pawnbroker held a party to show the sculpture and had it deliberately broken in front of many guests who would certainly spread the news. As the news reached the trickster, he immediately came to the pawnshop to redeem the piece, thinking that not only could he keep the 1,000 ounces of silver, but also bluff the pawnbroker into giving him more money as compensation for the supposed Han jade.

Comment: Thus the trickster was paid back literally in his own coin. Incidentally, Xu Wenchang was a well-known playwright, essayist, artist and man of letters in the sixteenth century during the Ming Dynasty.

2. THE MISSING SEAL

> When a wealthy man acts meanly, he acts poorly and cannot enjoy his wealth for long. When a smart man seeks to show off, he shows off his folly and will fail sooner or later.
> —*Vegetable Roots*

A corrupt mayor ruled in a county near present-day Shanghai in the mid-sixteenth century during the Ming Dynasty. He was very much upset when word came that an imperial emissary was on an inspection tour to the county.

Not far from Shanghai, in the city of Suzhou, there was a well-known thief. It was said that he could scale walls without a noise as though he were walking on the ground. In fighting, he looked calm and relaxed but attacked with lightning speed. He was also a generous man.

Why not solicit the assistance of that famous thief? The mayor thought.

So the mayor dispatched a messenger to Suzhou with costly gifts for the thief. The thief was flattered and immediately set out for the county to see the mayor.

"Thank you very much for the nice gifts, Your Honor," he said. "What can I do for you?"

"I want to have a private word with you," said the mayor after having dismissed all others from his office.

"The imperial inspector has arrived at this county," the mayor continued. "I have a hunch that he is going to make trouble for me. I want you to go to his yamen and get his official seal for me. Without the seal, he cannot carry out his official mission and he will lose his job at that. I'll give you 100 ounces of gold for your work."

"No problem, Your Honor. I'll get it for you in no time."

Later in the night he returned with the seal and the mayor was elated.

"You've done a wonderful job," the mayor said, giving the thief the gold as he had promised. "Now there is no point for you to hang around here. You'd better leave as soon as possible."

"Your Honor, you are generous with me. I'd like to offer you a word of advice before I leave?"

"What is it?" asked the mayor.

"When I was hidden on top of the beam in his office," said the thief, "I could not help noticing the way His Lordship worked, going through the documents quickly and writing down his instructions without a break. It seems to me that you are up against an extremely capable and sharp-witted man. A man of that calibre is not to be fooled. I think it would be the best for you if you hand back the seal tomorrow. Just tell him that it was found by your night patrols but the thief had run off. Even if the inspector smelled a rat, he would think twice before picking on you."

"It doesn't make sense to return the seal," said the mayor. "The seal means authority. With his seal in hand, he'd be able to do whatever he likes with me. You'd better go home and leave me alone."

The next day the imperial inspector discovered that his seal was missing. He ordered an immediate search, but to no avail. "The mayor must have something to do with the theft, knowing I am not his friend," the inspector said to himself. "This is his territory, and it is easy for him to place spies around me. But I'll get him just the same."

He locked the seal box and put it back, and bade his subordinates not to breathe a word about the theft. Then he said he was ill. For the next few days, he did not go to work.

The mayor was laughing up his sleeve. But, just like other local officials, he had to pay a visit to the imperial inspector as a matter of protocol.

When the mayor called upon him, the inspector seemed in good mood. They talked over a cup of tea about administrative matters, local customs, taxes and budget and what not. The mayor started to feel a bit embarrassed seeing the inspector totally unsuspecting and hospitable. Just as they were chatting, a servant rushed in.

"Fire, fire! Your Honor, the kitchen is on fire."

The inspector's face changed color. He jumped up from the couch. Grabbing the seal box, he handed it to the mayor. "We have to get out. Take care of this for me. Please get more help to put out the fire."

Caught off his guard, the mayor could not refuse. He had to leave the yamen with the seal box. When the fire was extinguished, the kitchen was damaged, but the main office of the yamen was safe. Now the mayor came to realize that the imperial inspector had given him the empty box deliberately. If he should return it as it was, the imperial inspector would certainly open the empty box in order to incriminate him. What excuse could he give? Finally he decided to put the seal back into the box.

The next morning the imperial inspector came back to work. The mayor handed back the seal box. The inspector opened the box in the presence of all the officials and affixed the seal on the documents he had left unsigned. He left the county that same day, then called on the governor of the province and made a full report about the theft. Shortly afterwards the mayor was removed from office.

Comment: Obviously the mayor did not know that sometimes a veiled threat is more effective because, among other things, it leaves others to imagine how much more you are capable of doing.

3. I AM COMING

> Do not make promises lightly when you are happy. Do not act on impulse. And never leave your goal one step short of completion when you are tired.
>
> —*Vegetable Roots*

In the Song Dynasty about a thousand years ago, there was a famous thief in Hangzhou by the nickname of I-am-coming. Each time he committed a theft, he left no trace whatsoever except for his nickname on the wall.

The residents of the city were upset because their houses were often broken into. An all-out search was launched and finally the man was caught and brought before the municipal magistrate.

"Do you have any proof to convict him?" the magistrate asked the police officer.

"There is no mistake," the officer replied.

But the man denied the charge vehemently.

"Your Honor, you have the wrong man," he protested. "The police were so desperate that they made me the scapegoat. They have no proof."

"We went through a lot of trouble getting hold of him, Your Honor. If you let go of him this time, it'll be difficult to catch him again." So the police warned the magistrate.

Although there was no evidence against the man, the magistrate ordered him to be taken into temporary custody pending further investigation.

Upon entering the jail a prisoner had to give some money to the prison guard, as was the custom then.

"I have nothing with me now," said the man to the prison guard. "They have searched me and taken away all my belongings. But I have some silver in the temple of the Mountain God. I'd like to give that to you. I hid it under a broken brick inside the shrine. Go there, pretend that you are praying and then just grab it."

The prison guard was not sure the man was telling the truth. Nevertheless, he went over, and found twenty ounces of silver. He was pleased and began to treat the man like a friend.

A few days later, the man said to the guard: "Thank you for being nice to me. I have another package hidden under the bridge. I'd like to give it to you, too."

"But the bridge is a busy place, how can I take anything without being noticed?"

"Take some clothes there. Pretend you are washing them and then just take the package and put it in your laundry basket."

The prison guard did what the man suggested and found three hundred ounces of silver in the package. He was grateful and bought some wine back to the prison for a drink with the man.

"I want to ask you a favor," the man said. "I would like to go home tonight. I'll come back before daybreak."

Seeing the guard was concerned, he said again: "Don't worry, my friend. Why should I try to escape? The police have arrested the wrong man and the magistrate cannot convict me. There is no evidence. I am sure I will be released soon. You have my word: I'll be back in four hours."

The guard thought: "Even if he does not come back, the case would not be too serious, since he is not convicted. And I can use some of the money he gave me to hush things up if the worst comes to the worst." So he obliged him.

Instead of going out through the door, the man jumped onto the roof and disappeared without making the slightest noise.

The prison guard was having a snooze when the man came back. He shook the guard awake.

"I'm back."

"Good! You do keep your words."

"I don't want you to get into trouble for me. Thank you for letting me out. I've left something in your house as a token of appreciation. I expect to be released soon."

The guard did not quite understand. He hurried back home.

"You're home at the right moment," said his wife excitedly. "I want to tell you that early this morning I heard a noise on the roof. Somebody dropped a packet into the house. When I opened it, I found it contains gold and silver. Heaven is shedding His blessings on us!"

"Hush!" the guard said. "Put them away. Don't say anything about it. We'll sell them later."

He went back to the prison, thanking the man profusely.

That day half a dozen households reported burglary the previous night. On the walls of each house there was the familiar word: "I-am-coming."

When the magistrate heard of this, he ordered the man to be released. Obviously the culprit was still at large.

Only the prison guard knew what really had happened but he kept his mouth shut.

Comment: No alibi could be more perfect.

4. RANSOM PRICE

Try to understand the original intention of a person whose endeavor meets with failure. Wait to see how a successful person winds off in the end.

—*Vegetable Roots*

Fan Li was a fabulously rich man about 2,500 years ago.

He had served as the commander-in-chief in the army of the state of Yue which was located on the east coast of China. At one time, the king of Yue, having been defeated by its neighbor, the state of Wu, had been held captive and forced to work as a slave in the stable of the king of Wu for three years. After he was released, the king of Yue spared no pains, for the next twenty years, to rebuild his country into a strong power. Finally he wiped out Wu and forced its king to commit suicide. So he had avenged himself for the humiliation he had borne. It was Fan Li who had played a vital role in making all this possible.

When his meritorious service was highly extolled by the king, Fan Li asked to be relieved from office, knowing that the king of Yue was the kind of person to share hardship with but not the fruits of victory, a good friend in adversity but not a good companion in times of peace and happiness.

With the handsome reward he got from the king, Fan moved to the state of Qi. There he successfully managed a farming estate and became a millionaire. He had three sons. One day his second son was arrested on a charge of murder in the state of Chu.

"If my son is convicted of murder," said Fan Li to his family, "he will be sentenced to death. But the son of a millionaire need not die on the execution ground." He gave his youngest son 20,000 ounces of gold and told him to go to Chu to see if he could get his brother out of jail.

"As the eldest son, I am supposed to go," protested his eldest son. "But you are sending my younger brother on my behalf. I feel ashamed that you won't let me do my duty. I must be an unworthy son of yours." And he threatened to kill himself.

Fan's wife intervened, "If you send the youngest one, he may or may not be useful. But we are going to lose the eldest son, too. What good will that be?"

Fan gave in and agreed to send his eldest son. He wrote a letter to a friend of his in Chu whose name was Zhuang.

"Give the letter and the 20,000 ounces of gold to Mr. Zhuang," he said to his son. "Let him do whatever he likes with the money and never argue with him."

His son departed, bringing some more gold of his own with him.

Mr. Zhuang's home was a very modest one. He read the letter and accepted the money.

"Please go home straight away," said Mr. Zhuang to the young man. "Please leave the matter to me."

But Fan's eldest son decided to stay in the city. He called on a senior government minister on his own initiative and gave him the gold he brought along with him.

Mr. Zhuang had an impeccable reputation in the country as a man of integrity. The king held him in high esteem. Zhuang had no intention to keep the gold and meant to return it to Fan Li as soon as he had rescued Fan's second son.

He went to see the King of Chu and told him that astrological signs pointed to an impending disaster.

"What can we do about it?" the king asked.

"An act of clemency may avert the danger," Zhuang proposed.

"Very well," said the king. Then he ordered the treasury be sealed up.

When the senior government minister got the news, he told Fan Li's eldest son that there would soon be an amnesty.

"How do you know?"

"Before an amnesty is granted," the minister explained, "the king always seals up the treasury for fear that robbers may take advantage of it, and he ordered to have the treasury sealed up yesterday."

The eldest son was delighted that his younger brother would be released soon. Thinking that there was no point to have given so much gold to Mr. Zhuang, he called on him again.

Mr. Zhuang was surprised to see him. "You're still here? I thought you've left for home."

"Yes, I am still here. I will go home with my brother now that there would be an amnesty. I am here to say good-bye to you."

Mr. Zhuang took the hint. "Come in and take the gold back," he said. The eldest son was only too glad to do so.

Mr. Zhuang was upset. He felt he had been tricked by the young man. He went back to the king.

"Your Majesty decided upon an amnesty after our conversation last time. But now it is the talk of the town that the son of a wealthy man, Fan Li, was convicted of murder and his family bribed your ministers. They say the amnesty was granted only to spare the life of a rich man's son, and not a gesture of clemency."

"What absurdity!" the king was upset. "The amnesty is not for the son of a wealthy man, you know that." In his anger, he ordered the immediate execution of Fan Li's second son and declared amnesty the following day.

The eldest son had to return home with the corpse of his brother. The whole family cried their eyes out, but the father kept his poise.

"I knew it all along," said Fan Li, "that things would come to this. Not that my eldest son does not love his brother, but he just could not help himself. He is close-fisted because when he was young, he went through a lot of hardship with me in building up the family fortune. My youngest son has lived a much easier life. When he was yet a child, he rode in luxurious carriages and went hunting rabbits on fine horses. He is a man of extravagant habits because he does not understand where money comes from. That was just why I wanted to send him to Chu for he could be generous with money. This is something my eldest son is not capable of. However, in the scheme of things, he ended up killing his brother."

Comment: Fan Li understood his eldest son well and anticipated what was going to happen. If he really wanted to rescue his second son, why, then, did he not go there himself? Why did he fail to communicate the weakness of his eldest son to his friend? For all his wisdom, he seemed to have failed his own son and his friend. This is very puzzling.

5. WOMAN IN BLACK

A great plan can be ruined by the lack of just a small measure of patience.

—*Confucius (551-479 B.C.)*

Mr. Zhu, a district magistrate in Jiangsu Province during the Qing Dynasty, was commissioned to transport a large amount of cash to the national capital, Beijing. The journey would take several days, and he had to make a number of stops on the way. One of the stops was in the suburbs of Linqing, in northwestern Shandong, reportedly an area to be infested with bandits.

The moment he arrived at an inn, which was the only inn in town, a few young women came up, eager to entertain him by singing. They were actually hookers. It was the practice in the north for the prostitutes to sing for potential clients in lieu of direct solicitation. After singing, if the guest would like to spend the night with any one of them, all he had to do was to ask her to bring a comforter to his room. The price they charged was only half of that in the south, but those hookers were often associated with local bandits. They would inform the bandits if they found their clients to be rich men.

Mr. Zhu had travelled a lot. He had heard about Linqing being a tough area in which to travel. He noted that these young hookers did not act haphazardly. They seemed to take cues from a girl in a black dress as to whether they should sing or dance or approach him directly. While other hookers wore heavy make-up and were dressed seductively, this girl did not use any cosmetics. But still she looked attractive. She was about twenty. Zhu figured that she must be the ringleader. The circumstances smelled trouble to him. The remote location of the inn made it virtually impossible for him to escape or get help.

Mr. Zhu decided to confront the girl directly. He had to take a chance. And that might be the only chance to avert imminent danger.

He dismissed the other girls and made it clear that he wanted to be quite alone with the woman in black. She seemed agreeable to his suggestion and accepted his invitation to dinner. Zhu began to tell her that he came from a poor family and got where he was through hard work. She said that her parents were too poor to support her so that she got into such a miserable profession to make a living.

Zhu listened with sympathy and then began to tell her stories of how some famous courtesans of ancient times became patriotic heroines and how they got married to distinguished scholars. Zhu expressed his admiration for those women. Zhu's words seemed to have struck her. The girl was visibly moved.

The conversation then turned to his mission. Zhu decided to be candid with her and told her that he was in charge of tens of thousands of ounces of silver to be transported to Beijing.

As they were chatting, a heavy snow began to fall, turning the land into a vast expanse of glistening white under the pale moonlight. The fire in the stove was low, the oil in the lamp was running out, and the room turned very cold. Seeing the girl was shivering with cold in her thin black dress, Zhu took out a fur coat from his luggage and wrapped it around her shoulders. They chatted on like close friends. But Zhu never touched the girl.

The first streaks of dawn were gleaming in the east before they knew it. As a rule, the prostitutes were supposed to clear out by daybreak. The girl rose to her feet, took off the fur coat, and was ready to go.

"Take it with you," he said, handing her the fur coat. "It's cold outside. You need it." He also put four ounces of silver in her hand.

"Thank you for your generosity. You should not pay me. I haven't done anything for you. Neither can I accept the fur coat."

"Please take the coat. I give you this out of my admiration and respect for you. You are no common woman. I have enjoyed your company."

She thanked him again and left. Zhu was still uneasy. About fifteen minutes later there was a knock on the door. It was the woman in black again.

"I must tell you the truth," she said in real earnest. "I am a robber and my father is the head of the local bandits. I act as his bait to ensnare travellers. But I am still a virgin. I do not let anyone touch me. If anyone tries to force me, I'll kill him with my knife. I do appreciate your kind interest in me. When I get home, I'll have somebody bring the coat back to you, together with something which will prove useful to you. Take it and get on your journey before the road becomes too slippery when the snow starts to thaw."

Zhu bowed to her, feeling very much relieved.

An hour later, a messenger came with the fur coat and a small parcel for Zhu.

"This is from our mistress," the man said. "It will come in handy in case of trouble on your journey. Now listen. Keep this until you have arrived at Yangliuqing and then give it to a man from the local security office who will approach you to ask for it."

Zhu wanted to tip the man, but he refused, saying that his mistress told him not to accept a penny.

Zhu was astonished by what he found in the parcel. It was a triangular flag.

Now he was ready to continue his journey, but the driver of the carriage he wanted to hire refused to set out, saying that the road was not safe. To the surprise of the driver, Zhu produced the flag and placed it on the carriage window.

"Where did you get this?!" the driver exclaimed. "Come on in! Let's get going. We are safe now."

After ten miles or so, they found themselves confronting a gang of more than twenty armed horsemen. They surrounded his carriage, examined the flag carefully and then just turned back without making any trouble. Similar encounters were repeated a number of times during the next few days until they reached Yangliuqing, which is about sixty miles from Beijing.

A man from the security office came to meet them and invited Zhu to a very good dinner. Late that night, he came to Zhu's room and asked Zhu how he managed to get that flag. Zhu told him about the woman in black.

"This is a most precious gift. She must like you a lot. Now you are in Yangliuqing which marks the boundary of their activities. You have no need for it any more."

Zhu gave the flag back, thanked the man and left the place the following day.

Comment: Mr. Zhu managed the crisis well. He was able to diffuse a dangerous situation by confronting the source of danger with tact and presence of mind. If he had panicked, he would probably have had no chance at all. In a critical situation, there is no margin for error.

6. THE BABIES' CHAPEL

Fortune cannot be had by willing it. But being happy breeds fortune. Misfortune cannot be avoided. But eliminating evil thoughts keeps disasters away.

—*Vegetable Roots*

The following story took place in the Ming Dynasty.

Located in Nanning, a city in southern China, was the Temple of Lotus, a monastery with a long history. It had several thousand acres of land and substantial real estate property. There were about a hundred monks residing in the temple. Visitors were usually given a guided tour and treated in a most hospitable fashion.

What made this monastery well-known and prosperous was its Babies' Chapel. A woman who wanted a child would get pregnant if she spent a night there praying.

The Temple of Lotus required that women who came to pray be young and healthy. They should fast for seven days at home before coming to the temple. In the temple, each would first consult a divining rod. If the oracle was favorable, the woman would pass a night in one of the rooms in the Babies' Chapel to pray in solitude. If the divining rod gave an unfavorable reply, the monks would ask the woman to pray very, very sincerely and then go home to begin the seven day fasting anew.

The rooms of the Babies' Chapel had no windows. When a woman entered there for the night, the monks insisted that one of her family members spend the night outside the door. Most women became pregnant after praying and had healthy babies born to them.

Many families in that area sent women to pray in the Babies' Chapel. Women from other places were attracted to the temple, too.

Every day there was a crowd of worshippers in the monastery. Offerings of every kind were poured in. When the women were asked how Buddha made her prayers work in the night, some said that Buddha told them in a dream that they would be expecting, others blushed and

refused to say anything. Some women never came a second time; others went there frequently.

The news reached a new governor of the city, Wang Dan.

"Why did the women have to spend a night in the temple?" The new governor was curious.

He went there to see for himself. The brightly decorated monastery was surrounded by tall pine trees and looked rather imposing. It was quite a busy place. There were a lot of comings and goings there.

As a monk saw the governor, he sounded the drums and bells to summon all the monks. Led by the chief monk, a procession was quickly formed to welcome the governor. Like other pilgrims, Governor Wang burned some incense and prayed before the statue of Buddha.

"I've heard the reputation of this Holy Temple," said the governor to the chief monk. "I intend to recommend you to the Emperor to put you in charge of all the temples and monks in the district."

The chief monk was delighted.

"I heard your Babies' Chapel performs miracles. How does it work?"

The chief monk replied that the women were required to fast for seven days and if they were truly sincere, their prayers would be granted in a dream during the night they spent in the Babies' Chapel.

Governor Wang asked if the Babies' Chapel was guarded at night time. The monks explained that there was no other entrance except the door to the prayer room. A family member of the woman was invariably asked to stay overnight outside the room.

"If so," said the governor, "I want to send my wife here."

"If Your Honor wishes for a child," said the chief monk, "it's not necessary for Her Ladyship to come here. She can pray at home. I'm sure her prayers will be granted."

"But why do other women have to come here?"

"When a noble man like a governor comes here to worship, I'm sure Buddha will appreciate and pay special attention to his prayers."

"Thank you," said the governor. "I would like to take a tour in the miracle chapel, please."

The hall was packed with visitors who were praying before the statue of Buddhisttava, the Goddess of Mercy, with one baby in her arms and four babies around her feet. Countless candles were lit and the hall was filled with the smoke of incense.

Governor Wang bowed to the Goddess of Mercy. Then he visited the prayers' rooms. All the rooms were carpeted. The beds, the tables and the chairs were all spotlessly clean. The only entrance to each room was the door. As there were no cracks in the walls, not even a rat could slip into the room.

But Governor Wang was still puzzled by the miraculous power of the Babies' Chapel. He wanted to solve the mystery. When he came back, he told his secretary to get him two prostitutes.

"Ask them to dress like housewives. You will hire them and send them to spend the night at the Temple of Lotus. Give one of them a bottle of black ink and the other a bottle of red ink. If anyone approaches them at night, tell them to mark his head with the ink."

His secretary found two whores, Zhang Mei and Li Wan. The secretary and another man from the governor's office posed as their husbands to take them to the monastery.

Besides these two, there were a dozen other women that day to spend the night in the temple. At eight o'clock, all the rooms were locked, and the family members of all the women took up their positions outside the doors. The monks retreated to their own quarters.

Zhang Mei took off her clothes, turned off the light and lay in the bed.

The bell rang at 10 o'clock. Silence reigned in the temple. Suddenly Zhang Mei heard some noise from under the floor. Then she saw a plank of the floor move to one side, and a shaven head emerged from under it. It was a monk's head.

She did not move. The monk tiptoed to her bedside, took off his robe and slid into bed next to her. Zhang Mei pretended to be asleep. She felt his hands reaching her legs.

"Who are you?" she asked, trying to push him away. "This is the holy chapel."

But the monk held her tightly in his arms. "I am sent by Buddha to give you a child," he whispered to her ears.

He started to have sex with her. Zhang Mei was experienced, but she felt this monk was among the more vigorous ones she had encountered and she had a hard time keeping pace with him. As he was coming to orgasm, she dipped her finger in the prepared bottle of red ink and made a mark on his bald head. Before he rolled off, the monk got up and gave her a small packet.

"Here are some pills to help you get pregnant. Take three-tenths of an ounce each morning with hot water for a week and you'll have a child."

Now the monk was gone. Zhang Mei was a bit tired. She was about to close her eyes to get some sleep when she felt a jab in the side.

"What? You again?" she cried, thinking it was the same monk. "I'm tired out."

"You are mistaken. I am a new one. I'm going to make you feel very happy."

"But I'm tired." She complained.

"Take this pill and you won't be tired all night." He handed her a packet. Likewise, she marked his head with red ink. The monk did not leave until dawn.

Li Wan had similar experience in her room. Just after the first monk finished, a second one appeared from under the floor.

"You've had your share," the second monk said to the first monk. "It's my turn now."

The first one whose scalp had already been marked by Li Wan with black ink chuckled and left. As the second one started to caress her body, Li Wan pretended to dodge him. But he took out a sweet-smelling pill and thrust it into her mouth, and forced her to swallow it.

"This pill will give you more energy and keep you excited," the monk whispered.

She felt as though her whole body was filled with a soothing warmth and she was going to melt. But she did not forget her assignment.

"What a nice sleek head you've got!" Stroking his head, she applied the black ink.

"I am a very tender and sensitive person. I am not like other monks. Come and see me often." He left her room at daybreak.

Governor Wang left his mansion at around 4 o'clock in the morning, accompanied by a squad of a hundred policemen.

When they reached the monastery, his guard announced his arrival by thumping heavily at the gate. The governor went straight into the chief monk's residence and found the monk was already up. The governor ordered him to hand over the register of the temple and summon all the monks to a meeting in the front hall.

The alarmed chief monk had the drums and bells sounded. Moments later all the monks were gathered. The governor then ordered them to remove their caps. Two of the monks were found to have red stains on the head and another two, black stains.

"Where did you get these marks on your heads?" asked the governor.

Looking at each other, the four monks did not know what to say. "Maybe somebody played a joke with us."

"Very well. I'll show you who played the joke with you."

Then the two prostitutes were brought in. They told the governor what happened that night. All the monks were panic-stricken.

Other women were brought in to testify, though some of them tried to deny. The governor ordered a body search. As a result, a small packet containing the same pills that the two prostitutes had was found on each of them. Amidst the general consternation, their angry husbands quickly took them home.

An investigation revealed that the monks had been doing this for years. The women were required to be young and healthy, and the monks working on them were required to be strong and energetic. They were all helped with the special pills that the temple had prepared. Hence, the high rate of pregnancy. When the women found themselves deceived, most of them kept quiet for fear of ruining their reputation and family life. Some were reticent because they liked to come again.

The governor arrested all the monks and had the Temple of Lotus burnt down.

Comment: When the days of the surrogate mother are here, can the days of the surrogate father be far away? The trouble is children sired by healthy robust monks are not going to look like their legal fathers.

7. LIE DETECTOR

He is still hopeful who has done something bad but is afraid of being found out. He is already blemished who has done some good deed but is eager to make it known.

—*Vegetable Roots*

In the Song Dynasty about a thousand years ago, there was a magistrate by the name of Chen Xiang, in Fujian, a province in southern China.

One night there was a burglary in a hotel involving a large amount of money. The police quickly detained all the suspects in the hotel and its neighborhood. There were fifteen in all. But no one admitted stealing.

At the initial hearing, Magistrate Chen did not have sufficient evidence to bring charges against anyone. Then he announced that in a temple north of the city, there was an old bronze bell that had the divine power of telling a thief from an honest person.

He sent a few policemen to borrow the bell. After it was placed in the courtroom, the magistrate bowed to the bell and solemnly asked it to pass its verdict on the case in question. The fifteen suspects were brought before the bell. Each was to touch the bell with his hands. He told them that if a man was innocent, the bell would remain silent when he touched it. But if the man was guilty, the bell would ring.

Then all the lights were turned off and the courtroom became pitch-dark. One by one the suspects walked up to the bronze bell placed behind a screen and put their hands on it. The bell gave no sound and the audience in the courtroom were disappointed as everyone had passed the test.

When lights were switched on, the magistrate asked them to stretch out their hands. Among all the black hands, there was a pair of clean ones.

"You are the thief," said Magistrate Chen, pointing to the man whose hands were clean.

Earlier the magistrate had the bell sprayed with soot. The thief dared not touch it for fear that it might betray him.

The man, now under custody, confessed to the theft he had committed.

Comment: This story brings to mind a modern device, the lie detector. Given that an experienced and determined person is known to be able to beat the machine, we probably should not give undue credence to the polygraph. If somebody has passed the test, that person is not necessarily innocent. If someone has failed it, the person is not always guilty, as the cause of the failure could be something resembling stage fright.

Faces and eyes can reveal more of a person than the pulse rate, the blood pressure or the breathing as measured by a polygraph. The problem is they cannot be quantified or documented, and therefore their interpretation is often given little validity. But quantitative measurement and documentation as used in science and technology is just one way of discovering the truth, not the only way. And in judging human beings, it is probably the least accurate.

8. THE WEDDING OF THE RIVER-GOD

To prevent a country from lapsing into lawlessness, severe punishments are called for. In a country that has long been in anarchy, lenient measures should be adopted to give the people a chance.

—*Zeng Guoquan (1824-1890)*

Ximen Bao was appointed governor of Ye, in the state of Wei (in modern northern Henan Province).

Upon arrival at his post, he called a meeting with the town-fathers and inquired about their livelihood. The town-fathers told him about the wedding of the River God, which had been the source of their misery.

The Ye County had been plagued with floods caused by the River Zhang. According to the local witches, it was the doing of the River God. If a girl was presented to him each year, the flood might be averted. So each year, the witches went around visiting every home in town. If they saw a pretty girl, they would appoint her to be the bride for the River God. Every year the local officials would collect several thousand ounces of silver from the people in the county to spend on the wedding. It was believed that, as a rule, they used about two or three hundred on the wedding but kept the rest to themselves. Girls of wealthy families could be exempted if they donated a large amount of money. Those who could not afford to pay had to surrender their daughter once she was chosen.

Before the wedding, the bride had to be bathed, dressed in a silk gown and made to stay in a specially built bridal bed by the river and fast for a few days before being presented to the River God. On the day of the wedding, the bridal bed was lowered into the river along with the dowry. She was supposedly to join the god down below.

This practice had been going on for several years. The local residents were terrorized. As more and more people fled the town, the town was more dead than alive.

Ximen Bao decided to go and have a look when the next wedding was to be held.

The next wedding took place in due course. The ceremony was attended by all the local officials and the witches. Thousands of local residents came out to see the ritual, too. The chief witch was a seventy-year-old woman who was accompanied by a dozen of junior witches.

Ximen Bao, who was present, asked the bride to be brought to him. Then he looked at her for a while.

"I don't think she is pretty enough," he said to the chief witch. "Could you go and inform the River God that a better-looking one will soon be chosen and the wedding is postponed until the day after tomorrow?"

He motioned the guards to throw the old witch into the river.

The crowd was shocked.

After a while, Ximen Bao said: "The old lady has gone for some time. We cannot wait for her all day. Better send someone else to hurry her a bit."

He ordered the guards to throw one of the junior witches into the water. She began to struggle and shriek. But the governor turned a deaf ear to her plea.

A few moments after she was thrown into the river, the governor ordered a third witch to be thrown into the river.

"She is too slow. We must send another one to find out why they are late." The governor became impatient.

After four witches were dispatched, Ximen Bao said: "Maybe the women are not doing a good job down there. We must send some man."

He turned to the local officials standing by.

An official who had collaborated with the witches was forcibly dumped into the river by the guards despite his protest. The governor stood on the river bank for a long time, looking rather solemn.

"None of them came back so far. What should we do now?" he asked other officials.

They were all on their knees, begging for mercy. Some of them kowtowed repeatedly until their foreheads were covered with blood.

"All right. Let's call it a day," Ximen Bao finally announced. "We'll wait until we have news from the River God."

Since then there was no more wedding of the River God.

Ximen Bao instructed local residents to dig twelve irrigation canals in order to redirect the flow of the river so that there would be no more flood to harass them. As a result, all the fields had ample water supply, though at first some people complained of the hard work of the project.

Ximen Bao remarked: "People prefer an easy life and do not want to work hard. If you try to get consensus from them on everything, nothing will get done. Sometimes you just have to tell them what to do. At present, they are complaining that I work them too hard, but future generations will be grateful for what I will have done for them."

Comment: The witches were getting a taste of their own medicine. It serves them right.

As many people are eager to give advice to others, many are anxious to seek advice from others. The best way to test whether the person really believes in the advice he gives to others is to see whether he himself lives by it.

9. KIDNAPPING

Without intelligence, a man can live up to a hundred years but remains a child. With intelligence, a child can do better than a man who has lived a hundred years.

—*Daoyuan (11th century)*

The Chinese New Year, which normally falls on the fifth of February, is a festive occasion for family reunions and sumptuous dinners, an occasion for visiting relatives and friends, settling debts and cleaning the houses. On New Year's Eve nobody goes to bed. Dinner that night is the most important event of the year.

The fifteenth day after the New Year is the Lantern Festival. Red lanterns are lit everywhere that night to celebrate the advent of spring. A kind of sweet dumpling stuffed with ground sesame is the specialty of the occasion.

In the Song Dynasty, the Lantern Festival began on the thirteenth day after the New Year and reached its climax on the fifteenth day. On that day, the emperor would step out of the palace to join the people in observing the holiday. He would ascend one of the towers overlooking Kaifeng, the capital city, to watch the gleeful illuminations and fireworks. This was a rare chance when the ordinary people could see the emperor. Music and theatricals were performed in the crowded city center square. But this was also an occasion criminals took advantage of.

On one such night, a five-year-old boy named Nan Gai was kidnapped.

Nan Gai came from a wealthy family. His father, Lord Wang Shao, was a government minister under Emperor Shen Zong, the sixth emperor of the Song Dynasty. Nan Gai was his youngest son and the darling of the family. To watch the celebration, most members of the family came out that evening to the city center. Like everybody else, Nan Gai was dressed in his festival best. His small hat, embroidered with pearls and precious stones, was particularly eye-catching. Studded on its front was a large cat's-eye worth nearly a thousand ounces of gold.

A servant named Wang Ji was carrying him on his shoulders. When they reached the city center square, a vast crowd of people was already gathered there to watch the emperor who was leaning over the battlements of the tower, smiling his gracious smiles. Standing on tip-toe for a glimpse of the emperor, Wang Ji had a hard time holding the boy.

After a while, he felt he was able to move his body more freely as though the burden on his shoulders was somehow lifted. For a moment he did not realize that something might have gone wrong. But suddenly it occurred to him that he should be carrying Nan Gai on his shoulders. He looked around, and the boy was nowhere to be seen.

Seized with panic, he hastened to push his way out of the crowd. Soon he came across a few other servants of the family.

"Have you seen Nan Gai?" he asked anxiously.

"Wasn't he with you?"

"I was standing in the crowd there when somebody took him off my back. I thought you might have taken him home."

Thrown into consternation, the group immediately went in different directions looking for Nan Gai. They shouted his name, but their voice was drowned by the noise of the crowd. There was no trace of the boy.

"Maybe others of the family have taken him home," one of them suggested.

"I guess somebody saw his hat and kidnapped him," said another.

They raced back home. At the report of the disappearance of Nan Gai, Lord Wang Shao did not look as anxious as the servants.

"Nan Gai will come back by himself," said Lord Wang. "Don't panic."

"What if he has been kidnapped by gangsters? Should we notify the police to ask them to launch an instant search?"

"No, not necessary."

The servants were confounded. Unable to see how Lord Wang could be so calm, they hurried to report the incident to Mrs. Wang.

Mrs. Wang was shocked. With tears rolling down her cheeks, she rushed to her husband. She wanted every possible measure to be taken to rescue the boy. But Lord Wang said: "If it's any other child, I will do everything possible to find him. But Nan Gai is different. I am sure he'll come back safe and sound."

He also rejected the idea of putting up a reward for any information leading to the safe return of the boy.

"Believe me. Nan Gai will be back, I guarantee." But no one believed him. His wife sent out people to look for the boy.

Sitting on Wang Ji's shoulders, Nan Gai was absorbed in watching the activities in the square. He did not even know it when someone gently carried him off. It was not until the man started to jostle his way out of the crowd that Nan Gai asked: "Where are you going, Wang Ji?"

As he looked down, he discovered that he was on a stranger's shoulders. He knew something had gone wrong: he had been kidnapped. His first instinct was to shout for help, but he held back because he did not see any familiar faces around. He suspected that the kidnapper was after his hat, so he took off the hat and hid it in his sleeve. The man was walking at a brisk pace; Nan Gai kept his silence, pretending that he took him for his servant.

When they got to the East Gate near the palace, Nan Gai saw some sedan-chairs carried by people in official uniforms approaching from the opposite direction. He decided that here was his chance for escape. As soon as the first sedan-chair moved to his side, Nan Gai shot out his hand and grabbed the carrying pole of the sedan, screaming at the top of his lungs: "Help! Help! Catch the kidnapper!"

The man was taken aback. He threw down the boy, made off, and soon disappeared into the crowd.

The passenger in the sedan chair got down. The man was a eunuch in the palace. He and his colleagues were on their way back to the palace from the square. Nan Gai told him what happened. The sympathetic eunuch took the boy into his sedan, and together they entered the palace. Eunuchs were fond of children as they themselves had lost the ability to have children. The eunuch offered him some fruit and cakes to eat and took him to spend the night in his mansion.

The next morning the eunuch briefed the emperor on the presence of Nan Gai in the palace. Emperor Shen Zong was very pleased at the news, because he regarded the arrival of Nan Gai at the palace was a good omen. He had not had an heir yet.

Nan Gai was brought before the emperor. Nobody had told him how to conduct himself in the royal court, but Nan Gai took out his hat, put it on, and bowed to the emperor.

"My name is Wang Nan Gai. I am the youngest son of Your Majesty's minister Wang Shao."

The emperor was surprised at his politeness and composure.

"How did you manage to get here?"

"Last night we were in the square to celebrate the holiday and to catch a glimpse of Your Majesty, some nasty fellow kidnapped me. On the way, I was rescued by Your Majesty's attendants when they were on their way back to the palace. That's why I have the honor of standing before Your Majesty today."

"How old are you?"

"Five."

"Your father must be very anxious now. You'll be sent back soon. But what a pity it is that the criminal was not caught."

"Your Majesty, it wouldn't be too difficult to find the kidnapper," Nan Gai said.

"Why do you say that?"

"When I discovered the man's intention, I took my hat off and hid it in my sleeve. Mother had attached a needle with silk thread to the hat because she said it could prevent evil. As I was sitting on the man's shoulders, I used the needle to make a stitch underneath the collar of the man's coat, leaving a small bit of thread there for future identification. Now if Your Majesty sends out detectives, they will be able to find him."

The emperor was surprised. "What a clever boy! I want you to stay here until the kidnapper is caught." Then he ordered the mayor of the city to have the kidnapper arrested in three days.

A special squad was quickly organized. Plainclothes detectives were dispatched to various bars and restaurants and other public places as the police believed that the kidnapper probably belonged to some gang, who, for the time being, was still in the city.

The kidnapper, indeed, was the ring-leader of a gang. He was nicknamed Hawk. There were a dozen or so of them in the gang. Hawk had been targeting the Wang family for some time. When he abducted Nan Gai, he thought what the boy could do was at most crying. Nan Gai's action totally caught him by surprise.

All members of his gang produced their spoils that night. Gold, jewels, pearls, jade, fur coats and what not. But he had nothing to offer. They asked him why he did not just take the boy's hat.

"There are gold and jewels all over his clothes and the boy would worth a lot more money."

"You bit off more than you could chew!"

It was the practice of the gang that each day one of them was to treat the rest to a good dinner by turn. So they went to a restaurant off the busy districts.

Detective Li happened to be making inquiries in that neighborhood. He saw these people inside a restaurant. He chose a convenient seat, ordered something for himself, and then carefully looked at each one of those people. He noticed that one of the men had a tiny colored thread thrusting out from under the collar of his coat.

Li went out quickly to gather enough policemen, took them into the restaurant and arrested the gangsters in the name of the emperor. Interrogations resulted in the recovery of many stolen goods and their confessions of other criminal activities.

The emperor was pleased at the news and ordered the execution of the kidnapper.

In the meantime, Nan Gai became the darling boy of everyone in the palace. He was clever and sweet. Gifts showered upon him. The empress, too, regarded the discovery of such a bright boy as Nan Gai an auspicious sign, for she was expecting. Nan Gai had a good time playing with everyone in the palace.

Now that the kidnapper had been brought to justice, it was time that the boy be sent home. A royal carriage arrived at the gate of Lord Wang Shao's mansion. When Nan Gai came out, the whole family was excited. Tears of joy were streaming down his mother's cheeks. The eunuch read an imperial statement:

We had the pleasure of finding your son who was lost on the night of the Lantern Festival. We enjoyed his company and are sending him back with our gifts as a token of our appreciation of his intelligence.

The next day Lord Wang took the boy to see Emperor Shen Zong to express his gratitude.

When he grew up, Nan Gai became a brilliant scholar and rose to a very senior position in the government.

Comment: Intelligence is essentially endowed by nature and defined in the early years of life. Experience and knowledge can be acquired later on. These two are different things but often get confused. With intelligence, a little experience goes a long way. Without intelligence, diligence goes a long way to make up for the gap.

10. SAILING UNDER FALSE COLORS

Move the deceitful with sincerity; the ruthless with gentleness; and the wicked and crooked with pride and a sense of honor.
—*Vegetable Roots*

In the Ming Dynasty, there lived in Huanggang, a town near modern Wuhan, a scholar named Wang. He was from a rich family and had dozens of servants in the household. An easygoing yet resourceful person, Wang loved to travel with his girlfriend Huifeng, a very attractive young woman who shared his liking for horseback riding and archery.

One day Wang and Huifeng took an excursion in Yueyang, a well-known scenic spot in Hunan Province, central China. After touring Lake Dongting and the famous Yueyang Tower, they took a short boat trip to the foot of the legendary Mount Jun where they visited an ancient temple. Then they went to the nearby Terrace of the Yellow Emperor, a vantage point, to enjoy the panoramic view of the scenery in all its magnificence. Close to them dotted on the mountain were ancient landmarks dated back to the beginning of Chinese civilization. In the far distance the waves of the river seemed to be beating at the sky, the color of the water and the sky merged in a harmonious hue. It was a breathtaking sight. The two lovers were lost in admiration.

Suddenly they noticed a bulky fellow coming in their direction from down the mountain. The man eyed Huifeng closely. When the two walked away, he followed them. Wang and Huifeng felt uneasy and quickly ran down the mountain. When they were about to board their boat, the man, closely behind them, whistled. All of a sudden, a dozen men emerged from another boat.

"Take the woman to the boss," the man shouted, pointing to Huifeng.

They jumped forward, snatched Huifeng away from her boyfriend, dumped her in their boat, and sailed away with all speed down the river.

Wang could only look on in distress. All of this happened so fast.

He did not know where they were taking her to, but he was determined to get her back. He immediately took action. He sent out his servants to make inquiries in all the towns and market-places in the area. Meanwhile he offered a reward of a hundred ounces of gold to anyone who could provide information as to the whereabouts of Huifeng. Notices to that effect were posted everywhere.

A few days later, Wang arrived at Wuhan, the provincial capital of Hubei. There, the regional military commissioner, General Xiang, was a friend of his. Xiang invited him to the famous Tower of Yellow Crane on top of a hill to the southwest of Wuhan for a view of the splendid scenery, but Wang was in no mood to enjoy it. He was deeply concerned about Huifeng's safety. Tears were streaming down his cheeks before he knew it.

He was just going to tell the general of what had happened, when the general's bodyguard said: "I heard your girlfriend has been abducted, Sir."

"How do you know that?" Wang asked.

"I saw the notice you posted. Don't worry. I know where she is."

"Really? Oh, please help me!"

"I live near Mount Helu and I know something about the gangsters there. The ring-leader is called Ke Chen. He and his brothers are engaged in smuggling and other illegal activities. Their group is the largest among gangsters in the lake area. I heard the other day that they had abducted a pretty girl on Lake Dongting. Ke Chen was so pleased that he held a feast to celebrate. I figured she must be your girlfriend."

"This Ke Chen is different from other outlaws," General Xiang said. "He is not a mean fellow and does abide by certain code of honor. He knows everybody in the local government, has good connections, and often make contributions to local authorities. It's going to be difficult to arrest him by force. If your girlfriend was indeed abducted by his gang, I'm afraid you might as well give her up and drop the matter. There are plenty of beautiful women around."

"How can you say that?!" Wang was angry. "I am not a real man if I allow my girlfriend to be kidnapped and do not try to rescue her. I must find her."

"It's not going to be easy, I can tell you," General Xiang said.

The next day Wang paid the bodyguard fifty ounces of gold for his information and promised to give him the remaining fifty ounces as soon as Huifeng was found. With the permission of General Xiang, Wang hired the bodyguard as a guide.

He then sent in a formal petition to the local government requesting action against Ke Chen and his gang.

"They are tough customers to deal with," said the police commissioner when he read Ke Chen's name. "I'm not sure if we can do anything about it. If we send armed personnel over, there is going to be a bloody fight."

"I do not expect you to send soldiers there," Wang replied. "All I want is an arrest warrant from you. I do not need your other help. I'll go there myself to negotiate the release of my girlfriend. There won't be any fighting."

The police chief was skeptical, but anyway he issued an arrest warrant and handed it to Wang.

Wang went back to General Xiang.

"I have officially petitioned the government to take action against Ke's gang. Now I need your help," he said.

"But I'm not going to send soldiers there."

"I am not asking you for that. I want to borrow your official cruiser and two patrol boats equipped with official flags and uniforms. I do not need any soldiers. I'll take only your bodyguard who knows the whereabouts of the gang."

"What are you going to do?"

"I'll tell you everything when my mission is over."

General Xiang obliged and lent Wang his cruiser and the patrol boats. Then Wang had dozens of his servants clothed in official uniforms and posed himself as a newly appointed district army commander. An insignia bearing his name and title was erected on the ship. Then they set out to Mount Helu.

Before they reached Mount Helu, Wang sent two of his men and the bodyguard of General Xiang to inform the local officials of his arrival. He also informed Ke Chen that he would like to call on him.

Ke Chen lived on a farming estate. He felt flattered when he was presented with the calling card of the new district army commander. When Wang's boat arrived, he and his men came to the harbor and joined the local officials to welcome the young district army commander.

Wang, dressed in a red silk official uniform, cut an imposing figure. When the welcoming ceremony was over, he instructed the palanquin to go to Ke Chen's place.

Ke gave Wang a warm reception. A banquet was held in Wang's honor. Ke Chen and his gang expressed their appreciation of the gesture of the new army commander, for his visit was bound to enhance their respectability in the local community. Many drinks were toasted and soon enough Wang and Ke were chatting like good friends.

"If you have any trouble on the river, Your Honor, just call us. We'll do our best to help you," Ke said.

Wang accepted his offer graciously and did not leave Ke Chen's until it was late into the night. The next day Ke Chen invited him over again. Afterwards Wang asked Ke and his associates to come to attend a reciprocal dinner on his official cruiser.

An elaborate banquet was held on board the cruiser, with a theatrical performance to come after it. Ke Chen and his men had never seen such an entertainment before. They were enchanted. As they were watching the opera, Wang ordered his men to lift the anchor. The boat began to move down the river quickly, but noiselessly. The current was swift. None of Ke Chen's men noticed anything. When the performance was over, the boat had already cruised several miles down the river.

Wang invited them to return to the dinner table.

"It's a great pleasure for me to have you here tonight," he announced. "There is something I would like to discuss with you. I need your help."

"What can we do for you, Your Honor?" Ke Chen asked.

Wang produced the official warrant and showed it to Ke.

"A gentleman by the name of Wang filed a petition against you. He charges that you people have kidnapped his girlfriend. Is that true?"

Ke and his brothers looked at each other in consternation.

"Yes, there is a woman by the name of Huifeng," Ke Chen admitted. "We took her a few days ago on Lake Dongting. She said she was from the Wang family. She is now at my place."

"A woman is no big deal," said their host. "But this Mr. Wang is not an ordinary man. He has a lot of clout. He intends to pursue this case to the top until those who abducted his girlfriend are completely wiped out. He has already sent in his formal petition to the authorities. This arrest warrant has been passed to me by my superior in the process for action. However, as I know who you are, I don't want to use any force. So I invited you here to meet my superior tomorrow. You'll have to confront Mr. Wang in the court of justice, I'm afraid."

Ke and his brothers were stunned.

"What? You want us to be thrown into jail!" They wanted to make off, but discovered that they were in the middle of the river, far from Mount Helu. They realized they were trapped.

"Please help us out," Ke Chen entreated.

"Right now, if you refuse to meet my superior, you are going to give me trouble; but if you do, you'll get into trouble. We must think out a way to render this warrant null and void. That may be the only solution."

"But how?"

"The whole thing was caused by the abduction of Wang's girlfriend. He is anxious about her safety. If you bring her here, the cause for action against you will be completely removed. I guarantee you won't face any charge."

"That's not difficult," Ke said. "I can write a note to have the woman be sent back here."

"Then, do it now! Do it quickly."

Ke Chen immediately scribbled a note addressed to his housekeeper at his home on Mount Helu. The message was then carried there by Wang's men in a patrol boat. While waiting, Wang asked Ke and his brothers to resume drinking and dining. But they were too restless to enjoy any more food or wine.

Toward daybreak, the patrol boat came back. Huifeng was escorted on board the cruiser right away. Wang toasted thanks to Ke and his brothers.

"Now I can report to my boss. You may go home."

Ke and his men were relieved now that the crisis was over. They thanked Wang for his assistance. Just as they were leaving, Wang stopped them.

"My friends, you want to know who that Mr. Wang is?" Wang said with a quizzical smile. "He is right here standing before you. There is no district army commander. I did this to you because I could not possibly give up my girlfriend. Now as she is safely back, I must say that I have enjoyed your company. Good-bye."

Ke Chen and his brothers looked at Wang with an expression of a man just awakened from a dream. At last they burst into laughter.

"You fooled us so cleverly. You are a wonderful man! We like your guts." Ke offered his compliment. "We do like you a lot. It's an honor for me to have met you. I hope to see you again in future. Please forgive me for having offended your girlfriend in ignorance. I am very sorry, very, very sorry indeed."

Each member of Ke's gang took some silver from his pocket, amounting to more than thirty ounces in total, for a gift to Wang.

"This is for your girlfriend's wardrobe, please accept it."

Wang declined, but they insisted that he accept it. Finally he took the money, as a friendly gesture. His patrol boat escorted Ke Chen and his men to shore and they bid farewell to each other.

Huifeng was sobbing when Wang came back.

"Don't cry, sweetheart. You are with me again."

The two lovers had a few drinks of celebration and took a good rest until they arrived at Wuhan.

"My mission is completed," Wang announced to his friend, General Xiang. "Now I want to return everything I borrowed from you. Without your help, General, I could not have pulled it off. Thank you very much indeed."

General Xiang was very impressed when he heard the whole story.

"With your resourcefulness, you could be a real army commander, my friend."

Wang gave another fifty ounces of gold to the general's bodyguard who was overwhelmed by Wang's courage and wit.

Comment: It is almost impossible to duplicate the way Mr. Wang managed to rescue his girlfriend.

But should someone dear to us meet with this kind of misfortune, to what length should we go to rescue that person? We could try to kidnap a member of the gang tit for tat and negotiate a hostage exchange. We could try to make a secret deal of some sort with the kidnapper to get our hostage back. Or we could bring in the full power of law enforcement in dealing with the gangster.

Our action may create a conflict between our moral obligation and our legal duty. But whatever decision we make, the life of the hostage weighs more with us than any other consideration.

PART II
EDUCATION, ETHICS AND FAMILY VALUES

11. THE UNCROWNED KING

Learn the Truth in the morning, and die content in the evening.
—*Confucius* (551-479 B.C.)

For more than two thousand years, Confucius has been the uncrowned king of China. Indeed, Confucianism is more than a cultural heritage for the Chinese. It is an integral part of the Chinese wisdom. It is part of the national consciousness of the Chinese. However, with the passage of time, Confucius seems to have become remote and strange, sometimes even impersonal to us. To better understand what he had preached, I should like to turn back in history, trying to find out what kind of a man Confucius was really like.

Here is the story of Confucius concentrating more on his life than his philosophy.

CHILDHOOD AND FAMILY

Confucius was a love child.

His father died when he was three; his mother died when he was seventeen.

In those days, people, as a rule, buried the coffins of their parents together. But Confucius could not do so unless he located the site of his father's tomb. His mother had never told him who his father was. So he took his mother's coffin, placed it at the crossroads leading to his village and there he stood by, making inquiries with passers-by about his deceased father. Finally, a kind old woman took him to his father's tomb and for the first time he was told the story of his own father.

At the age of seventy, his father, a member of an ancient aristocratic family and a well-known soldier in Lu, present-day Shandong Province, fell in love with a farmer's daughter, a seventeen-year-old girl. And a child was born to them in the year 551 B.C.

The child was named Qiu after a mountain called the Ni Qiu. Confucius was not his real name. It was a title of courtesy, a Latinized

至聖先師孔子寶像

乙亥戴敦邦拜制於滬上

form of "Kong Fuzi", meaning "Master Kong"—an appellation accorded to him years later by his three thousand student-disciples, because his family name was Kong.

Legend had it that his mother often went to pray to a shrine at the foot of the Ni Qiu Mountain, located to the southeast of Qufu County in the state of Lu. One night after her return from her pilgrimage, she had a strange dream in which she saw a fabulous one-horned horse, the so-called *qilin*, a symbol of intelligence and good fortune, emerge from the edge of a forest, clenching between its teeth a book made of jade. The beast threw the book at her feet and plunged back into the woods. Shortly afterwards, she was pregnant. When the baby was born, she called him Qiu.

Qiu was the second son of the Kong family, for he had nine sisters and a brother, all of them the children of his father's first wife.

After the death of his father, he was brought up by his mother. Little has been recorded in history about his childhood. He got married at nineteen. Little is known about his wife, too. He had a son and a daughter. His son was not very talented, but his grandson grew up to become a famous scholar. Confucius gave in marriage his only daughter to a student of his. At the time of the wedding, the bridegroom was in jail on a false charge. But Confucius believed his student to be innocent, so he gave the couple his blessing.

SELF-EDUCATION

Confucius seldom talked about his early life except for once when he said, "When I was young, we were very poor. Perhaps that's why I have learned to do so many odd jobs like a laborer."

Although 6.4 feet tall and strongly built, Confucius did not want to follow his father's career as a soldier, the most esteemed profession of his day, because he had no interest in the military.

Confucius was a self-taught man. He had never received any formal education. But he loved books, books about the wisdom of sage kings of a former age who ruled the country not by force, but by virtue. He often mentioned how people enjoyed living in peace and prosperity during the early stage of the Zhou Dynasty.

"When I was fifteen," he said, "I set my mind on learning. I once spent all day thinking without eating and all night thinking without sleeping, but I gained nothing. So I decided to learn."

Obviously it was his assiduity and perseverance that had made his great career possible, his career as the greatest teacher, thinker and philosopher in the history of China.

Through self-teaching, Confucius had trained himself to be well-versed in the six requisite skills for a gentleman at that time: proper conduct, writing, arithmetic, music, archery and chariot driving.

Take music for example, Confucius was fond of music and could sing and play the lute. He believed that music could have a beneficial or a harmful impact on the mind and the character of a person, and even on society as a whole.

"When you see the type of a nation's dance and music," he once observed, "you will know the general character of that nation."

One day he had a chance to listen to a choir of blind singers from the capital of the Zhou kingdom, the present-day Luoyang, in Henan Province. He was so deeply moved by the music that he announced he could forget the taste of meat for three months. After that he always cherished a special feeling for the blind, often helped them and bowed to them even though they could not see him.

Confucius studied music with a well-known music master of Lu.

"You do play well now." the music master once said to him after he had practiced a piece of ancient music on the lute for ten days. "Let's move on to something else."

"No, Master," said Confucius. "I have learnt the melody but not the rhythm yet."

After some more practice, his tutor said: "Now you've got the rhythm. We can try something else."

"No," Confucius objected. "I haven't got the mood yet."

After a while, the music master suggested again that he had practiced enough.

"Not yet. I am trying to get a feel as to what kind of a man the composer is."

So he played again and again. Sometimes the music came out solemn and thoughtful, other times bright and breezy. The music master was very pleased.

A few days later while Confucius was playing the same piece of music, his face suddenly lit up.

"Master, I found it!" he shouted rapturously. "I've found who he is. He's a tall, big man, somewhat dark-skinned. He has a majestic air about him. He has a heart that embraces the whole world. He must be King Wen who founded the Zhou Dynasty six hundred years ago."

The music master was astonished at Confucius' musical intuition. Involuntarily he bowed twice to his student.

"Yes, you're right!" he said. "My tutor did tell me that it was composed by King Wen."

Later when he became a teacher, Confucius made music a part of his teaching curriculum.

One day Confucius was playing the lute in his room. His student-disciples Zigong and Zeng Shen were listening outside. Suddenly Zeng Shen detected in the music a note of ferocity quite uncharacteristic of Confucius.

When Zigong told him about Zeng Shen's comment, Confucius laughed.

"Shen has good ears," he said. "I saw a cat chasing a rat. As I hated to see the rat run faster than the cat, I was anxious to kill the rat. So I felt murder in me at the moment. My feeling must have got into the music."

AN EXEMPLARY TEACHER

As a young man, Confucius got his first job as the keeper of a granary for a local baron. After a while he was appointed to be superintendent in the Department of Land and Herding and subsequently to supervisory positions in various offices in the civil service in the state of Lu. And he began teaching in his spare time in his late twenties.

Confucius did not just teach knowledge and skill. He taught how to cultivate one's mind and attain integrity.

At that time, education was meant only for the privileged aristocracy. But Confucius broke this monopoly of education. He believed that in education there should be no distinction of class, that everyone, regardless of his background, deserved an equal opportunity to receive education. He announced that whoever wanted to learn was welcome. He rarely mentioned money, and accepted students regardless of how much they paid him.

Yan Hui, a young man of humble origin, was afraid he could not afford the tuition. But he heard Confucius say, "I won't refuse anyone, even if he can only afford to pay ten slices of dried meat as tuition." Pretty soon, he became Confucius' student.

Students, old and young, rich and poor, gathered around him. He had some three thousand of them. Of those, seventy-two were close personal disciples, the most famous being Zilu who was enthusiastic, direct and bold; Zigong who was intelligent, diplomatic, charming and well-balanced; Ran Qiu who was competent, calculating and ready to compromise on principles; Zeng Shen who was known for his filial devotion; and Yan Hui, Confucius' most favorite disciple, who was diligent, capable but reticent and poor.

Confucius conducted his instruction in the form of panel discussion. His students were encouraged to raise questions and express their own opinions freely and independently. He tailored his tutorial method to the individual.

Once Zilu asked him whether he should immediately practice what he had learnt, Confucius told him to first consult his father and brother before taking any action. But when Ran Qiu put the same question to him, Confucius told him to put what he had learnt into immediate practice. One of his disciples was puzzled by the different answers to one and the same question. Confucius explained: "Ran Qiu tends to hesitate, so I urged him on. Zilu is too enthusiastic, so I tried to hold him back a little."

Confucius insisted that his students should think for themselves.

"If I explain one corner of a subject, I expect him to grasp the other three himself. If he doesn't, I'll let him go."

He told his students, "The highest are those who were born with wisdom. Next are those who become wise through learning. Next to them come those who turn to study after encountering difficulties in life. Those who still do not try to learn are the lowest type of men.

"You must study as though you would never be able to master what you have learnt, and hold it as though you were afraid of losing it." But "studying without thinking is labor lost; thinking without studying is dangerous."

Confucius loved young people. "Young people," he said, "should be treated with respect. How do you know they will not be your equal one day? It is those who have reached the age of forty or fifty without having accomplished anything that do not deserve respect."

His reputation as a teacher and scholar spread rapidly. Even government ministers sent their children to study with him.

THE GENTLEMAN

His aim was to educate his students to be gentlemen with knowledge and of a high moral standard. He proposed that the best career for such gentlemen was in the civil service to work for the happiness of the people and to bring about a better world. In a sense, Confucius was training an elite group based not on wealth or family background, but on ability and moral integrity. His criteria for selecting students were intelligence combined with an eagerness to learn.

Confucius said many things concerning the qualities that a gentleman should have:

A gentleman is modest, generous, open-minded, diligent and kind-hearted.

A gentleman understands what is just and right; a small man only understands what is profitable.

A gentleman helps others to realize what is good in them and takes no part in their wrong-doing; a small man does the opposite.

A gentleman is worried about his lack of ability, not about whether or not his ability is appreciated.

A gentleman makes demands upon himself; a small man makes demands upon others.

A gentleman has a broad social circle; a small man is partisan.

A gentleman first practices what he preaches and then preaches what he practices.

A gentleman is slow to talk but quick to act.

The following anecdote also illustrates what he had in mind regarding the qualities of a gentleman.

One day when hiking in the hills, Confucius sent Zilu to get some water. Zilu encountered a tiger on his way. After a fierce fight, he killed the beast by grabbing its tail.

He cut the tiger's tail and brought it back when he returned with the water, eager to show Confucius his trophy. But first he asked: "Master, how does a superior man kill a tiger?"

"A superior man kills a tiger by aiming at its head," the master replied.

"How does an average man kill a tiger?"

"An average man kills a tiger by getting at its ears."

"How does a lower man kill a tiger?"

"A lower man kills a tiger by grabbing its tail."

Zilu felt ashamed and threw away the tiger's tail.

"Why did the master send me for water in the mountain?" he thought after a little while, "Didn't he know tigers lurk in highlands? He must have wanted me killed."

So he carried a big piece of rock behind him and intended to kill Confucius with it.

"How does a superior man kill a man?" he asked before taking action.

"A superior man kills a man with his pen."

"How does an average man kill a man?"

"An average man kills a man with his tongue."

"How does a lower man kill a man?"

"A lower man kills a man with a stone."

Zilu turned around sheepishly and tossed away the rock. He had been given some food for thought.

Once Confucius asked his students to talk about their wishes.

Zilu said without hesitation: "My ambition is like this: take for instance a kingdom of a thousand chariots that has been invaded by big powers and is suffering from famine. I'll put things right for that country in three years."

"Give me a small country," said Ran Qiu, "and I can make the people rich in three years. But for good manners and music appreciation, I have to leave it to others."

"I want to be a master of ceremony presiding over various rituals in public places and in diplomatic conferences," said Gongxi Hua.

"My wish is different from yours, I'm afraid," said Zeng Xi who was the last one to talk about his wish. "When spring comes, I'll put on light clothes, get a few friends to go swimming in the river. Then I'll enjoy the breeze in the woods, and come back home sauntering all the way and singing to my heart's content."

"That sounds good," Confucius smiled. "I like your wish the best."

Zilu asked him what his wish was.

"To bring comfort to the old; to be faithful to friends and to cherish the young," was the master's reply.

One day a fishmonger wanted to give Confucius a fish as a gift. At first Confucius declined.

"I've sold all my fish today except this one," the fishmonger said. "It's a warm day. Rather than throw it away, I think I should give it away."

Confucius thanked the man and accepted the fish. Then he told his disciples to clean the room, for he would like to offer the fish as a sacrifice to God.

"This is a fish the man almost threw away," one of his disciples objected. "Why do you want to offer it to God?"

"If a man understands charity and gives away what he does not need," said the master, "he should be regarded as a saint. Now I have received a gift from a saint, can't I offer it to God?"

Filial piety was an important topic which he often dwelled on. "At home respect your parents. When you are away from home, respect your elders. Be honest. Love your fellow men, and love what is good. Then pursue your studies if you still have the time and energy to."

"Let your parents have no anxiety except when you are ill," Confucius admonished his students. "You should always keep in mind the age of your parents and let their advancing years be your joy and fear at the same time."

A man who set great store by propriety and the observance of decorum, Confucius respected religious ceremonies as part of established custom. But he never talked about ghosts, the supernatural, the occult, and the exotic. He said, "We do not know life; how can we understand death? We do not fully understand our obligations to the living, what can we know of our obligations to the dead?" .

For pastime, Confucius liked fishing, but would only use a rod, not a net. He liked hunting, but would not aim at a bird at rest because he felt that to do so would be unfair to the animal.

One day his stable burned down. When he came back, he asked whether anybody was hurt. He did not ask about the horses.

INVOLVEMENT IN POLITICS

Confucius lived in the Zhou Dynasty in Chinese history. The founders of Zhou overthrew the last ruler of the Shang Dynasty about a thousand years before Christ. In the early years of the Zhou Dynasty, the kings were powerful and the country enjoyed peace and prosperity. But by Confucius's time, China was divided into various states which were formerly fiefs controlled by members of the ruling clans. Those states made war on each other for dominance. Domestically there were also succession disputes and constant strife between the ruler and other aristocrats around him. Violence and political intrigues were the order of the day. The welfare of the ordinary people was totally disregarded.

Once when he happened to pass by the foot of Mount Tai in the state of Lu (in present-day Shandong Province), Confucius saw a woman weeping beside a grave. He sent Zilu over to have a look.

"My uncle was killed by a tiger some time ago," said the woman. "Then my husband was killed by a tiger, too. Now my son..."

"Why didn't you leave the place and go somewhere else?"

"But there is no tyrant here to terrorize us," the woman replied.

"You see," Confucius said to Zilu after a while, "a tyrannical government is worse than a tiger."

Confucius was not content to be just a teacher. He wanted to practice his ideals and hoped that some ruler would give him a chance to do so and set a reform program in motion. "If only somebody would use me," he observed, "I could accomplish a lot in one year, and make a real difference in three years."

When Zigong asked about government, Confucius said: "Sufficient food, sufficient defense and the trust of the people are the essentials for a government."

"If you have to part with one of the three, which one would you give up?" asked Zigong.

"Defense."

"Suppose you are forced to give up one of the remaining two, which would it be?"

"Food. It is true that without food, people die. However, death has been the lot of all men since the beginning of time. But a nation will not stand if the people have no confidence in the government."

But playing politics was not in his vein, for he was outspoken and regarded it beneath him to flatter the powerful. Just as he said, "To hide one's feelings and pretend friendship with those one does not like—I am ashamed of such conduct." He considered the best thing was to be liked by the good and disliked by the bad.

He was thirty when the ruler of Qi, Duke Jing, paid a visit to him. Confucius told him that the strength of a prince lay in a benevolent government and good officials. He preached on good government, proper social order, and the importance of moral cultivation.

He was thirty-five when a civil war broke out in his native land between Duke Zhao, the ruler of Lu, and his generals. Confucius took some of his favorite disciples and fled to Qi. Duke Jing of Qi again sought his advice on good government.

Confucius said: "Careful spending is the main thing a good government should pay attention to.

"A prince's conduct should be worthy of a prince, a minister's worthy of a minister, a father's worthy of a father and a son's worthy of a son." In other words, Confucius believed that each should perform his own duty and leave others to do theirs.

He pointed out: "A person may have sufficient intelligence to secure himself a high office but needs virtue to keep that position. Otherwise, he will certainly lose it even if he has it now. A person may have sufficient intelligence and virtue to secure and keep his office but he will not have the respect of the people if he does not treat them with dignity. A person may be intelligent and virtuous and respected, but he is still imperfect unless he conducts himself with propriety."

The duke wanted to appoint Confucius to a high government position in Qi, but his prime minister and other officials opposed. They were not pleased that a scholar from another country should be allowed to be their equal.

Confucius stayed in Qi for three years, but was never given a post. So he left Qi and came back to Lu to resume teaching for the next ten years.

At that time, the power of the Lu government was in the hands of Yang Hu, a shrewd and ambitious politician of dubious reputation. He was a dictator and a usurper of state power. Knowing the high prestige Confucius enjoyed in Lu, he urged Confucius to join him and repeatedly offered Confucius senior government positions. But Confucius turned him down.

Yang Hu was persistent. One day, he sent Confucius a young pig as a present when Confucius was out so that he could not refuse. This obliged Confucius to pay Yang Hu a courtesy visit, according to the rules of etiquette at the time. Confucius, too, chose a time when Yang Hu was not at home to call back. But he ran into Yang Hu on his way home.

"I would like to have a word with you," Yang Hu stopped Confucius. "Do you think a man can be called benevolent if he possesses priceless treasure but ignores the plight of his country?"

"No," Confucius replied.

"Do you think a man can be called wise if he wants to serve his country but lets go good opportunities of working for the government?"

"No."

"Time is flying. It waits for no man, you understand?"

"All right. I'll accept public office," finally Confucius said.

But he was only trying to extricate himself out of an awkward encounter. He never actually took office under Yang Hu.

It was not until 501 B.C. when Yang Hu fled Lu after he failed in his attempt to murder one of his political rivals that Confucius began to participate in the politics of Lu.

At fifty-one, Confucius was appointed mayor of the city of Zhongdu by Duke Ding, the ruler of Lu. In one year, Zhongdu became a crime-free model city. Doors did not need to be closed at night for there were no burglars. Lost properties could always be retrieved because they invariably lay where they were left behind.

"In handling a lawsuit, I am no better than other people," Confucius said. "But my aim is to bring an end to lawsuits."

He believed that high moral principles and good manners would help develop a good conscience and propriety and, thereby, lead to peace and good social order whereas the enforcement of the law only made people try to evade punishment without developing conscience.

The following year Confucius was promoted to be the Minister of Justice and then the Prime Minister of Lu.

Lu's economy boomed under his administration. People came from other countries to Lu to see for themselves the prosperity and peace of the country.

"To maintain a country of a thousand chariots calls for honesty, diligence, thrift, fair employment and love for one's fellow men," was Confucius' idea of governing.

Confucius also scored a diplomatic success when he accompanied the duke of Lu at a peace conference with Qi and negotiated the return of three cities that had been taken away from Lu. This was due to his understanding of the importance of negotiating from a position of strength. Before going to the conference, he suggested that the Minister of Defense should go with the delegation.

"If you want peace, prepare for war," he told the duke.

This was the happiest period of his life.

"I heard that a gentleman never shows fear in the face of danger, nor does he feel complacent over success," one of his students teased him.

"True," Confucius replied. "But he is delighted because he is humble despite the high position he holds."

Confucius was unassuming and quiet at home, but brilliant and eloquent at government meetings and ceremonious gatherings. He was serene with high-ranking officials, but affable with those of lower ranks. He was polite but not stiff, strict but not harsh, gentle yet firm, dignified yet approachable. He did not have any foregone conclusion, or arbitrary opinions, and never viewed things only from his own perspective.

THE WANDERING MASTER

Confucius had held government offices for four years and the prosperity of Lu caused anxiety in its neighboring state, Qi. At the suggestion of his new prime minister, the duke of Qi sent a troupe of eighty beautiful dancers and a hundred and twenty splendid tattooed horses as a gift to the duke of Lu. The duke was so tempted by the luscious entertainment of the Qi dancers that he began to ignore his duties. Confucius' exhortations fell on a deaf ear. This was exactly what Qi had hoped to happen. In the meantime, certain members of the ruling hierarchy in Lu were eager to push Confucius out of politics because Confucius had tried to curtail the power of the aristocracy. Confucius was vexed, but he waited for the duke to see his own mistake and repent. What he got at last was a calculated insult: he was deliberately left out of the most important annual religious service of the country. He was so hurt that he decided to leave Lu.

In the ensuing fourteen years, Confucius led the life of an exile like a lost dog, in his own words. He was wandering about in various countries in the hope that he might be useful in some other countries. On their journey, he and his followers experienced many perils and ordeals.

Once Confucius was arrested due to mistaken identity. For this reason, his disciples were rounded up one by one, only Yan Hui was missing. Confucius was deeply concerned about his safety. When Yan Hui was brought in after five days, Confucius was greatly relieved.

"I thought you were dead!" exclaimed Confucius.

"So long as my Master lives, how can I dare to die?" replied Yan Hui.

All his followers were concerned about Confucius' safety. Feeling a sense of mission, he comforted them: "God has entrusted me with this civilization of ours. If God had wished to destroy it, He would have done so long before and we would never have had the chance to educate ourselves. Obviously God intends to preserve it. What, therefore, can these people do to me?"

Another time when he was on his way to the State of Wei, he was waylaid by a rebel chief who was fighting Wei. The chief told Confucius that he would not let him go unless he promised to give up his plan of visiting Wei. Confucius gave him his word. But as soon as the rebel troops left, he turned straight off in the direction of Wei.

"Master, is it right to break your promise?" asked Zigong, puzzled.

"I do not keep promises made under duress," said Confucius. "Even God would disregard such promises."

When they arrived in Wei's capital, they found it was a busy, populous city.

"Ah, so many people." Confucius said.

"What would you do for them if you had the opportunity?" Ran Qiu asked.

"I would make them rich."

"What next?"

"I would teach them."

Yet another time, they were surrounded by the troops of Chen and Cai who tried to stop him from going to their common enemy, the state of Chu, for fear that the wise counsel of Confucius might turn Chu into a very strong power which would mean a threat to Chen and Cai.

The troops did not lift their encirclement until their supplies ran out. All along Confucius went on teaching, even singing and playing the lute.

"Do we have to put up with such hardship?" Zigong asked anxiously.

"A gentleman," answered Confucius, "can withstand hardship in a time like this, but a small man loses self-control and goes wild."

Knowing that his disciples were in low spirits, Confucius posed a question to them.

"Is there anything wrong with my ideas? In theory, if my ideas were right, I would be successful. We would never have been driven to this wilderness like animals."

"Maybe we do not have the virtue and wisdom as we thought," Zilu answered. "People do not trust us or listen to us."

"Perhaps you are right," said Confucius. "But what would you say on behalf of all the great men who met with misfortune? If wise and virtuous men are automatically honored, none of them would have to meet with misfortune."

"I think your teachings are just a little too highbrow," said Zigong. "What about stooping a little bit to bring them closer to the understanding of the ordinary people?"

"A good farmer does not always have a good harvest," said Confucius. "A craftsman has superb skill, but his style may not appeal to the fancy of his time. I can modify, reorganize or simplify my ideas but still may not be accepted by the world. If you want to stoop in order to please, your ideal will suffer."

"Your teaching is the truth," Yan Hui said firmly. "And just because of that, it is not accepted. But we ourselves ought to live by it. What does it matter if it is not accepted by others. It is their fault. The fact that people find your teachings hard to accept shows their recognition of it."

"My son, if you were a rich lord, I would want to be your housekeeper," said Confucius, greatly pleased with Yan Hui's reply.

In the end they were rescued by King Zhao of Chu. To show his appreciation of Confucius, the king wanted to give him seven hundred square miles of land to live on. But his brother stood out to stop him.

"Among your diplomats, is there anyone whose skill is equal to Zigong?" the king's brother asked.

"No," the king replied.

"And among all your generals, is there anyone the equal of Zilu?"

"No."

"And among all your advisors, is there anyone as wise as Yan Hui?"

"No."

"Then, do you think giving Confucius seven hundred miles a good idea? I heard the sage kings who founded the Zhou Dynasty started with only a hundred miles of land and finally ruled the world. With his wisdom and learning and all his disciples, would it turn out to our advantage?"

The king of Chu treated Confucius royally but gave up the idea of asking Confucius to stay.

Wherever they went, there the heads of states and their government ministers all gathered to listen to Confucius' ideas on government and social organization. As though he had a mandate from Heaven, Confucius always urged them to embrace the ideal of virtue. His long trips turned into a sort of crusade for better government and better society. While rulers of various countries treated him politely, they did not follow his advice.

"The world has gone astray for a long time," Confucius lamented. "No one would listen to me. Indeed, they do not understand what I'm talking about."

LAST DAYS

At the age of sixty-eight, Confucius was welcomed back to Lu by the new ruler of the country, Duke Ai. The duke asked him about the key factors of a good government.

"Choose the right people," said Confucius. "If you put honest men above the dishonest, the people will have confidence in the government. If you put the dishonest above the honest, you will lose their confidence. But first of all there should be no greed in you yourself. Then those under you will not steal, even if you pay them to do so."

By that time, Confucius was no longer interested in politics, though a number of his student-disciples became government ministers, ambassadors and governors of towns and cities.

"I cannot realize my ideals," mourned the great master. "But can I leave something behind for the future generation?" So he devoted his time entirely to teaching and writing and editing ancient classics. His love for music was unabated. He collected ancient ballads and poems into a book called *The Book of Songs*.

To his great grief, his most favorite disciple, Yan Hui, died at the age of only forty-one.

"Oh, Heaven has destroyed me!" wailed Confucius, stricken with agony, for he had meant Yan Hui to be his successor.

He had barely finished his work *The Annuals of Spring and Autumn*, an account of Chinese history covering a period of two hundred and forty years when news came that another of his favorite students, Zilu, was killed in a battle in Wei. Confucius was struck ill.

Confucius knew he would not be around for long. Looking back, he summarized his life as this:

"At fifteen, I set my mind on learning; at thirty I became firm in my purpose; at forty I was free from doubts; at fifty I came to know fate; at sixty I could tell truth from falsehood by listening to other people; at seventy I followed my heart's desire without trespassing the norm of conduct."

He spent his whole life advocating reforms aimed at making a better society founded on virtue and benevolence. He had in vision an ideal state with its ruler setting an example of virtuous conduct for the people to follow, with a host of scholar-officials of high principles to guide the ruler in his administration. By now he realized that he had largely failed to accomplish what he had hoped for.

"I don't blame Heaven; I don't blame man," said the great master. "All I tried to do is to acquire knowledge as best as I could and I aimed high. Perhaps only Heaven understands me."

Weighed down with sadness, he wept and composed a song for himself to sing:

Mount Tai is falling,
A pillar is collapsing,

Oh, philosopher,
Like grass, you are withering.

This was his swan song. He died seven days later after he wrote this song at the age of seventy-three. He was buried in Qufu, Shandong. Many of his students stayed by his grave-side for three years in mourning. Zigong stayed there for three more years.

The sayings of Confucius were recorded in the *Analects*. His tomb and temple became a mecca for most Chinese.

Comment: It is somewhat disappointing to find that, for a man whose teachings have influenced the life, thought and language of the Chinese, Confucius had not had a very dramatic life.

Confucius's view on the government and the individual is probably the most important element of his doctrine.

He believes that the aim of the government is the welfare of the people. The best way to govern is by moral values and virtuous examples from the above, not by negative means of law and punishment. The best candidates for government are those who are equipped with qualities of human kindness and profound knowledge. For that reason, Confucius is concerned with the development of the individual.

Confucius's thought centers around the ideal of humanity, or benevolence, whose chief qualities are courtesy, tolerance, good faith, diligence, kindness, moderation, bravery, loyalty and filial piety. Confucius holds that these virtues can be acquired through education and personal cultivation. Hence the importance of learning.

Moreover, Confucius points out, without learning, love of benevolence may become stupidity; love of bravery may lapse into recklessness; without learning, love of honesty may degenerate into gullibility, love of uprightness into impetuosity; without learning, love of wisdom may lead to superficial generalization, and love of loyalty may cause one to hurt others.

Confucius holds that intrinsic moral qualities are more important than one's outward appearance. But inner virtues are necessarily embodied by good behavior. At the same time, he believes that manners make the man. Good manners, whether in public or private, have a subtle impact on character. They tend to push one towards goodness and keep him from wrongdoing. Just as listening to music brings harmony to the mind, so good manners bring harmony to the character.

For Confucius, the ideal person is a man of wisdom and virtue.

Confucius's emphasis on education, his advocacy for moral principles, his respect for the scholar and the teaching profession, his belief in the role of the family, and the importance he attached to the civil service have, for centuries, exerted profound influence not only in China, but also in Japan, Korea, and other Asian countries.

12. FATHER TALKS

Zigong asked: "Is there a single motto that one can live by in all one's life?"

The Master said: "It is perhaps to be considerate towards your fellow men. Never do to others what you do not want to be done to yourself."

—*Confucius*

Yan Zhitui (531-591) was a noted scholar of the sixth century. His family had a long record of government service and scholarly achievement. Yan lived in a period of turmoil in Chinese history known as the Northern and Southern Dynasties. For one hundred and seventy years, China was divided into two parts: north and south. During that time, the ruling regime in the north changed hands four times and in the south five times. Yan served under two governments, was twice taken prisoner by opposing forces, and lived through five regimes in his sixty years of life.

Based on his belief in family value, his attention to personal growth and development, and his moral convictions, Yan wrote Family Instructions *for his children, with lessons drawn from his checkered experiences in life, his personal sufferings and the vicissitudes of his career. The book highlights many of the values shared by ancient Chinese.*

The following is taken from his Family Instructions, *which has become a handbook for Chinese families for generations since his day.*

CHILD EDUCATION

It is your bounden duty as parents to provide your children with good education. Love does not mean just to feed and clothe the children well and to take care of their material needs. To love also means to educate. And education should start even before the child is born.

When a woman is pregnant, she should read the right books or listen to good classics read to her, and be in the right company. She should not overexert herself or let anything frighten her. She should not seek for sensory satisfaction through such stimuli as drugs or sexual indulgence. She should avoid quarrelling and not talk too much.

In short, she should see no evil, hear no evil and say no evil words. Then she will have a bright and healthy baby born to her. Otherwise she may cause afflictions on her child. So a woman has a lot of responsibility for educating the unborn.

If a child has not received proper education before his birth, education should start as soon as he is able to recognize people's faces and tell their expressions. Train him to listen to you and follow your instructions regarding what to do and what not to do, when to play and when to rest. A child brought up in this way needs no physical punishment when he grows bigger.

Praise the child when he deserves. Do not praise him when you ought to talk to him seriously. Do not laugh it away when you ought to give him a dressing-down. Otherwise the child may misunderstand you or get confused. If his bad behavior becomes a habit, then it may be too late to change him. Habit is second nature. By the time a bad habit is already formed, even physical punishment may not avail. Your punishment will only cause resentment in the child. Such a child is bound to have trouble when he grows up.

There are times when physical punishment is necessary in child education. Those who say that they cannot bear to punish the child actually do him more harm than good. Some parents argue that they do not punish the child because they do not want the child to lose self-respect. But let me ask you: "If a person is sick, would you withhold medicine from him because the pills are bitter?" Parents who punish the child by no means take any pleasure in doing so. It is only because they have no option but to take such stern measures under the circumstances. The worst thing is to punish the child after you have spoiled him.

Education, by my definition, is not of much use to a genius or an idiot. It is meant for the average child.

FAMILY RELATIONSHIP

There are three fundamental human relationships. First there is the relationship between husband and wife; next comes that between parents and children, and then that between brothers and sisters. All other relationships are based on these three.

What is the ideal relationship between a father and his child? It is love mixed with respect and affection coupled with dignity. A father loves his child and at the same time, he should command respect from him. He loves his child but maintains a degree of dignity. Only love combined with dignity can inspire filial piety in the child.

Confucius said that a father should keep a proper distance from his own son. Without a proper distance, it may not be easy to foster a relationship in which a father loves the child and the child cherishes a filial devotion to the father. Over-intimacy may cause the child to slight the father. Therefore the father should preferably not share the same room with the child.

It is advisable that a father does not teach his own son. Certain things such as sex education are better taught by others rather than the parents.

The teacher can demand the student to work hard. He is supposed to show anger if the student does not behave. But if a father gets angry with his child, the child may think that though his father teaches him to behave, yet he himself does not practice what he teaches. This may lead to estrangement, and nothing is worse than estrangement between father and son. That is why in ancient times, fathers only taught other people's children, but not their own.

I hope you appreciate this subtle point in child education.

Brothers and sisters love each other. When you grow up, you eat at the same table with your brothers and sisters; you study and play together, or even share clothes with each other. It is only natural you are attached to each other. It is also natural that you expect a lot from your brothers and sisters. If they disappoint you, you get upset easily but make it up quickly, too. Sibling relationship is a special one, different from ordinary relationships. If there is a crack in your relationship with your siblings, you must fix it up without delay. Never allow it to grow big.

Oddly enough, I find some people are very nice to their friends, but do not seem to cherish the relationship with their siblings. They treat outsiders well but are hard on their own folks. Some are even able to command the loyalty of tens of thousands of people, but cannot be kind to his own siblings.

It seems difficult for a lot of parents to love all their children equally. But parents must bear in mind that partiality has bad consequences. A bright and well-behaved child deserves love and approval, but a dumb and stubborn child deserves love and sympathy, too. Partiality toward a child can make him too conceited to get along well with his brothers and sisters.

Children normally follow their parents' example. If a parent is nice to a child, the child is bound to love the parent. If the elder brother is cold to the younger one, the younger one will not respect him. If a husband is unfaithful, he cannot expect his wife to listen to him. But what if the child is unruly when the parent is nice to him, or if the younger brother is recalcitrant when the elder one treats him well, or if the husband is faithful and loving but the wife is a shrew? Such people are inherently bad, and only punishment can deter them.

Moral influence has its limit. There is a point where moral persuasion ends and punishment begins. Without appropriate punishment, a bad child will go from bad to worse. Running a household is not unlike running a country. Without legal justice, you cannot run the country. Without a reward for good behavior and an appropriate punishment for bad behavior, you cannot manage a family. Too much leniency is as bad as harshness. The best is a balance between the two.

MARRIAGE AND COMPANIONSHIP

In marriage, if there is a big difference in the background between the husband and the wife, they may have different sets of values. This difference may pose a potential snag in their relationship. A person from a rich family may be haughty to a person of modest origin. The person who comes from a poor family may have inferiority complex. If they allow their in-laws get involved in their relationship, things will become more complicated. That is why I usually do not advise people of very different backgrounds to get married.

I was born in a time of turbulence. I travelled everywhere in the country and met a lot of people. Whenever I met a virtuous man, I was always attracted by his personality. I wanted to learn something from him. When you are young, you are malleable. If you are in the company of a man of virtue, you will imitate him before you know it, even though you may not be conscious of what you are doing. He is bound to have some influence on you.

To associate with people of noble character is like going into a room full of fragrant orchids. If you stay in the room long enough, you will acquire the pleasant smell yourself. On the contrary, to expose yourself to bad company is like going to a fish market, you will get the stink if you hang in there long enough.

Watching a dyer of silk at work, the famous philosopher Mo Zi (468-376 B.C.) made the following comment:

"What is dyed in blue becomes blue. What is dyed in yellow becomes yellow. After being dyed a few times, the original color of the silk is beyond recognition. This is true not only with silk, but also with an individual or a country. An individual can be influenced by what kind of people he associates with. A country can be changed by the kind of influences it is placed under."

Therefore you must choose your friends carefully. Confucius said: "Don't make friends who are not equal to yourself." So, associate with those from whom you can learn something. As long as someone is better than you in some respect, make him your friend.

Some people tend to believe what they read in the books, but overlook what they see in real life. They think great men only existed in the past and do not accept that there are great men in our time. Some may believe there are great men in foreign countries and are eager to meet them. But they do not recognize great men among their friends and fellow students and may even make fun of them. Familiarity seems to have blinded these people. Actually they do not have to look far away or look back into the past for greatness. The fact is there are great men here and now.

In Confucius' time, people in his own country, Lu, did not give him recognition. Confucius had to leave his own country. The king of Yu, in the Spring and Autumn Period in history, lost his country because he did not take seriously the far-sighted advice of his friend who was very close to him.

STUDY

Study serves two purposes. One is to cultivate one's mind and broaden one's horizon. The other is to enable one to make contributions to the society. Unfortunately nowadays most people regard the cultivation of their character as a means to secure lucrative positions. Whatever service they offer to the society is lip service.

Study has its practical value as well as idealistic. In addition to cultivating character, study enables you to improve your overall ability and to master specific skills to make a living. Your skill will stand you in good stead especially in times of uncertainty when no permanent employment and no family support are available. Your survival depends on your education. A useful skill is better than money. Whether you are bright or dumb, you must study. It is always good to have more knowledge and know more people.

The best time to study is when you are young and your mind is fresh. What is learnt in the cradle lasts till the tomb. As you grow up, you will be distracted by many other things. Concentration becomes more difficult. That is why you should not squander your youth. I still remember what I learnt when I was a seven-year-old boy. But what I learnt after twenty, I tend to forget after only a month.

Due to circumstances, some people were not able to devote themselves to studies when they were young. In that case, they have to receive adult education and redouble their efforts. Adult education is of course one step late, as adults cannot compete with young people. But they must never write themselves off as hopeless. Let me tell you a story.

Shi Kuang was a blind musician (in the sixth century B.C.).

One day the king of Jin said to him: "I want to study, but I am afraid I'm too old. I am already seventy. It's too late."

Shi Kuang said: "Too late? Why not light some candles?"

"I am serious. Why are you joking?"

"I am not, Your Majesty. A young man fond of studying is like the morning sun. He has a bright future. A middle-aged man is like the noonday sun. He still has half a day's good time ahead. An old man who has knowledge is like the light of a candle. He is still better than a blind man like me who have to grope in darkness."

Learning is like growing plants. You reap what you sow. You have to aim high. If you do not set a high goal for yourself, you may fall below average. To learn something really well, you have to study the classics in your chosen field and learn from experts at the same time. Respect authorities but do not treat them as gods. Otherwise you will never surpass them. Only by using their achievement as your starting point, can you hope to surpass them. In every field, there are great masters. But the chances are that you may not meet them. Most people can only learn from those who are not experts. Do not let them limit your potential.

In every professional field there are certain guiding principles to follow. If you do not grasp them, you cannot make great achievement. So don't just concentrate on technical skills.

I am not against being well-read. But you have to choose your profession. The pre-requisite of being a learned man is that you are already well-versed in your own field. It is difficult enough for most people to master everything in their chosen field. At most they can learn probably two-thirds, which is already quite good. If you are learning a specific skill, it is essential you learn under the instruction of a master. It is better to know everything about something than to know something about everything. A lot of smart people do not realize all the excellent potential in themselves because they are not specialized.

Books can teach children their duties toward their parents, and turn the proud to be humble, the mean to be charitable, the miserly to be generous, the cruel to be gentle, the timid to be brave, the selfish to be considerate, the impetuous to be patient and the narrow-minded to be tolerant.

However, a lot of people, who can quote what they have read in books, never practice what they have learnt. Study is supposed to help you improve yourself. But I have noticed some people tend to get supercilious just because they know something that others do not. They look down upon their contemporaries and do not respect their elders. As a result, others dislike them. If knowledge makes them behave like that, it is better not to have any knowledge at all.

SUCCESS IN LIFE

My father told me: "Always love truth and be ready to defend it. Cultivate your character and make a career when opportunity comes along. If you uphold moral principles and still do not succeed, it is the will of Heaven. There are many ways of achieving success in life. Some people have secured good positions through doing shameful things, through nepotism, bribery, disparaging others in order to advance themselves. They have no scruples in promoting their self-interest. To me, these people are like thieves."

Some parents ignore ethics on account of the career prospects of their children. But career success at the expense of moral integrity is the worst example which parents can set for their children.

Some people try very hard but success evades them. Others seem to succeed easily. In life we should not ignore the element of luck. Sometimes no matter what you do, you cannot succeed. But if you are in luck, you will find fame and fortune even if you are not seeking them.

Life is a paradox. Success may not be entirely of your own making. It depends on the will of Heaven. But before that day comes, prepare yourself. Make yourself worthy of God's favor. Acquire more knowledge and pick up a specialty for yourself.

When you do attain success, remember not to indulge yourself and not to use up your prosperity. The most ideal position is an office of middle rank with fifty people above you and fifty below. Stick to the middle course and do not accept too high a position which invariably exposes you to danger. Then you are shielded from shame or disgrace; your risk is minimized. Be modest, humble and willing to suffer some losses so that disaster may stay away.

The world has its limit, but human desire knows no bounds. You only need enough food to eat, enough clothes to keep you warm and a house for shelter. Set a limit to your desire. Do not pursue luxury and do not be enslaved by too many desires. A contented mind is a perpetual feast.

The truth about nature and about the universe is that excess is dangerous; it incurs penalty.

Comment: Yan Zhitui lived in a male-dominated society, which, as a matter of course, had an impact on his views and even his choice of words. Nevertheless this ought not to hinder us from appreciating some of the simple, plain truths that he talked about.

Speaking of family value, the Chinese tradition regards filial devotion as the fount of all virtues. A loving husband, a faithful friend, or a good citizen is, first and foremost, a responsible child to his parents. Of all human relations, the relation between the child and its parents is the most fundamental for it constitutes the basis of society. Respect for and obligations to the aged are its natural expression.

But Yan Zhitui does not take filial devotion for granted; he spells out the duties of parents explicitly and emphatically, suggesting that parents have to earn it. After all, it is not the child who asks to be born. It is the decision of the parents that brings the child into the world. So it is only proper that before filial piety come love and care from the parents.

Our society, in many respects, is undoubtedly a quantum jump forward from Yan Zhitui's days. However, the success of our society in educating the young is still doubtful.

Some parents are being baffled, challenged and rebelled against by their children. Some have lost their sense of balance and appropriateness while trying to "catch up" with the changing environment and to be "trendy." Some even choose to neglect, abuse, or abandon their children.

Some of us believe that education of the young starts at and belongs to the school alone. Some abrogate their own moral responsibility and assert that law and police are the sole answer to crime. We are also laboring under the notion that money can solve every problem, money can raise our educational standard, money can cure social evils—as though we have not spent enough already.

We are living in a permissive society. We have so much freedom. But often we are not held responsible for our own behavior. Our freedom is somehow separated from our responsibility; our right from our obligation. Various theories of behavior science, or rather pseudo-behavior science, try to explain away all sorts of wrong-doings. Family value, conscience, willpower, discipline, character building and moral value seem to have ceased to be meaningful.

For this reason, it is refreshing to hear Yan Zhitui talk even though one may not agree with him on everything.

13. VIRTUOUS MOTHERS

A great man is one who has not lost the child's heart.
—Mencius (372-289 B.C.)

The role of the mother in a traditional Chinese family could never be stressed too much. The most famous Chinese mother is Mother Meng, mother of Mencius. Her wisdom is known to virtually every Chinese parent.

NEIGHBORHOOD

Mencius lost his father when he was only three years old, and his mother had to weave in order to make a living. Mother Meng placed a great hope on her son.

They lived not far from a cemetery. Mencius often played games with other boys to mimic how people buried the dead and mourned for the dead. Mother Meng decided to move out, believing that this neighborhood was no place to bring up a child.

She found a house near a marketplace. But before long Mencius began to play at hawking goods and haggling prices with neighborhood kids like street peddlers and shopkeepers. Mother Meng decided that the environment was not good for the boy, either.

Again she moved. This time she took care to examine the neighborhood before moving in. Their new home was near a school. There they settled down. The boy began to pattern himself after the pupils in the school. Mother Meng was pleased.

Comment: This is one of the first stories a Chinese child is told. It has caught the fancy of the Chinese. It probably explains why many Chinese have an obsession of living in a good neighborhood.

THE LOOM

In time Mencius went to school. Once the boy came home earlier than usual.

"Why did you come back so early today?" Mother Meng asked, still weaving at her loom.

"I miss you, ma'am."

Without a word, Mother Meng took out a knife and cut the yarn on the loom right in the middle. Mencius was startled.

"For you to suspend your study at school is just like for me to cut the yarn on my loom. We are poor. That is why I've been working so hard. You have to study hard to establish yourself. If you do not concentrate on your studies and stop halfway, we will never be able to break the bondage of poverty. We will always have to lead a precarious life."

From then on, Mencius devoted himself completely to learning.

Later, Mencius had a chance to study under a disciple of Zi Si, the grandson of Confucius. He was greatly inspired and became a famous scholar.

Comment: What a vivid metaphor! Mother Meng's point is well taken.

PRIVACY AT HOME

Mencius married the daughter of a friend of his father's.

One day when entering his wife's room, he found her half naked. He was displeased. His wife went to her mother-in-law to ask for permission to go back to her own home.

"I heard that between husband and wife there should still be some privacy," she complained. "Now my husband is not happy because I was only partially dressed when he barged into my room. I felt being treated unfairly. I don't want to stay here."

Mother Meng called in Mencius.

"You should ask whether there is anyone inside before you enter a house," she said to her son. "You should knock on the door or make a sound to give notice before you enter a room. You should look down when you open the door of the bedroom to avoid seeing what others may not want you to see. This means respect for others and it is good manner. You didn't behave yourself today. How can you blame your wife? Is that fair?"

Mencius apologized to his wife and begged her to stay.

Comment: Respect is the foundation of any relationship. And a marital relationship is among the most important ones. We can show our respect to our spouse by not violating his or her privacy. Mother Meng well understood this.

THE RIGHT THING TO DO

Mencius was born a century after the death of Confucius at a time known as the Period of Warring States in Chinese history, a time characterized by social anarchy, political instability and constant wars.

Mencius believed that the king ruled with the mandate of Heaven. Such mandate was not given in perpetuity. If the king lost moral qualities and abused his power, the mandate would be taken away from him.

When he was serving as a minister in the state of Qi, he tried very hard to persuade the king to adopt his idea of government.

"The people have to have a stable job and real property for a living," Mencius advised the king. "Once the stability of livelihood is gone, they are likely to lapse into wrongdoing.

"If you wait until they lapse into crime and then punish them, it is like setting traps for them. An enlightened ruler never sets traps for his people. He makes sure that they have stable jobs and real property to support their families, and that they live well in good years and in bad years. Only then will he urge them to be good and honest.

"But today under your policy, people do not have enough to support their families or parents. In good years they have to work hard all year round. In bad years, they struggle just to survive. What leisure do they have for cultivating proper behavior and nurturing virtues? You have to reverse your policy and turn to what is fundamental."

The king, however, only interested in power and wealth, turned a deaf ear to Mencius. Therefore, Mencius was thinking of resigning from his post, but he was concerned about providing for his elderly mother.

One day Mother Meng heard him sighing and asked to know the reason.

"I heard that a gentleman examines his own ability before taking up a position. He does not sail under false colors to seek personal gains. He is neither vain nor greedy. To stand in a king's court where his principles cannot prevail - that is a matter to be ashamed of. He will not serve the king who refuses to listen to him. Now the king of Qi won't take my advice, I want to quit and go elsewhere. But I am concerned as you are getting old."

"Do the right thing. Don't worry about me," Mother Meng said. "You have your principles to follow just as I have my duties to do."

So, Mencius resigned from his post.

He traveled from one state to another, trying to find a ruler willing to put Confucian idea into practice but all to no avail. In the end, he decided to devote himself to teaching and writing in order to spread the gospel of Confucianism. He is honored as the Second Sage by the Chinese.

Comment: Mencius's view on human nature is particularly significant. He believes when left to follow its natural inclination, human nature will do good. All men have a sense of mercy, a sense of shame, a sense of respect and a sense of what is right and what is wrong.

For example, if we see a child about to fall into a well, we will feel horrified and try to rescue the child. It is not because we want to gain the favor of the child's parents or seek approbation from friends and neighbors, or fear that we may be blamed if we do not rescue the child. It is only in our nature to want to do so.

As we cannot bear to see others suffer, the outcome will be human compassion if we extend that feeling to all the people we meet with. And the outcome will be righteousness if we extend that feeling to whatever things we do.

If a man can fully develop the feeling of not wishing to harm others, his human compassion will be inexhaustible. If a man can fully extend the feeling of not wanting to steal, his righteousness will be inexhaustible. If a man can fully expand his desire of not wanting to be addressed to by others in contempt, he will behave honestly wherever he goes.

The feeling of compassion is the beginning of humanity. The sense of shame is the beginning of righteousness. The sense of respect is the beginning of propriety. The sense of what is right and what is wrong is the beginning of wisdom.

All of us have these four intrinsic qualities just as we have the four limbs. They are inherent in our nature, only we do not think about them consciously. Therefore if we seek, we will find them. If a man pretends that he cannot find them, he is simply destroying himself.

So Mencius urges us to fully realize and develop these innate qualities and claims if we can fully develop these qualities, we will have all that is needed to govern the world. But if we fail to do so, we cannot even take care of our own family.

ARMCHAIR GENERAL

Zhao Kuo's father was a brilliant general in the state of Zhao. Zhao Kuo studied military science since he was a boy. He became so eloquent in the theories of military strategy that he even beat his father once in a discussion on the subject. But his father did not think that he could really make a good general.

"War is a matter of life and death," said the father when Zhao Kuo's mother asked to know the reason. "But when our son talks about war, he makes light of it. I hope he would never be an army general. Otherwise he is bound to destroy the whole army."

After his father died, Zhao Kuo became an army officer.

When Qin invaded Zhao, the king of Zhao decided to appoint Zhao Kuo to be the commander-in-chief to fight the enemy. His mother hastened to petition to the king imploring him not to do so.

"When I married his father, he was an army commander. He took good care of his soldiers and shared with them whatever Your Majesty gave him. When he led his men to fight, he devoted all his attention to his job, never once allowing domestic matters to divert his mind. But Zhao Kuo is different. He became arrogant as soon as he was appointed army general. He does not share anything with his soldiers and is keen on buying properties for himself. Your Majesty are making a grave mistake if you appoint him commander-in-chief on account of his father's reputation. Zhao Kuo has only book knowledge of war. He doesn't know how to apply what he has learnt in the book to a real battle."

"Leave this to me, madam," the king replied. "I've made up my mind."

"If so, I will have nothing to do with it," said the mother. "Don't tell me I haven't warned you if he disappoints you."

After he assumed the command of the army, Zhao Kuo first replaced all the earlier appointments and then changed the strategy of his predecessor. The army of Qin was led by an experienced general. He fooled Zhao Kuo by feigning retreat in the battle, then cut the supply line of the Zhao army in a surprise attack, split them into two isolated sections unable to support each other and besieged them for more than forty days. Zhao Kuo was killed when he tried to break through the enemy encirclement. His forces sustained a devastating defeat and the enemy nearly captured the capital of Zhao.

Comment: A mother's warning is not to be ignored for few people know a child better than the parents.

OLD WOUND

When Kou Zhun was a boy, he loved playing and hated studying, and was careless in everything he did. One day his mother got so angry that she threw the sliding weight of a steelyard at him, hitting him in the foot. His foot was hurt and blood came out. After that, Kou Zhun changed his way and began to study earnestly.

By the time he became a prime minister under Emperor Zhenzong of the Song Dynasty, his mother had already died. Kou often stroked the scar on his foot. Sometimes he would stare at the old wound and cry because he was thinking of his mother.

Comment: Kou Zhun might not appreciate at the time that his mother hit him because she loved him and wanted him to be good. We are not in favor of such corporal punishment. But without a strict mother, Kou Zhun probably would never have become a prime minister. In certain circumstances, "shock treatment" may be necessary for the good of the child. This certainly should not be equated with child abuse.

SNAKE WITH TWIN HEADS

When Sun Shuao was a small boy, he saw a twin-headed snake one day. He killed it on the spot, dug a hole in the ground and buried it.

Then he went home crying.

"Mother, I won't be with you for long," said the boy to his mother. "I heard that whoever saw a twin-headed snake would not live long. I saw one on my way home," the boy said.

"Where is the snake?"

"I killed it. I have dug a hole and buried the dead snake. I did not want other people to see it and go home and die, too."

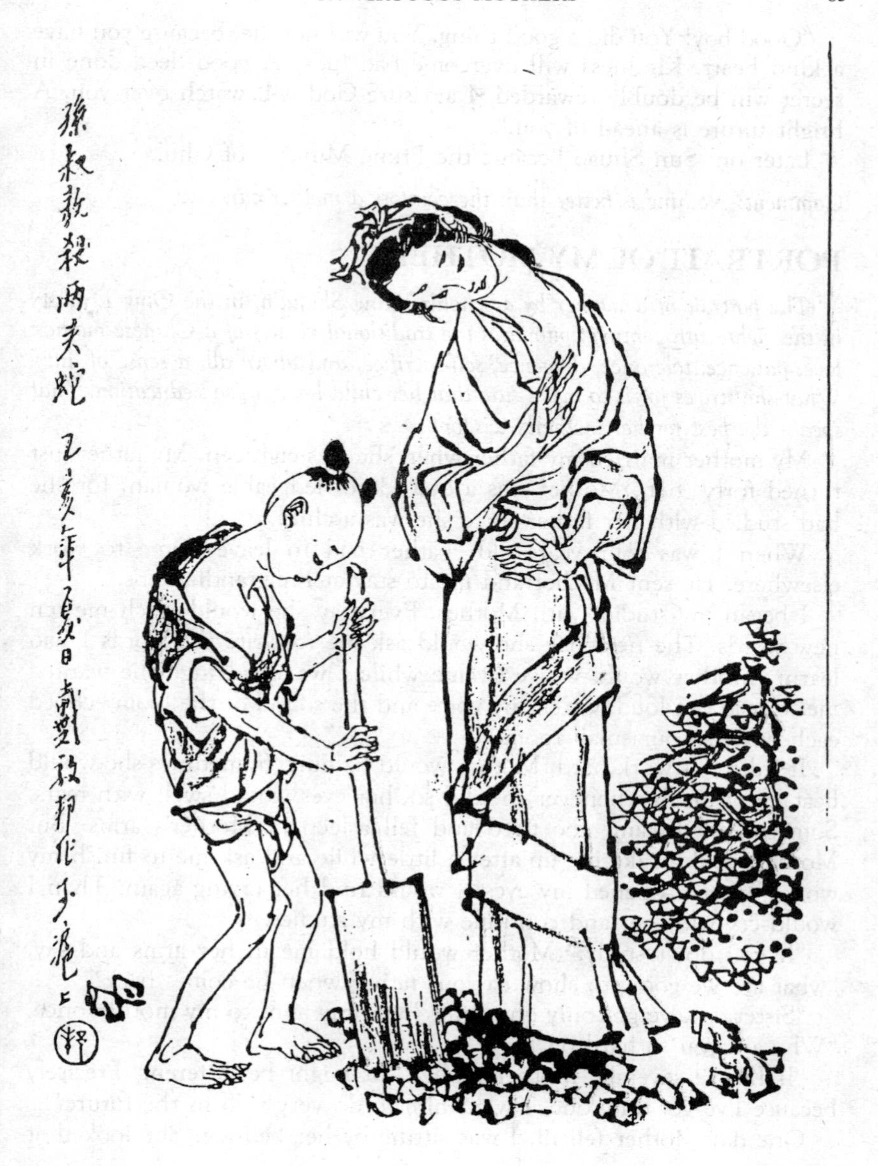
孫叔敖殺兩头蛇
乙亥年夏日戴敦邦作于滬上

"Good boy! You did a good thing. You will not die, because you have a kind heart. Kindness will overcome bad luck. A good deed done in secret will be doubly rewarded. I am sure God will watch over you. A bright future is ahead of you."

Later on, Sun Shuao became the Prime Minister of Chu.

Comment: Nothing is better than the comfort a mother can give.

PORTRAIT OF MY MOTHER

The portrait of a mother by a scholar, Jiang Shiquan, in the Qing Dynasty in the eighteenth century epitomizes the traditional virtues of a Chinese mother: love, patience, tolerance, diligence, self-sacrifice, and above all, a sense of duty. What she strives for is to make sure that her child have a good education. That speaks the best for her motherly wisdom.

My mother married my father when she was eighteen. My father just turned forty then. Mother was a quite knowledgeable woman, for she had studied with her father since she was a child.

When I was four years old, Father had to leave home to work elsewhere. He sent Mother and me to stay at my grandfather's.

I began my studies with Mother. Everyday she would teach me ten new words. The next day she would ask me to write the words I had learnt. Mother would weave by me while I was studying. She wanted me to read out loud. Often my voice and the sound of the loom echoed each other in our small room.

If I did not work hard, Mother would be hurt. Sometimes she would beat me, though whenever she did so, her eyes would swell with tears. Sometimes I became too tired and fell asleep in Mother's arms. But Mother would wake me up after a little while and ask me to finish my work. When I opened my eyes, I would find her crying again. Then I would cry with her and continue with my studies.

"If you don't study," Mother would hold me in her arms and say, "what are we going to show to your father when he comes back?"

"Sister, you've got only one child," said my aunt to my mother once. "Why are you so hard on him?"

"If I have several," Mother replied, "it might be different. Precisely because I've got only one, I want him to do very well in the future?"

One day Mother fell ill, I was sitting by her bedside. She looked at me and I looked at her, our hearts filled with an indescribable feeling of love bordering on sorrow.

"What can I do to make you happy, Mother?" I asked.

"If you can recite what you have learnt, I'll be happy."

So I stood up, reciting loudly and clearly what I had just learnt.

"I feel much better now," Mother said, her face beaming with smile.

My grandfather's family was never rich, especially after a few poor harvests when things got worse. All my clothes and shoes were made by Mother. As a matter of fact, her handicraft works were so good that they became the admiration of the local community. Whenever anything she had embroidered appeared in the market, it would be sold out in an instant.

When my grandmother fell seriously ill, Mother waited upon her for forty days and forty nights. But she never showed any sign of fatigue. Before serving a meal or a decoction of herbal medicine to Grandma, she would first taste it herself to make sure it was all right. When Grandma passed away, Mother was so distraught that she did not eat a morsel of food for seven days.

Father finally came back when I was ten. The following year he took us to where he was appointed a magistrate. Whenever Father had an important case to hear, Mother would urge him to exercise the best of his judgment.

"You know you must not make a mistake lest there should be retribution on our child," she would warn Father. And Father always nodded readily.

If Father did something wrong, Mother would point it out. But when Father got impatient and refused to listen to her, she would drop the matter for a while until later when she found Father in a better mood. Then she would raise the matter again and talk to him until Father admitted his mistake.

Father died when Mother was forty-three. She cried so hard that she fainted several times. At the funeral, Mother gave a short memorial speech. Plain as it was, it carried such a touching note of deep love and heart-rending grief that everyone at the service was moved to tears.

I got married at the age of twenty-one. Mother treated my wife like her own daughter. The following year when I passed the imperial examinations, Mother's happiness was beyond description.

I had to work away from home. When Mother missed me, she would write poems to pour out her feelings for me. But she never sent me any one of her poems.

Not long ago I came across a very good portrait artist. I asked him to paint Mother's portrait. For the background scene, I asked Mother for her opinion.

"Mother, I hope the portrait will make you happy. Please tell me what you would like to be put in the picture."

"Well," Mother heaved a sigh. "My parents and my husband have all gone. There is really no happiness to talk about. But if my son and daughter-in-law know how to teach their children, I will be satisfied."

So, the artist painted a portrait with my mother weaving at the loom, my wife sitting by her side to give her a helping hand, myself studying by the desk under a big candle, and a boy and a girl playing under the moonlight in the garden outside where trees and flowers were gently swaying in the autumn breeze.

Mother liked the portrait very much. So I am writing a profile of my mother to commemorate the occasion.

Comment: An ordinary yet great mother.

14. NO JOKING MATTER

To be poor is not shameful; it is to be poor and to have no high aspirations that is shameful. To hold a lowly position is not dreadful; it is to hold a lowly position and not to improve your ability that is dreadful. Getting old is not lamentable; it is getting old and having wasted your life that is lamentable. To die is not a sad thing; it is to die without anyone knowing you that is really sad.

—*Chinese proverb*

TO KILL A PIG

Zeng Shen was a disciple of Confucius.

One day Zeng Shen's son was crying because his mother refused to let him go shopping with her.

"Be a good boy, and stay at home," said the mother. "When Mother comes back, we are going to kill a pig and cook a nice meal for you. I know you like pork."

The boy nodded and stayed home.

When she got back, she saw Zeng Shen ready to kill a pig in the family's pigsty. She hastened to stop him.

"I was only joking. You needn't kill the pig today."

"This's no joking matter," Zeng Shen said. "Make sure you never lie to a child. A child does not know what is right and what is wrong. He imitates his parents. Now if you deceive him, he will think that it is all right to deceive. And he will not believe you any more. This is not the way to teach a child."

Thus Zeng Shen killed the pig and cooked some pork for the boy.

Comment: Example is better than precept and credibility begins at home with the children.

FILIAL THOUGHTS

When Bo Yu did something wrong, his mother used to spank him, but he would not cry even though it hurt.

曾子殺猪
乙亥

One day he again did something wrong. His mother again beat him with a stick. This time, however, he cried.

His mother was surprised.

"Why do you cry today? You never cried before when I hit you."

"Mother, in the past when you beat me, it always hurt. But this time, it doesn't hurt any more. I realize it is because you are getting old. That's why I am crying."

Comment: Bo Yu was too sincere to realize the dig in his remark.

CHANTING

Being a devoted Buddhist, Zhai Yongling's mother chanted the name of Buddha all day long. Yongling had tried many times to persuade her not to do so, but to no avail.

One day Yongling found some pretext and called to his mother, "Mother!" "Yes," she answered. Yongling called again. Again she answered. Then he called for the third and fourth times. His mother got annoyed.

"What's the matter with you? Why are you calling me so many times today?"

Yongling said:"Aha! You get annoyed when I only called you a few times. But you call Buddha a thousand times a day. How annoyed he must be!"

Since then, his mother no longer chanted the name of Buddha the way she did before.

Comment: A light-hearted way of following Confucius's teaching that it is a son's duty to speak out when he thinks what his parent does is wrong.

GENERAL WU QI

When General Wu Qi of the state of Wei led an army to attack the state of Zhongshan, he wore the same clothes and ate the same food as a rank and file member of his army. He slept with the soldiers and marched on foot instead of riding a horse or in a carriage.

One day he learnt that one of his soldiers had a boil from a wound, he went to see him. In front of all the men there, he knelt down and sucked the pus out of the boil with his own mouth.

When the soldier's mother heard of the news, tears ran down her cheeks.

"Why should you weep?" someone asked her. "Your son is only a foot soldier, but the general is taking good care of him."

"You don't know," said the mother. "A few years ago, General Wu did the same thing for the boy's father. He was so grateful that he fought bravely until he was struck down by the enemy. Now the boy will surely die for the general, too. That is why I am weeping."

Comment: Action speaks louder than words.

BEGGAR'S EXCUSE

A beggar was cooking his meal in the street. He was about forty and there was a boy of about seven or eight by his side.

"You're a robust young man. Why don't you find a job for yourself instead of begging in the street?" somebody asked him.

"It's all because of my mother," the beggar replied.

"How so?"

"I came from a wealthy family. My father died early. When I was a small child, my grandfather urged me to study and learn some useful skill. But my mother pampered me. She wouldn't let me work hard. Whatever I wanted, she would give me until I was totally satisfied. In the end, I had very little education. I fell into bad company and squandered away all my money. My wife divorced me, leaving behind her this child. Sure I want a job, but I have no education and no skill. Who wants me? I can only go begging. Isn't it all my mother's fault?"

Comment: But blaming mother, even if with some justification, will not solve anything; it is never too old to learn. Confucius said that the real fault is to have faults and not to amend them.

MOTHER'S MILK

A man was about to be executed for a serious crime. On the execution ground, there was a placard with the words: "It Is Too Late Now!" written on it.

Before the execution, the man asked to see his mother for the last time. His request was granted and his mother came.

"Mother, I'm not going to see you any more. Could I have a taste of your milk?"

His mother unbuttoned her clothes and let him suck her breast. Suddenly the man bit off her nipple. She screamed in agony and nearly passed out.

As the man was being dragged away, he shouted: "Mother, I hate you! It's all your fault. If you had raised me properly, I would not have come to this today."

Comment: A gruesome reversal of Oedipus complex. Indeed, most Chinese would consider that the man's parents were at least partially responsible for his lapse into crime.

FOUND AND LOST

It was in the Yuan Dynasty in the thirteenth century.

Early one morning, a young man went to the market to buy some vegetables. On his way, he found a bundle of money. It was still dark. He hid himself away and waited until daybreak to count his windfall. To his surprise, the bundle of money was worth a hundred and fifty ounces of silver. So he took an ounce of silver and bought some meat and rice instead of vegetables.

When he got home, his mother asked him why he did not buy any vegetables.

"Look, Mother, I found so much money in the street. So I bought some rice and meat for you."

"Don't lie to me," the mother said. "People may drop one or two bills accidentally, but not a bundle of money like this. I hope it's not stolen money. You should know that ill-gotten wealth never brings luck."

The son kept silent. The mother became angry and threatened to inform the police on him.

"I honestly found it in the street. I don't know whom to return the money to, Mother."

"Just wait there where you found it. When the owner comes looking for it, give the money back to him. We are poor. We don't have the money to buy this much meat and rice. But if you keep what does not belong to you, you are inviting bad luck."

The young man went back to the spot where he had found the

money. Soon a man came to look for it. The young man was a simple-minded person. Without asking how much the man had lost, he handed him the bundle of money.

Some bystander saw this and suggested to the owner that he give the young man some money as reward. But the man was something of a miser.

"I lost three hundred ounces of silver. Here is only half of it. Why should I reward him?"

His remark triggered a quarrel between the young man and himself.

To resolve their dispute, they went to the local magistrate. The magistrate secretly sent for the young man's mother, questioned her separately and found what she had said corresponded to her son's account.

He asked each man to sign a sworn statement regarding the exact amount of the money lost or found.

"All right," he announced. "The money found is not the money lost. It must be a god-send to a good mother."

He ordered to have the money given to the young man's mother and told her to go home with her son. Then he turned to the other man.

"You must have lost your three hundred ounces somewhere else. Go and look for your money there."

His verdict won the approval of the audience in the court-room.

Comment: Cheats never prosper. Dishonesty often has a boomerang effect.

FOUR TIMES SEVEN

"Four times seven is twenty-eight," said one man.

"Four times seven is twenty-seven," said another.

The two men argued and argued until both became so furious that they got into a fist fight, and were brought before the local magistrate who ruled that the first man be caned.

The man shouted his protest.

"You were so foolish," said the magistrate solemnly, "as to come to blows (or: fight) with a man who was ridiculous enough to suggest four times seven is twenty-seven? Shouldn't you be punished?"

The man, at length, nodded in agreement, admitting that the magistrate had a point there.

Comment: Silence is golden when it is plain meaningless to argue. If the first man were really sensible, he probably would not have got himself into trouble for taking a fool so seriously. But in a sense, the second man's punishment is even worse than the first man's: for he would never know he was wrong.

PART III
WIT, WILL AND THE ART OF WINNING

15. THE ART OF COMPETITION

Zilu asked: "If you were leading a great army, what sort of a person would you want to be with you?"

The Master said: "I would not take the person who fights a tiger with his bare hands, or crosses a river without a boat. I want somebody who approaches difficulties with caution and who chooses to succeed by strategy."

—*Confucius*

The Art of War *is one of the most widely read books in the world. Its author Sun Zi was a military advisor to the king of the state of Wu, a region in modern Zhejiang, east China, about two thousand and five hundred years ago during the Spring and Autumn Period. During that period and the subsequent Period of the Warring States, China resembled a microcosmic world of today. More than three hundred wars were fought among various states over a time span of a hundred and fifty years. The weapons they used were very different from today's, but the objectives of war were the same—for survival or dominance.*

Although we do not know much about the activities of Sun Zi, there is little doubt that he was a genius of his time. The following is based on that world-renowned book.

ORGANIZATION AND LEADERSHIP

War is a serious matter. Its outcome depends on whether or not it is a just war and whether or not it has wise military leadership. It also depends on the geographical and climatic conditions, the range and distance of the battlefield. Organization, logistics, and communication are also of paramount importance.

To manage an army is a matter of organization. To manage a small army is as much a matter of organization as it is to manage a large one. Good communication is essential to success. The same is true with commanding a small army as it is with commanding a large one.

The duty of a general is to defend his country. The king must place

孫子兵法十三篇

full confidence in him. If the king interferes with the orders of the general, he can cause confusion and bring disaster upon the army. Military matters are different from civilian. If the king appoints a civilian who is totally ignorant of military matters to lead the army, he may cause the army to lose confidence in its leadership. Mistrust between the king and the general invariably weakens the fighting effectiveness of the army.

War is full of contingencies. There are occasions when a general need not obey orders from the king. He only fights when he is sure of victory. In that sense, even if the king orders him not to fight, he should fight. Likewise he should not fight if he believes that he may meet with defeat. Even if the king orders him to fight, he should not fight. He does not engage the enemy and hope to win by luck. The decision to fight or not should solely be based on whether it is in the best interest of the country, not on any personal consideration such as fame or shame.

A good general is somebody who knows when to fight and when not to fight, who is well-prepared to seize any favorable opportunity that presents itself, who knows how to make use of a small force as well as a large one, who has the whole-hearted support of his officers and soldiers, and who is competent and free from interference from his king.

A good general should be able to command his many soldiers like one man. He often engages his soldiers in friendly conversation in order to create mutual trust. When a general treats his soldiers like his own children, they will rally round him wherever he goes, even at the risk of their lives. At the same time, he should exercise his authority and be consistent. He may alienate his soldiers if he punishes them before they have a chance to get to know him and develop loyalty to him. And alienation leads to disaffection.

He will not have good soldiers if he is too easy-going to demand obedience from those who are loyal to him or if he fails to enforce discipline on those who have violated rules and regulations in the army. Among the rank and file members, the conviction of the moral cause of the war ought to be combined with the enforcement of discipline. Only then will they act like one man and become invincible.

A strong general with a weak army or a weak general with a strong army spells defeat.

A general does not always explain everything explicitly when he gives orders to or sets targets for his soldiers. He is serene, reasonable, strict, impartial and a little inscrutable.

When called for by contingencies, he should have the flexibility to issue orders to suit the situation, and not be constrained by prefixed rules and regulations.

There are five weaknesses in the commanding officer that may lead to failure:

A reckless commander may get killed.

A commander who fears death may end up as a war prisoner.

A short-tempered commander may be easily provoked to take stupid actions.

An over-sensitive commander may not be able to endure insults and plunge into battle prematurely.

A commander who is unduly concerned with the safety of the civilian population will be subject to enemy harassment.

CAREFUL PLANNING

Careful planning is a prerequisite to winning a war. Victory is secured before one goes to the battle. The more carefully one plans before he goes into a battle, the more likely he will win. A less carefully planned action reduces the chance of winning. No planning in advance invites defeat. In that sense, the outcome of a war can be foretold from how carefully the war is planned.

A good general should be familiar with the quantitative and qualitative comparisons between his forces and those of his foes.

He outlines different scenarios, and then plans his action and anticipates the action of the enemy accordingly, taking into account both favorable and unfavorable factors in each scenario. Under favorable conditions, he does not overlook negative factors, thus making sure that the final victory is his. Under adverse circumstances, he does not lose sight of positive factors. Thus he keeps up his confidence.

If a general knows the strength of his army but not that of the enemy, his chance of winning is only fifty-fifty. If he knows the strength of the enemy but not his own troops, his chance of winning is still fifty-fifty. If he understands neither, he has no chance of winning. If he understands the strengths of both his own army and the enemy's, but does not know which is and which is not the right place for him to fight, his chance of winning is still fifty-fifty. Only when he has a good knowledge of the environment, geography and climate in connection with the battle he is going to fight, can he win for sure.

If a general is able to anticipate when to fight and where to fight, he can defeat the enemy even if he has to travel a thousand miles to fight. If not, he cannot even send his left wing to the rescue of his right wing.

THE BEST WAY OF WINNING

War is a most serious undertaking. A general must be on guard against his own emotions. If it is not in the interests of the country, he must not go to war. If he can succeed without resorting to war, he should not use troops. A king should not start a war because he is angry. Nor should a general go into a battle because he hates the enemy. The one important consideration before going into war is: If one does fight, can he win? Anger may give way. Hate may be soothed. But the consequences of a war are irreversible. Those who died at war are lost forever.

The best way of winning a war is to win it without fighting, to conquer the enemy nation without destroying it and to subdue the enemy troops without killing. To fight a hundred battles and win a hundred is not the best of the best. The supreme triumph lies in defeating the enemy without a fight, in making the enemy surrender, in making them see that the odds against them are so overwhelming that it makes no sense for them to put up even the smallest resistance. This is surely the best of all victories.

To win a war this way may not be very exciting. A general will not have the opportunity to show his ability and courage to earn glory and praise. But this is the best kind of victory.

The best way to win a war is to defeat the overall strategy of the enemy. The next best is to beat them on the political and diplomatic front. Then the next option is to fight a war with the enemy troops. The worst way to win a war is to lay siege to enemy cities and defeat them at the expense of heavy casualties of one's own forces in a protracted campaign.

If you have ten times the forces of your enemy, surround them.

If you have five times the forces of your enemy, attack.

If you have a two to one advantage in number, try to split up the enemy and attack.

If you have about the same forces as the enemy has, take the initiative and attack first.

If the enemy is stronger than you, go away quickly and do not fight.

To win a war that everyone expects you will win, you do not deserve extra reward. To conquer the enemy by way of mass destruction hardly entitles you to any honor.

If you have won the war but failed to consolidate your victory and achieve your strategic objective, it amounts to defeat.

POSITIONING

The most difficult part of formulating a strategy is positioning. Sometimes correct positioning may not bring direct or immediate benefit, but it will be to your advantage in the long run. A wise general should have the foresight to take what seems a long shot in order to achieve the final victory.

When fighting, place yourself first in an impregnable position and then wait for an opportune moment to attack. Your defense is largely a function of your own effort whereas to defeat the enemy you have to wait for the right moment which probably has to be provided by the enemy through their own mistakes.

Moreover, the requirements for defending yourself and defeating the enemy are different. You may have more than sufficient manpower and firepower for defense but not enough for engaging the enemy in an offensive. Then the priority is to preserve your manpower and firepower for they are the ultimate means to your eventual victory. Therefore, although a good general cannot guarantee to defeat the enemy, he is able to ensure that he is not to be defeated.

A general does not win victory simply because he insists on winning. A good general creates conditions that his officers can take advantage of rather than make unrealistic demand on them. If you have a good strategy, remember you can create external conditions in such a way as to facilitate the implementation of your strategy. Order or disorder, courage or cowardice, strength or weakness are also a function of your positioning.

If you get to the battlefield early, you will have time to rest and wait for the enemy. If you are late and the enemy is awaiting you, you have to rush into action immediately upon arriving at the scene. You are not in your best form then. A good general forces the enemy to the battlefield rather than being forced into fighting by them.

By the same token, do not give the enemy a breathing space. Do not allow them a chance to recover from their fatigue. Always keep them tense to wear them down.

Some battleground is such that whoever get there first will gain advantage. Try to pre-empt the enemy. But if the enemy get there ahead of you, do not try to seize the stronghold from their hands, because it may be too costly for you to conquer it.

Some terrain is easy to get in but hard to get out. Avoid it. Wait until the enemy gets half way there and then attack.

Some area is of strategic interest to a number of parties concerned. If you control such an area, you have much leverage. Step up your diplomatic activities and strengthen ties with your allies.

STRATEGY AND TACTICS

If a war is unavoidable, the best is to fight a quick war. If the war is protracted, the morale of the troops may be affected; the resources may run out; inflation may occur; the economy of the country may suffer. A prolonged war is never in the interests of a nation. It is especially so when you are fighting a war far from your home base.

Even if you do not have the best commanders in the world, you should fight a quick war. If the war efforts cause financial difficulties, even the most brilliant think tank cannot be of much help.

Therefore those who know the benefit a war may bring about must also be fully aware of its potential risk.

At the initial stage of the battle, morale tends to be high. Then it begins to flag a little. Towards the end of the battle, it fizzles out. So a wise general avoids the enemy when they are in high spirits but attack them when their morale is sagging.

Do not attack them if they are in good array.

Do not attack if the enemy occupy a vantage point in the battlefield.

Do not stop them when they retreat. Give them a way out. The defeated enemy can still put up a formidable fight if they are pushed to desperation.

A war is a combination of the expected and the unexpected. A regular battle just repels the enemy. It is a surprise attack or an extraordinary manoeuvre that wins victory for you. If the enemy seem to be well-organized and large in number, attack its vital part, and force them to react in a way that can be turned to your advantage. You should move at a faster speed, take unexpected routes and catch the enemy when and where they are least prepared.

Always use your strong points to attack the weak points of the enemy.

If you want to fight but the enemy do not, attack some target that they are compelled to rescue in order to lure them out. Alternately, if you do not want to fight but the enemy do, mislead them by unexpected raids so as to divert the thrust of their attack.

The battle may take place on your own territory, or on the enemy's territory, or on a third party's territory.

If it is on your own territory, try to avoid fighting if you can, because even if you win, you may cause much destruction to your own land.

If you are fighting inside the enemy territory, avail yourself of their resources to provide for your troops.

If your troops are put in a life-and-death situation and they understand there is no way out unless they smash the enemy, then they will not fear death and will fight to win.

If your troops are fighting deep inside the enemy territory, you can expect them to be automatically more vigilant, more mutually supportive, and more courageous because of the danger they are facing.

Treat prisoners of war well. Reward the brave. You may exceed the normal limit set to the reward so as to show your appreciation of extraordinary valor.

DECEPTION

Warfare is essentially based on deception, that is, to hide your real intention and keep the enemy guessing.

When you are capable of attacking the enemy, pretend that you are not. When you are actively making preparations, pretend you are not.

Give the enemy some minor advantage and lure them out, then ambush them. Provoke them and then attack. Encourage them to be complacent by pretending that you are inferior to them, and then beat them. Employ stratagems and put up a false front to induce the enemy to act the way you want. Sometimes a devious route can get you to your destination faster than an apparent short-cut if the enemy do not suspect. If the enemy seem united, try to create confusion and sow dissension among them. If the enemy occupy an apparently vulnerable position, they may be holding out a bait for you. Be careful.

You can pretend that you do not understand the real intentions of the enemy and are doing exactly what they want you to do. But in the meantime, get your forces ready for a surprise attack on the enemy.

The best general conceals his action plan so well that even the enemy spy cannot detect anything. For that reason, he does not explain everything to his soldiers or disclose his master plans to his own troops. For fear of enemy espionage, the communication between his troops and the external world should be kept to a minimum. He permits no rumors to spread in the army.

Be careful about the deception of the enemy. When the enemy talk humbly, they may be preparing for an attack. When they talk tough and take a hard stance, they may actually want to back down and find a way to retreat.

Your tactics should vary with circumstances and change with the conditions of the battlefield as water adapts itself to whatever terrain surfaces it flows in. Never let the enemy see through your tactics. Never repeat the same tactics. Your tactics should have no fixed form or pattern. The best tactics is everybody can see the apparent moves you make, but, when victory comes, nobody understands how you have managed to win.

The size of the forces committed to a battle may not be a decisive factor. If the enemy do not know when and where you are to attack, they have to put up defense in all places. This causes their forces to split up and necessarily weakens them at one particular point. If they concentrate their forces on the right side, their left side will be weak. Similarly if they focus their forces in the front, the rear will not be as strong. When they are forced to be on the defensive all the time, they lose the advantage even though they outnumber you. You gain advantage because you are able to focus your smaller forces more effectively on the larger but scattered enemy troops. This shows the importance of keeping the enemy in the dark while you are well-informed about them.

Naturally the success of a deceptive strategy hinges on your swift action once the right moment comes. Timing and speed are key success factors.

INFORMATION GATHERING

More than anything else, information about the enemy is essential to victory.

War is an expensive undertaking. Compared with the cost of war, the cost of running information gathering activities is small. If a general is unwilling to allocate sufficient resources for information gathering or grudges intelligence officers rank, honor, or money, then he does not really understand what is at stake. To put it strongly, he does not really care for the well-being of his army.

Information has to be gathered by human efforts. It is not something that you can infer from past experience or by deductive thinking. Information should be collected by those who have a good knowledge of the enemy. They understand what information is valuable to your cause.

Among your forces, intelligence officers should get the best treatment. Only men of the highest integrity and capability can be trusted with intelligence work because their work concerns the outcome of the war. The action of the entire army largely depends on information provided by your intelligence network.

You can also use insiders such as officials of the enemy country to provide information for you, or turn the table around and recruit spies sent by your foes to work for you. Allure them with generous reward.

If necessary, you can fight a small battle which you need not win. Its purpose is to sound out the enemy and ascertain the pattern of their behavior. In doing so, you may obtain valuable information which otherwise eludes you.

Comment: The Art of War is a classic on the science of war, the psychology of war and the philosophy of war.

It is interesting to note that General Norman Schwarzkopf had each of his soldiers read Sun Zi's Art of War during the Gulf War. But the principles expounded in this legendary book go well beyond the scope of military warfare.

The end of Cold War means that superpowers will no longer try to settle their disputes on the battlefield with infantry, tanks and nuclear weapons. But war on another battlefield, the global economic battlefield, has intensified, even among military allies. The economic competition is perhaps more cutthroat, more protracted and more difficult to win than a military confrontation. We must understand this new paradigm of competition and maintain combat readiness. A national industrial and competitive strategy must be drawn up in the same way as a military strategy was once mapped out. And resources must be mobilized accordingly in order to fight and win this war.

The Chinese, Japanese, Korean and Singapore business people have made a careful study of Sun Zi's book, regarding it almost as a textbook on modern business competition where the market is the battlefield, the managers and employees are the officers and soldiers, and the products weapons. For this reason, I entitle this chapter the Art of Competition.

Sun Zi's insightful analysis on human nature, organization, leadership, the effects of environment, and the importance of information has as much bearing on economic warfare as it has on military warfare.

16. REVENGE IS SWEET

> Someone said: "Repay an injury with kindness."
>
> The Master said: "If you reward injury with kindness, with what, then, will you reward kindness. You should repay an injury with justice and kindness with kindness."
>
> —*Confucius*

During the Period of the Warring States in Chinese history about two thousand and five hundred years ago, military science was a useful subject of study. As numerous kingdoms and states incessantly waged war on each other, knowledge of military strategy and tactics was in great demand.

This is a story about a most distinguished strategist named Sun Bin who was a descendant of Sun Zi, author of the Art of War, *a famous book on military strategy and tactics as described in the previous chapter. It is a story of friendship displaced by treachery, jealousy turned into murderous intent. It is a story of Sun Bin's survival and revenge through a clash of wit and will with his tormentor.*

Sun Bin, a native of Qi, and Pang Juan, a native of Wei, had been friends and fellow students studying military science under one same mentor. Later Pang Juan became a successful general in Wei.

However, Pang Juan believed that his mastery of military science was not as good as Sun Bin's. Pang was concerned that if Sun Bin went to work for other countries he would pose a challenge to Wei's security. But if he came out to work for the king of Wei, it would mean a formidable threat to his own position as the king's right hand man. Pang turned the matter over and over in his mind until he had an idea.

He invited Sun to come to Wei and recommended him to the king of Wei. The king was impressed with Sun's knowledge and appointed him a senior advisor. Sun was grateful and took Pang Juan to be a trusty friend.

"How are your family in Qi?" Pang Juan asked one day. "Why not bring them over to join you here?"

"Truth to tell," said Sun Bin with a sigh. "My parents died when I

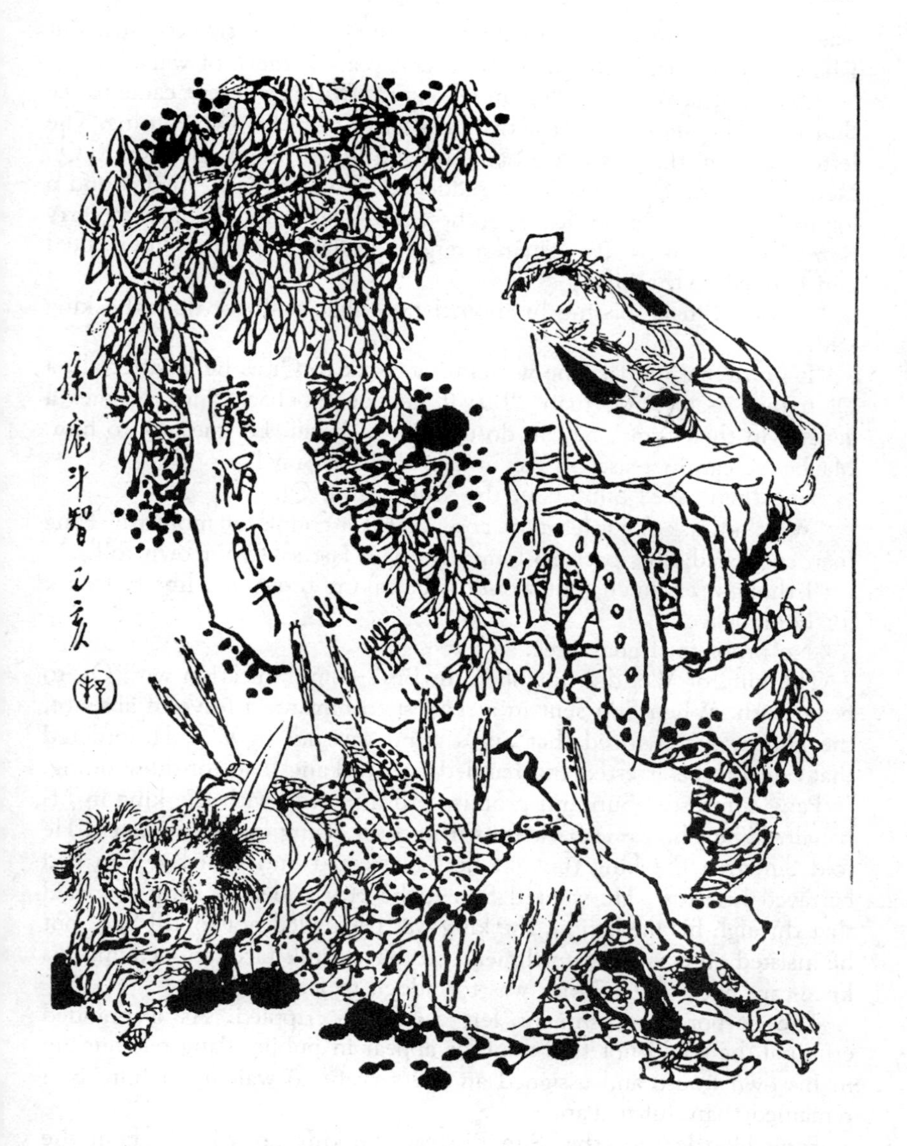

was yet a child. I was brought up by my uncle. I have two cousins. But I have lost contact with them for several years because of wars."

About half a year later, a man who spoke with Qi accent came to see Sun Bin. The man brought with him a letter from his two cousins. The letter told him that his uncle had died and urged him to go back to Qi. News of the death of his uncle saddened Sun. But as he had found a job in Wei, he could not leave. So he wrote a letter for the man to carry home to his cousins. Pang Juan arranged to have the letter intercepted and handed to the king.

"So Sun Bin is missing his homeland, what shall we do?" the king said.

"It's only natural that he wants to go back to Qi as he is, after all, a Qi native," said Pang Juan. "But if he does go back and becomes a general in their army, he can do us a lot of harm. Let me talk to him. Maybe we can increase his pay and ask him to stay."

Pang then asked Sun about the visitor from Qi.

"Why not ask for a leave of absence for a couple of months?" Pang Juan suggested. "It's been so long since you last saw your own folks."

"I thought as much, but would it be taking too much liberty to ask for home leave?"

"No problem, I guarantee."

The king of Wei did not like Sun Bin's communication with Qi, to begin with. When Sun sent in a request to him for a leave of absence, the king was convinced that Sun's mind was not in Wei. He ordered that Sun Bin be arrested and handed over to Pang Juan for questioning.

Pang comforted Sun and promised to intercede with the king in his behalf. When he came back from the court, Pang looked dejected. He told Sun that the king thought he had treated Sun well but Sun had betrayed his trust. He wanted Sun to be put to death. Pang also said that through his mediation, the king was persuaded not to kill Sun, but he insisted on a severe punishment - to have Sun's face tattooed and his knee-caps cut off. And Sun was forbidden to leave Wei.

The corporal punishment left Sun Bin crippled. As a branded criminal, he could not find a job or appear in public. Pang put him up in his own house and assigned an old servant to wait upon him. Sun remained thankful to Pang.

Pang Juan learned that Sun Bin was working on a book about the art of war like the one written by his ancestor, Sun Zi. He asked him about it. Sun Bin was eager to do something for Pang Juan, so he offered to dedicate his book to Pang.

His writing progressed slowly, partially because he could not sit properly due to his handicap and partially because he was often depressed. From time to time Pang asked the old servant who waited on Sun about the progress of his work. When he heard that Sun only wrote a few lines a day, he looked displeased.

"When is he going to finish the stuff if he drags on like that? Hurry him up!"

The old servant was puzzled. One of Pang Juan's aides confided to him that Sun was allowed to live only because General Pang was interested in what he was writing. As soon as he finished the book, he would have him put to death.

The old man was alarmed. He took pity on Sun and told him what he had heard. It was like a bombshell. Sun was so shocked that he nearly fainted. When he came to, he threw all he had written into the fire. He felt that he had awakened from a nightmare. He wished he had seen through Pang Juan earlier.

When Pang came to see him, Sun suddenly burst into an uncontrollable laugh and then cried convulsively. He laughed again and cried again.

"Help! Help!" he shouted at Pang.

"It's me. I am Pang Juan."

But Sun did not seem to recognize his former fellow student.

"Has he gone mad?" Pang thought. But he suspected that Sun feigned insanity. So he had Sun dragged into a pigsty. Sun fell onto the pile of pig dung, tossed about in the filth, covering himself all over with dirt, and then fell into a stupor.

Still suspecting, Pang secretly sent a man with some wine and food to see Sun in the pigsty. Sun threw all the nice food to the ground and put some pig feces into his own mouth.

"Delicious!" he shouted.

When his spy reported what he had seen to him, Pang was convinced that Sun was really insane and surveillance on Sun became lax.

From then on, the pigsty was Sun's home. In the day time, he would go out and wander in the street. In the evening, he would come back to sleep with the pigs. Sometimes he slept in the street, too. Everyone knew that he was a sick man. However, Pang continued to spy on him.

One night as he was sleeping in the street, Sun was wakened by a man. Sun recognized that the man was an old friend of his from Qi. He told Sun that an envoy from Qi was visiting Wei. As the Qi's envoy heard of what had happened to him, he wanted to smuggle him out of the country.

Sun said he was under constant watch by Pang Juan's men. His friend had one of his subordinates change into Sun's clothes to take Sun's place in the street.

The next day Sun hid himself inside the carriage of Qi's envoy and was taken out of Wei. Two days later, Sun's impersonator disappeared. Pang ordered an immediate search, but to no avail.

When Sun went back to Qi, General Tian Ji asked him to stay at his house. The general held Sun in great respect and admired his extraordinary knowledge of military strategy.

General Tian liked gambling on horse races with the king of Qi and other aristocrats. More often than not he lost. Sun noticed that all the racehorses were divided into three classes and their quality did not differ very much within the same class.

He asked General Tian to bet heavily on the next race.

"I promise you will win," he said.

Tian put down a thousand ounces of gold betting against the king. In the first round of the race, Sun told Tian to use his third class horse to compete with the king's first class horse. In the second round, Tian's first class horse was used against the king's second class horse. Then at the final round, Tian's second class horse was made to run against the king's third class horse.

In the end Tian lost the first round but won the second and third rounds of the race. The king lost a thousand ounces of gold. After the race, Tian Ji introduced Sun Bin to the king and explained how Sun Bin had helped him to win the horse race. The king admired Sun Bin's strategy and appointed him senior military advisor.

As he was settled down in Qi, Sun made an inquiry about his uncle and cousins. They were nowhere to be found. Sun realized that the man who spoke with Qi accent was a phony. Pang Juan had sent him. The alleged letter and the news of his uncle's death were all part of Pang

Juan's trick.

In 354 B.C. the capital of Zhao, Handan, came under fierce attack by an army of 80,000 strong led by Pang Juan. Zhao asked for help from Qi. The king of Qi intended to appoint Sun Bin as the commander-in-chief to lead an army to Zhao's rescue. Sun declined, because, he said, as he was supposed to be a convict in Wei, it would not be appropriate for him to be Qi's commander-in-chief. Therefore, Tian Ji was made the commander-in-chief and Sun Bin the chief of staff.

Tian Ji wanted to advance straight toward Zhao. Sun had a different idea.

"To unravel a knot, you need patience to find the end of the thread. To stop a fight, you should not get yourself drawn into it. Right now the best troops of Wei are all in Zhao. Only the weak ones are left to defend their own country. It is already too late to rush to Handan. But if we invade Wei itself, cut its supply line, and overrun its military positions where the defense is weak, Pang Juan's army will be forced to come back to defend its own land. But then we will not only have lifted the siege of Handan but also harassed Wei."

Tian thought it was a great idea.

Hardly had Wei's troops overrun Handan when they heard the news that Qi was invading their country and their own capital was under attack. Pang Juan ordered his troops to turn back.

The forces that were attacking Wei's capital, Daliang, which is modern Kaifeng in Henan, was only part of the Qi army. The main forces were waiting in ambush on the route Pang Juan was to take in his retreat. Pang lost 20,000 men in the ensuing battle, and Wei was forced to make peace with Zhao.

By now, Pang Juan had learnt, much to his dismay, that Sun Bin was still alive and working in Qi's army.

A few years later Wei invaded Han. Han was a small country unable to defend itself against the strong army led by Pang Juan. Its king appealed to Qi for help.

The king of Qi held a meeting with his advisors. The prime minister maintained that Qi needed to strengthen its own defense and should not mind other countries' business. General Tian Ji argued that without outside assistance, Han was bound to be defeated. If that happened, Wei's power would be boosted too much for the comfort of Qi. Sun Bin supported General Tian's position but suggested not to plunge into battle prematurely.

"Qi's army fights for Qi's interest, not for Han's. If we go there too early, we would be doing the fighting for Han. But we must help Han for our own sake. The best course of action to take would be to let Han know we are coming to their rescue. Once they have our assurance, they will fight with all their strength. After both sides have gone through much fighting, we can then commit our forces to win the final victory. So, we can achieve the maximum results with minimum effort."

Qi's assurance boosted the morale of Han's troops. But they were no match to Wei's fierce offensives. The situation became desperate.

At that point, the army of Qi invaded Wei as they did last time. Pang Juan's earlier bitter experience was still gnawing at his heart. This time he pulled back his troops of 100,000 strong from Han for a decisive battle with the army of Qi. So, Han's siege was automatically lifted.

Sun Bin read Pang's mind perfectly well, and he also knew that the army of Wei always thought themselves as among the best in the world and tended to look down upon others. He formed his battle plan accordingly.

Qi's army was not going to engage Wei's head-on. When Pang Juan hurried back, Sun Bin ordered a retreat. Just as Sun had anticipated, Pang Juan responded by a hot pursuit. As the troops of Qi were retreating, Sun Bin instructed that camp-fires sufficient for 100,000 people be built on their way the first day, for 50,000 on the second day and for 30,000 on the third day.

After chasing the army of Qi for three days, Pang Juan was delighted to find that each day the number of camp-fires was reduced.

"I know the troops of Qi are no good," said Pang Juan gloatingly. "When they heard we are fighting back, more than half of the soldiers have deserted in three days."

To speed up, he organized a lightly armed crack force to be formed to pursue the enemy.

Sun Bin reckoned that Pang's army would arrive at Maling on the evening of the fourth day. The road to Maling was narrow, and there were mountains on both sides. Sun ordered five hundred picked archers to hide on both sides of the road in ambush. They were ordered to shoot when they saw a flame. Then he instructed that all the trees, except for a tall one, be felled to block the passage. He had that unfelled big tree stripped of its bark on the trunk to bear the following words in black ink.

"Pang Juan shall die under this tree."

Just as Sun Bin had expected, Pang Juan arrived at Maling toward the evening of that day. They found that the road was narrow and the fallen trees were blocking their way. Pang ordered his soldiers to remove them, thinking that Qi's army were trying to slow down their pursuit by felling the trees.

He noticed that all the trees around the area were cut down except a very big one. There seemed to be something written on its exposed trunk. It was too dark to see clearly. Pang had a torch lit in order to read. When he saw the inscription, he realized that he had walked into a trap. But it was too late. Barely had he issued the order to back off when arrows came toward him like rain. The army of Wei was thrown into panic. There was no escape.

Pang was wounded in many places, knowing he was finally outwitted by his former fellow student.

"The bastard—I should have killed him," he growled. "He is going to make a name at my expense."

He mouthed a torrent of curses on Sun Bin and cut his own throat with his sword.

The army of Qi won a decisive victory of this strategic battle. The crown prince of Wei was taken prisoner. Since then Wei had never recovered from its defeat.

After the battle of Maling, Sun Bin resigned from office. He had his revenge. When his book on the art of war was completed, he presented it to the king of Qi.

Comment: Sun Bin's book on the art of war was discovered in 1972 when Chinese archaeologists excavated a tomb of the Han Dynasty.

If Sun had only endurance but not iron will, he probably would not have survived. If he had only the will power to survive but not the knowledge of the art of war, he probably could not have wrought his revenge upon his enemy. It was the combination of these qualities that made him one of the most extraordinary figures in Chinese history.

17. THE BATTLE OF THE RED CLIFF

Give more than you receive, so that even the greedy will feel grateful to you. Keep enough wits in reserve, so that in case of the unexpected, you will not be forced to the wall.

—*Vegetable Roots*

The battle of the Red Cliff which took place in the beginning of the third century is the most famous battle in Chinese history.

It was the battle of the Red Cliff that led to a power balance among the three kingdoms, Wei, Wu and Shu, which had emerged on the ruins of the Han Dynasty. It was the battle of Red Cliff that during which Cao Cao, the ruler of Wei, led an armada of 200,000 strong down the Yangtze River and returned with only 28 men after his ignominious defeat by the joint forces of Wu and Shu. It was during the battle of the Red Cliff that the wisest man in Chinese history Zhuge Liang made a name that has shone throughout all ages, a name which is even now a household word in China.

Towards the end of the Han Dynasty, the longest of China's dynasties, three states, Wei, Wu and Shu, were contending against one another for sovereignty. Cao Cao who was the ruler of Wei, the most powerful of the three, dominated the north. He was also the prime minister of the Han court who exercised complete control over the young emperor of Han. In the name of the emperor, he gave out orders and attacked those who did not obey him. He intended to destroy Shu and Wu and expand his rule to all over China. A versatile man, Cao Cao was not only a good professional soldier but also a prominent man of letters. But he was cruel, treacherous and suspicious. His notorious motto was: "Rather let me betray the whole world than let the world betray me."

The ruler of Wu was Sun Quan, a descendant of the famous general Sun Zi who wrote the *Art of War*. The Sun family had control over the lower reaches of the Yangtze River for long years. Sun Quan refused to submit to Cao Cao without a fight, but his army was not as strong as

Cao Cao's.

The weakest of the three was Shu whose ruler was Liu Bei. Liu was a descendant of the Han house. A kind, compassionate and modest man, he was neither very learned nor very talented, but he had sympathy for the ordinary people. He and his two sworn brothers took upon themselves the mission to restore peace and the legitimate rule of the Han Dynasty in China. His cause got a tremendous boost when Zhuge Liang joined him a few years after he rose and took arms against Cao Cao.

Zhuge Liang was a man of extraordinary talent. He had been living in reclusion when Liu Bei visited him. It was upon the third visit that Liu was able to meet him and persuaded Zhuge to work for him. Zhuge Liang's knowledge of politics, military strategy, physical sciences and insight into human psychology were matchless in his time. At the time, Cao Cao had won a strategic battle in central China over Liu Bei. Zhuge Liang's analyses of the political and military situation enlightened Liu who had been groping in the dark since his defeat by Cao Cao. Zhuge became the architecture of an alliance between Shu and Wu.

This is what is called the period of Three Kingdoms in Chinese history. It was one of the most interesting periods in history.

In 208 A.D. Cao Cao mustered an army of 200,000 men, ready to cross the Yangtze River to invade the kingdom of Wu in the southeast.

There were two factions in the Wu government: one was in favor of submission to Cao Cao and the other preferred to fight. Liu Bei, still recovering from his recent setback, sent his chief strategist Zhuge Liang to Wu to negotiate a collective response to Cao's threat. Both Wu and Shu regarded Cao Cao as a traitor who used the emperor as a puppet to further his own ambition. Zhuge Liang convinced Sun Quan that for the survival of his kingdom, the only possible way was to line up with Liu Bei, and the combined strength of Wu and Shu stood a good chance of routing Cao Cao's army.

Liu Bei paid a visit to Zhou Yu, the commander-in-chief of the Wu army, and thus the two kingdoms became allies. They joined forces at the Red Cliff, near modern Wuhan, central China, for a showdown with Cao Cao.

Cao Cao's army vastly outnumbered the combined forces of Wu and Shu of 50,000. They were stationed on the north bank of the Yangtze. An initial fray with Wu's navy inflicted heavy casualties on Cao's troops.

Most of Cao's soldiers could hardly keep their footing on a moving boat because they were northerners who had virtually no experience in naval warfare. Therefore Cao Cao ordered two newly recruited generals, Zhang Yun and Cai Mao, who were formerly Wu's naval officers and now defected to Cao Cao's camp, to train his men. Naval camps were set up; military exercises were performed day and night; the torches lit up the sky.

Seeing the bright lit sky and the glowing water from his headquarters on the south bank, Zhou Yu felt uneasy. He got on a boat to spy on Cao's army himself. What he saw really worried him: the two former naval generals of Wu really knew their trade. He was discovered by Cao's sentinels. But he and his team made a quick escape down the river easily.

Zhou Yu's reconnaissance upset Cao Cao.

"Zhou Yu and I used to be fellow students," said one of his advisors named Jiang Gan. "If I go to the south bank, probably I can win him over to our side."

Cao agreed to let him have a try.

Jiang Gan arrived at Zhou's camp in a ferry.

"It's no easy job to cross the river," said Zhou Yu after exchanging courtesies with Jiang. "Are you coming as an envoy from Cao Cao."

"Oh, no, no," Jiang denied. "I haven't seen you for so long. I miss you. What makes you think that I am sent by Cao Cao?"

Zhou smiled. "Forget it then! Since you have no such intentions, let's talk about nothing but old times. No politics."

He turned around and introduced Jiang to his officers.

A dinner party was held in Jiang's honor. They drank till late into the night. Zhou seemed in high spirits. He rose to perform a sword dance to a warm applause. When the party was over, Zhou, looking quite drunk, took Jiang Gan to his bedroom.

"It's been a long time since we shared a room together," mumbled Zhou Yu. "Let's spend the night here."

Zhou Yu flung himself onto the bed and immediately fell asleep.

Jiang Gan could not sleep. Looking around, he saw a pile of papers on the table. Jiang went over to the desk to examine them. They were letters. One letter bearing the signature of General Cai Mao and General Zhang Yun caught his eye. It was to the effect that they did not surrender to Cao willingly, but were driven to do so by circumstances. Now they were not really training the navy, but trapping them in the naval camps. And they promised to get in touch with Zhou Yu again.

Jiang remembered that these two generals were formerly Zhou Yu's men who had defected to Cao Cao. Good gracious! He hid the letter in his clothes and went to bed. Zhou was still snoring. Around two o'clock, he heard a guard coming to wake up Zhou. "Someone from the north is here to see you."

"Hush! Speak low," said Zhou.

He called Jiang, who pretended to be asleep. Zhou went out. Jiang strained his ears, trying to catch the conversation outside the tent. He vaguely heard the names of Cai Mao and Zhang Yun mentioned. Soon Zhou Yu came back.

"Hi, buddy!" Zhou Yu called Jiang again.

He did not respond. Then he heard Zhou Yu go back to sleep.

At 4 o'clock in the morning, Jiang got up. He called Zhou. No response. Jiang slipped out of the room and left the headquarters of Zhou Yu's army.

"Who are you?" A guard challenged him.

"I've got to go now," Jiang said, identifying himself. "I'm General Zhou's old friend. I don't want to wake him up so early."

He was let go without further questioning.

As soon as he returned, he showed the letter to Cao Cao.

"Although I failed to persuade Zhou Yu, I've found something of interest."

The letter threw Cao Cao into a rage. He summoned the two naval generals at once.

"I want you to start attacking now," he told them.

"But we have not completed our training yet."

"They won't be trained, I suppose."

The two officers were confused. Cao ordered to have them beheaded. As soon as they were executed, Cao realized that he had been tricked by Zhou Yu. But it was too late. When other officers asked for the reason, he replied: "They lacked discipline."

At that time, Zhuge Liang was staying in the Wu army headquarters to formulate a common strategy with Zhou Yu. The Shu-Wu alliance was not an easy one from the beginning. Zhou Yu was a handsome,

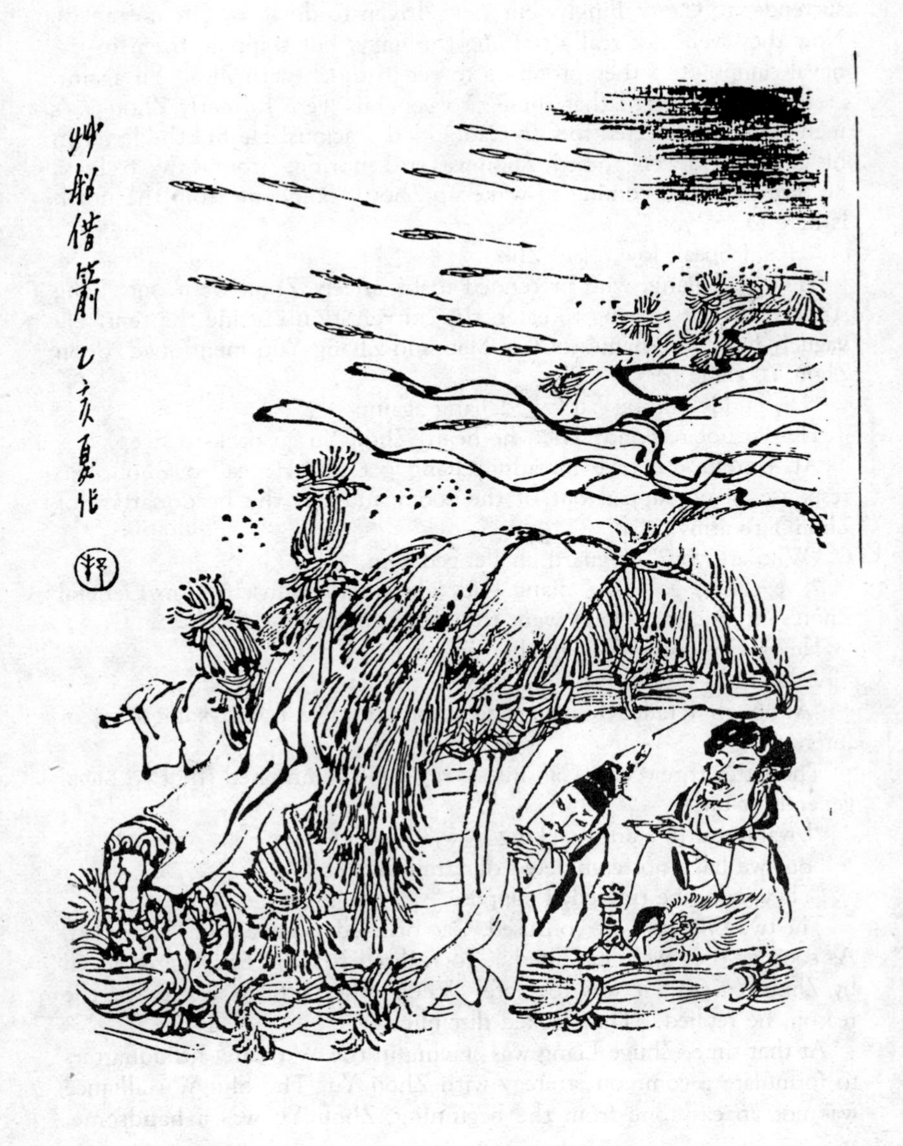
草船借箭
乙亥夏作

elegant, talented young general, but he sensed that Zhuge Liang was superior to himself in intellect and ability. He felt insecure and regarded Zhuge Liang as a serious potential threat to Wu. He wanted to kill Zhuge Liang, but his advisor Lu Su argued that at the moment he should make use of Zhuge Liang to deal with Cao Cao. He could lay his hands on him after Cao Cao was defeated.

When Lu Su went to see Zhuge Liang, Zhuge offered his congratulations for Zhou Yu's success in getting rid of the two southern generals in Cao Cao's army.

"You can only fool Jiang Gan," said Zhuge Liang. "You cannot fool Cao Cao. He must have realized his mistake soon enough, though he wouldn't admit it. The two new generals he has just now appointed to replace Cai Mao and Zhang Yun are imbeciles. But don't tell Zhou Yu what I said to you. I know how he feels about me."

Lu Su promised not to say anything, but he reported all that Zhuge Liang had said to Zhou Yu, anyway. Zhou was troubled by Zhuge's insight into his mind. He decided to find some way to embarrass Zhuge.

The next morning, Zhuge was invited to attend a meeting with Zhou Yu and his military officers.

"What weapons are most important in a naval battle?" Zhou asked Zhuge.

"Arrows are the best," answered Zhuge.

"I agree with you. But our supplies are running short. Would you help us replenish the arrows? We need 100,000 of them for the forthcoming battle. I hope you won't refuse."

"I certainly will do my best," said Zhuge. "When do you need them?"

"Can you do it in ten days?"

"The enemy may come any time. Ten days would be too long."

"How much time do you think you need?"

"I'll have them ready in three days."

"There is no joking in the army!"

"How dare I joke with you, General. If I can't deliver them in time, I am willing to accept any punishment. I am willing to give you a written guarantee. It's too late to start today. I'll start tomorrow. Three days from tomorrow, you will please send five hundred men to the river side to collect the arrows."

Zhou was pleased. He had a written guarantee drawn up to be signed by Zhuge. Zhou secretly ordered that materials needed to make arrows be withheld and the workmen go slow. He was sure Zhuge could not get away with it this time. Nevertheless, he sent Lu Su to see what Zhuge was doing.

Zhuge blamed Lu for not keeping his word and asked him to help him out.

"But you yourself brought trouble on you. How can I help you?"

"You can. I'd like to borrow twenty boats from you, with a crew of thirty men on each boat. Please fix at least a thousand jacks of straw covered by black cloth and have them lined up on both sides of each boat. But you must not let Zhou Yu know this time, or my plan will fail."

Lu Su was puzzled, but obliged him. The vessels were ready without Zhou Yu's knowledge. The first and second day went by. Zhuge Liang did not make any move.

At 2 o'clock before daybreak on the third day, Zhuge Liang secretly went to see Lu Su.

"Come on to my boat. We're going to get the arrows."

"From whom?"

"Don't ask. You'll see."

The twenty vessels were fastened together with long ropes, and they set out for the north shore. A dense fog hung over the river like a veil. Visibility was reduced to a few feet. By 4 o'clock, the ships were near Cao Cao's camp. Zhuge Liang ordered the crew to beat drums and shout battle cries.

Lu Su was alarmed. "What if the enemy come out and attack us?"

Zhuge laughed. "I would be surprised if Cao Cao will venture out in this weather. Let's have a drink and we'll go back when the fog lifts."

When he heard the drumming and shouting, Cao Cao suspected an ambush. To prevent the enemy from landing, he ordered the marines to shoot arrows at the coming vessels. An additional reinforcement of six thousand infantry soldiers were dispatched to the river bank to assist the marines.

Zhuge Liang ordered the boats to turn around and get closer to the shore to take more arrow shots while the crew on the boats continued to beat the drums and shout. Arrows fell on the boats like rain.

When the sun rose and the fog began to lift, Zhuge Liang ordered the boats to speed back home, with the straw men on each boat bristling with arrows. He ordered the crew to shout:

"Thank you, Prime Minister, for your arrows!"

By the time Cao Cao got the report, Zhuge's light craft were already miles down the stream beyond overtaking.

"You are a genius," Lu Su was amazed. "How did you know there would be such a fog today?"

"A general who is ignorant of astronomy, geography and probability will never rise above mediocrity. I figured three days ago that there would be a heavy fog this morning. That's why I took a chance on the three-day limit. As Zhou Yu offered me ten days but withheld labor and raw materials, obviously he did not want me to succeed so that he could punish me. But how can he harm me as my fate is linked with Heaven?"

Five hundred soldiers were waiting on the south shore to collect the arrows. The final count exceeded 150,000. Astonished at Zhuge's ruse, Zhou Yu was obliged to offer him his compliments.

Then they sat down to discuss ways of launching their offensive. Zhou Yu suggested that he had some idea but was not too sure about it. Zhuge Liang said: "Don't say it. Let's write it on our palms to see if we think alike."

The two laughed when each saw the word "*Fire*" on the other's hand.

Cao Cao was exasperated at the loss of so much ammunition. To get information about the enemy movement, he gathered, spies had to be sent. So he summoned the two cousins of General Cai Mao, who was killed as a result of Zhou Yu's trick, generously awarded them and asked them to go to Wu to collect intelligence.

"They won't suspect you if you surrender," Cao Cao told them. "When we win the war, you'll be richly rewarded. Don't betray me."

"Please rest assured. Our families are in here. How dare we think otherwise?"

When the two men arrived at the camp of Wu, Zhou Yu welcomed their defection, awarded them, and let them stay in the headquarters.

That night Zhou Yu had a confidential conversation with a senior officer named Huang Gai.

The next day Zhou called a general meeting of all his military officers. Zhuge Liang was also present. Zhou told them to prepare for a hold out with Cao Cao for three months. Barely had he finished when Huang

Gai interrupted him.

"Three months? What's the use even if we can manage to hold out for thirty months? If we can't win in a month, we may as well give up and surrender."

"How dare you talk about surrender?" Zhou shouted. "Our mission is to defeat Cao Cao. Whoever talks of surrender should be executed!"

He ordered the guards to drag Huang Gai out. Huang became abusive. Zhou was enraged and ordered instant execution. At that point, many other officers came up to plead on Huang Gai's behalf because Huang's family had been serving the state of Wu for generations.

Zhou relented but ordered the guards to lash him fifty times. Huang was stripped and beaten so severely that he lost consciousness. All the officers went down on their knees begging for mercy.

Lu Su called on Zhuge Liang again. He asked Zhuge why he did not intervene in his capacity as a guest-advisor.

"Why should I meddle in Zhou Yu's ruse? He has seen through Cao Cao's trick in sending the two cousins of Cai Mao here. Now he planned to make the two men report the punishment of Huang Gai to Cao so that Huang Gai could pretend to defect. Isn't all that obvious?"

When Lu Su confirmed this with Zhou Yu, he marvelled at Zhuge's insight.

A few days later, Cao Cao had a visitor from the south who claimed to be a friend of General Huang Gai. The visitor submitted a letter in Huang Gai's handwriting to Cao Cao. In the letter, Huang Gai expressed his resentment of his treatment at the hands of Zhou Yu and his desire to defect to Cao, promising to bring over with him ships and equipment. Cao suspected foul play.

"If your friend really meant to defect, why didn't he fix a time?" he questioned the visitor.

"How can he set a time in advance when he has to act without being noticed."

At the same time, a letter arrived from the cousins of General Cai confirming the beating of Huang Gai. Cao was half convinced. He still needed somebody to go over the south shore to find out the truth. Jiang Gan volunteered again.

"Last time I failed. Now I am willing to risk my life to find out what is really going on."

This time Zhou Yu did not come out to welcome his former fellow student. As soon as Jiang entered his office, Zhou accused him of betraying his trust.

"If it's not for old times' sake, I would have you executed." He ordered the guard to take Jiang Gan to a deserted temple on a nearby hill and put him under house arrest until after the battle with Cao Cao was over.

Jiang was so worried that he could not eat or sleep properly. That night, he took a walk in the backyard of the temple when he heard somebody reading out loud. Following the voice, he slipped out of the temple and found a small cottage close by. He knocked at the door. To his great surprise, it was none other than Pang Tong who was standing before him - a man who was well-known for his knowledge of military strategies and whose reputation was almost equal to that of Zhuge Liang.

Pang Tong told him that he had offered his service to Zhou Yu, but Zhou Yu was too conceited to take his advice. That was why he was staying at home. Jiang tried to persuade him to join Cao Cao, and Pang asked Jiang to introduce him. That same night Jiang Gan escaped with Pang Tong back to the other side of the river.

Cao Cao was delighted to meet Pang Tong and was eager to seek his advice. He took him on a tour in his naval camp. Then they discussed the art of war over dinner. Pang complimented Cao on the excellent training of his men but Cao wanted Pang to make suggestions for further improvement.

Knowing some of the soldiers had fallen ill because they were not used to the climate in the south, Pang asked whether there were good medical services in the army. This, indeed, had been bothering Cao for some time. Pang suggested that all the vessels be fastened with iron chains in groups of thirty or fifty and covered with planks. In this way men and horses could walk from ship to ship as if they were walking on dry land in spite of the rough waves and winds.

Cao Cao thought this was a great idea. One of his advisors objected: "True, to chain the boats together makes them steady. But if the enemy attacks us by fire, we'll be in deep trouble."

Cao Cao laughed. "Good thinking! But you overlooked one thing. An attack by fire depends on the force of the wind. Now in the middle of winter, the wind only blows from the north or the west, not from the south or the east. We are on the northwestern shore, they are on the south bank. If they use fire, they will burn themselves out. We have nothing to fear."

Thus the advice of Pang Tong was duly implemented. Pang told Cao that Zhou Yu was not a tolerant man. As a result, quite a few talented men in his army had become disaffected, and if he went back, he would be able to recruit some of them to come over to work for Cao Cao.

Cao Cao was pleased and promised to recommend Pang to the emperor.

"Please don't think I am after fortune or status," said Pang Tong. "I simply want to help the ordinary people. When you cross the river, Prime Minister, please do not kill."

Cao promised that he would not, and, at Pang's request, signed a safe conduct warrant for him and his family. Then Pang Tong left.

In fact, it was not a chance meeting that caused Jiang Gan to get acquainted with Pang Tong. It was set up by Zhou Yu. Knowing that Zhou Yu and Zhuge Liang intended to use fire, Pang Tong, who was on Zhou's side, volunteered to persuade Cao Cao to chain his entire fleet together so that when one boat caught fire, all boats would be burnt.

The issue of the wind was very much on Zhou Yu's mind, too. In fact, he was so anxious that he fell ill. Zhuge Liang went to see him.

"I know what is bothering you, General," he smiled at Zhou. "I have a prescription that may help."

He wrote on a sheet of paper: "To break Cao Cao, we must use fire. Now we have got everything except the east wind."

"I suppose that is the cause of your illness," he handed the paper to Zhou Yu.

Zhou was shocked. "What cure do you have, then? You know, I am in a critical condition."

"I happen to know how to call up winds through praying to Heaven. I need an altar to be built on Mount Nanping specially for the purpose. I'll go there and pray for a strong southeast wind to blow for three days and three nights."

"Just one night will suffice. Speed is the essence."

"I will call up the wind on the 20th of December and make it end on the 22nd."

So, an altar was built on the mountain to the specifications of Zhuge Liang. It had three tiers all encompassed with flags representing various stars.

On the 20th day, Zhuge Liang went up Mount Nanping and ascended the platform, burned incense, looked up to the sky and began praying. He walked up and down the altar three times, but there was no wind.

In the meantime, Huang Gai had prepared twenty ships all loaded with combustibles, their prows studded with giant nails. Inside the ships were stacks of reeds and straws soaked in fish oil and overspread with substances such as sulfur and saltpeter. All were covered with black cloth.

The entire Wu army was ready. But there was still no sign of a wind. Evening dragged on. Toward midnight, suddenly the sound of wind was heard. Banners on the boats began to flutter in the northeastern direction. Moments later, a strong southeasterly wind was blowing.

Zhou Yu dispatched a hundred armed men to the altar looking for Zhuge. He was nowhere to be seen. An immediate pursuit, simultaneously by land and water, was ordered. Now it was high time to get rid of Zhuge Liang, that supernatural man. Actually Zhuge was already aboard a boat. Beside him was the bravest soldier of Shu, General Zhao Yun. Zhou's men were speeding up after them in a fast boat.

"What's the point of chasing me?" Zhuge Liang shouted to the pursuing boat. "Go back and tell Zhou Yu to use his forces carefully. I have asked General Zhao to take me home because I can read Zhou Yu's mind like a book."

Twang! General Zhao shot down the sail of the pursuing boat and his boat sped away.

Zhou Yu executed the two spies sent by Cao Cao. He knew, from the beginning, their defection was a hoax because they did not bring their families with them. He asked them to stay only to pass misinformation to Cao Cao.

Cao Cao was having a meeting with his officers when it was reported that there was a southeasterly wind. At the same time, a secret message from Huang Gai came. It read: "I have been under strict surveillance so far. But we have a new shipment of grain coming and Zhou Yu has put me in charge of the convoy. I will redirect the grain ships to your camp. Please expect me at midnight. My flag bears a green dragon."

Cao was overjoyed. He went aboard a large ship and stayed up waiting for Huang to come. At midnight, Huang's fleet loomed in the distance. The easterly wind grew stronger and stronger. As the ships drew nearer, Cao became suspicious. Why were the ships moving so fast, if they were heavily loaded with grain?

He ordered his men to stop Huang Gai's ships. But Huang Gai, standing on his flag ship, waved his sword to motion the first row of the ships to be set on fire. Instantly the flame was sped by the wind. Twenty ships dashed toward Cao's fleet like flying arrows. Cao's ships were chained together. When one caught fire, others could not flee. Fire tongues rose high; the sky was lit up. Huang Gai's burning ships came in from all sides. In no time, the naval camp of Cao Cao was turned into a raging inferno. Cao Cao's tents on land caught fire, too. Cao Cao's entire army was thrown into a pandemonium. The battle of the Red Cliff had started.

Everything was ablaze. Escorted by his guards, Cao Cao had to escape through the burning forest. They had hardly cleared out of the woods when they were attacked by the joined troops of Wu and Shu waiting in ambush.

After surviving two such ambushes, Cao's remaining forces were reduced to a few hundred. Hungry and exhausted, they came to a crossroads.

"Which is the shorter route to our next stop Huarong?" asked Cao, as they were going back northward to his stronghold, Xuchang, in modern Henan.

"The highway is smooth but it takes a long time to travel. The Huarong Trail is the shortcut but it is rough and narrow."

Smoke could be seen along the Huarong Trail but the highway appeared quiet.

Cao Cao decided to take the shortcut.

"But there is smoke," his officers objected. "Could there be troops in ambush?"

"No," said Cao Cao. "One should never trust appearances in fighting. Zhuge Liang has lit the fire so that we dare not go that way. I am sure he has laid an ambush on the highway. This time I won't fall into his trap."

Huarong Trail was muddy, narrow, and full of potholes. Horses were bogged down in the mud. The soldiers had to throw away much of their equipment in order to be able to walk. They had to repair the road step by step as they trudged along.

After they had crossed this difficult part of the trail, the road became easier. Cao Cao laughed.

"If Zhuge Liang were smart, he would have us sniped here."

Barely had he finished his sentence, five hundred swordsmen of the Shu army appeared on both sides of the trail. For Zhuge Liang knew that Cao was a good strategist. The only way to induce him to Huarong Trail was to let him see smoke in the sky. When he saw smoke, he would think it a ruse and would take the trail instead of the highway.

At the sight of the enemy ready to engage them in a hand-to-hand combat, Cao's men were frightened out of their wits. They had lost their will to fight. Cao Cao was in despair, thinking that his doom was sealed.

One of his advisors reminded him that the Shu general, Guan Yu, who was now confronting him, had once been his guest and warmly treated by him.

Knowing that Guan Yu was a man of honor, who would never forget an act of kindness done to him, Cao Cao moved forward and bowed to him.

"How have you been, General, since we met last?" he said to Guan Yu.

General Guan bowed back. "I am under order to capture you, Prime Minister."

"My army is defeated. I am desperate. Please have mercy on me for our old friendship."

"But I am on official duty here," Guan Yu replied.

"Do you still remember that you once killed six of my generals, but I didn't blame you. I am sure you still remember how I treated you. You are a man of honor. Please do not destroy me."

Guan Yu had not forgotten Cao's hospitality and past kindness. He had a keen sense of obligation. Looking at the deplorable condition of Cao and his men, he could not bring himself to take Cao Cao prisoner. He ordered his men to make way for Cao Cao and his men to run past.

Suddenly Guan Yu shouted to them to stop as though he regretted his decision. At that point, Cao's men all got down from their horses, knelt before Guan and wept. Guan took pity on them. With a deep sigh, he finally let them pass.

Of Cao Cao's original army of 200,000 only twenty-eight survived the Battle of the Red Cliff. With the weakening of Wei's military forces, a power balance was established among the three kingdoms of Wei, Shu and Wu.

Comment: Zhuge Liang was twenty-eight when the Battle of the Red Cliff was fought. The battle could not have been won without the easterly winds, which were ostensibly invoked by Zhuge Liang's prayers. The real purpose of Zhuge Liang to have staged such a show on Mount Nanping was to make his escape possible.

As we note in his scheme to "borrow" arrows from Cao Cao, Zhuge Liang had expert knowledge about the weather. As he had lived for a long time in that area, he probably knew that the winter solstice usually brought about a change of winds. Since he came to the camp of Zhou Yu, he had been under the watchful eyes of the Wu general. He was fully aware of Zhou's jealousy and the potential danger he was facing. To pray for easterly winds was a perfect reason to ascend Mount Nanping, which gave him the chance to get away.

Zhuge Liang (181-234 A.D.) has been regarded by Chinese for ages as the most brilliant strategist and tactician in China's ancient history. His name, a household word in China, is proverbially synonymous for wisdom and resourcefulness.

Through his efforts, a geopolitical power balance was created among the three contending states after the demise of the Han Dynasty which was founded by Liu Bang in 206 B.C. He won many battles for Liu Bei and had been his prime minster for years. He served with utmost diligence and unswerving loyalty until his death at the age of fifty-four. He had also outstanding literary talent. His letters to Liu Bei and to his own son are literary masterpieces.

Here is another celebrated example of his feat.

One day, his main forces were away but an enemy battalion of 150,000 strong was seen approaching an isolated city garrisoned by only a handful old soldiers of Shu. Zhuge Liang was in the city. To deal with the emergency, he ordered all the flags in sight be taken down and all the city gates thrown open. He had twenty soldiers dressed as street cleaners to sweep the streets at each of the four city gates. No one was permitted to move about or make any noise. Then he himself, dressed in his usual white robe, sat on the city wall, lit a stick of incense and began playing a piece of peaceful music on the lute.

When the enemy commander saw the scene, he immediately suspected a sinister trap and decided to withdraw.

Zhuge Liang had a reputation for being too careful to play with danger. But this time he could not help it. The enemy commander was a recognized shrewd general of Wei. He loved deception in strategy but often fell victim to his own suspicion. Zhuge Liang gambled on his suspicion and won.

Another example was his campaign against the marauding Burmese. Zhuge captured the Mantse king seven times and seven times he released him to regroup his forces and spring into battle once more. When his officers protested, Zhuge Liang said: "I can capture him just as I can get something out of my pocket. What I want to do is to overcome and win his heart." When the Mantse king was taken captive for the seventh time, he fell to his knees before Zhuge Liang.

"Even though I am not cultured, I still have a sense of shame. I will put up no more resistance," he said.

In the end, Liu Bei failed in his attempt to restore the rule of the Han Dynasty. The three kingdoms were replaced by another dynasty. But the legend of Zhuge Liang lives on. To many Chinese, he was the personification of wisdom.

18. QUICK WITS

Those who learn to appreciate health after illness and learn to appreciate peace after war are not wise. Those who foresee and anticipate are truly wise.

—*Vegetable Roots*

THE HORSE

A man had an excellent horse for sale. For three days he stood with his horse in the marketplace, but nobody paid him any attention. So he called upon the famous horse trainer Bo Le.

"I have a great horse to sell but I have stood in the market for three days and nobody showed any interest," he complained to Bo Le. "Could you come over and have a look at my horse? Please walk around it, look at it closely, and then go away. But be sure to look back when you walk away. For your trouble I'll give you all my profit for the day from my other sales."

The next day Bo Le came. He walked around the horse and looked at it up and down. As he walked away, he kept looking back. That very day, the horse was sold for ten times its worth.

Comment: If one was not told that this story is 2,300 years old, few would have guessed that the idea of celebrity endorsement in product promotion began so early in history.

THE FIDDLE

In the Tang Dynasty, candidates for government posts were selected through imperial examinations held every year in its capital of Chang'an, a city now renamed Xi'an, in present-day Shaanxi Province.

Among those who sat for the examinations was a young man named Chen Zang. Although he had passed, he was not yet appointed to any office as there were hundreds of candidates like him. He came from Sichuan and knew nobody in the capital. Networking was out of the question.

H.T. 94.D.

One day as he was walking in the street, he saw a man selling a fiddle. The asking price was 1,000 ounces of gold. A big crowd was looking at the expensive music instrument, but none could tell whether it was worth the price.

Chen pushed his way through to the front.

"I'll buy it," he told the seller. "Please come with me to get your money."

The crowd looked at him in astonishment.

"You play the fiddle?" someone asked.

"Yes. I'm a virtuoso player," replied Chen.

"Could you please play it for us?" another one suggested.

The crowd all agreed.

"Sure," said Chen Zang with a smile. "Tomorrow I'll play it for you in front of the temple in the city center."

The next day, many people gathered there. Holding the fiddle in his hand, Chen Zang announced: "My name is Chen Zang. I am from Sichuan. Here are my resume and a collection of my writings. Please take a look. I wanted to present them to senior officials in the government, but I have no access to the imperial court because I am a stranger here. As for the fiddle, I don't know how to play. I am not really interested in being a musician."

With this remark, he smashed the fiddle on the ground.

Before long, he was offered a good position in the government.

Comment: For those who rack their brains to get the attention of the world, here is a quick way, though it is not cheap.

FORESTALLMENT

Gan Mao was the prime minister of Qin. One day one of his subordinates overheard the king talking to Gongsun Yan when they were taking a walk.

"I'll name you the prime minster."

The eavesdropper told Gan what he had heard.

The next day Gan Mao went to see the king and offered his congratulations. "Your Majesty has selected an excellent candidate as my replacement."

"You are the prime minister. Who is going to be your replacement?"

the king was surprised.

"I heard you are going to appoint Gongsun Yan to be the prime minister."

"Who told you so?"

"Gongsun Yan himself."

The king was so annoyed that he sent Gongsun Yan into exile on account of having disclosed a confidential matter.

Comment: A cheap shot. But leaks do spoil then as they do today.

SHEEPSKIN

Duke Mu, the ruler of Qin, married a princess of Jin. Included in the dowry offered by her father, the ruler of Jin, was a slave named Bai Lixi, who had once been a government minister of Yu. He came as a slave from Jin because he had been taken captive when Yu was overrun by Jin.

On his way to Qin, Bai managed to escape. But while passing through the territory of Chu, he was arrested for a spy and was made to attend the cattle.

While checking up on his bride's dowry, Duke Mu of Qin found Bai Lixi was missing. He asked the person who escorted the dowry who this slave Bai Lixi was.

"He is a man of outstanding talent and integrity, but he has no luck," said the escort.

Duke Mu ordered an inquiry. Finally he found out that Bai Lixi was raising cows in Chu. He prepared large amounts of expensive gifts, ready to offer them to the King of Chu in exchange for Bai.

His minister Gongsun Zhi stopped him.

"If the King of Chu knows that you are willing to pay this much for a slave, he will understand that Bai is no common man. He may want to keep Bai in Chu and use him. Then you will never get him."

The duke took the advice and sent an envoy to Chu with five pieces of sheepskin, the market price for a slave.

"Bai Lixi is wanted in Qin because he has committed a crime," the envoy told the King of Chu. "He is in your country. Please hand him over. We want to punish him."

The king accepted the sheepskin and handed over the slave.

Comment: The value of a merchandise lies in its perception.

TREES

One day Xi Simi, a government minister in Qi called upon Viscount Tian Cheng. Tian was the most powerful man in Qi at the time. He took his guest to a tower to look at the scenery. The view was splendid except for the fact that it was obstructed in the south by the trees grown in the garden of Xi Simi's house. The viscount did not say anything, though.

When he got home, Xi ordered his servants to chop the trees down. Just as they started cutting, he stopped them.

"Why did you change you mind?" his secretary asked.

"There is an ancient proverb which says troubles are awaiting those who can see fish in a deep valley. The viscount is working on some big scheme in secret. If he knew that I can read his mind, I would be in danger. Not to cut down trees won't be much of an offense but knowing something that somebody would not like you to know may have serious consequences."

Comment: Sometimes knowing too much may be just as bad as knowing too little. By and large, it is better for us to know than not to know. Only when we have the knowledge first can we decide whether or not it is necessary to show what you know.

WINE

A man was away from home for three years on an official mission. His wife had turned to love another man.

When the man finally returned, his wife intended to kill him. So she prepared a glass of poisoned wine for him. Their maid happened to know the secret. When the wife told her to give the wine to the husband, the maid hesitated. "If I give my master the wine, he'll die. But if I tell him the truth, he is going to get rid of his wife. Either way is no good."

So she deliberately tripped herself and knocked over the glass of wine.

"I especially prepared the wine for you, my dear," the wife said to

her husband, upset. "But she was so careless. She should be punished."
The husband bound the maid and whipped her.

Comment: Would you do the right thing for someone at the risk of offending that person?

ELEPHANT

During the Period of the Three Kingdoms as described in the previous chapter, Cao Cao, the ruler of Wei in the north, got an elephant as a gift from the ruler of Wu in the south. This was the first time people in the north had ever seen such a huge animal. Cao Cao was curious about its weight. There was no scale big enough to hold the elephant and none of his ministers knew how to weigh the animal.

Cao Chong, the young son of Cao Cao, then five years old, offered to help.

He asked the mahout to bring the elephant onto a boat in the river. The weight of the elephant forced the boat to submerge into the water. Cao Chong got on another boat and moved close to the boat carrying the elephant. He bent down and made a mark on the water line of that boat.

Then he had the animal taken ashore and the boat loaded with stones. When the boat was lowered to the water line previously marked, Cao Chong said: "Now take the stones out and weigh each one of them. The total weight of all the stones is actually the weight of the elephant."

Comment: Every child in China knows the story. But how many can repeat what Cao Chong did?

RAT BITES

Here is another story of Cao Chong.

Cao Cao loved horses and had some very precious saddles kept in the storeroom. One day the man in charge of the store-room found one of the saddles there was damaged by rat bites. He was frightened, knowing Cao Cao would not easily forgive him. He thought he'd better report to Cao Cao what had happened to the saddle and be ready to accept any punishment.

Just at that time, Cao Chong came over. He noticed the man's anxious look, and asked him why. Upon learning what had happened, he told the man to wait for three days before reporting the incident to his father.

The next day Chong poked a few holes in his own shirt with a penknife. The holes looked like rat bites. Wearing a sullen expression, he went to see his father.

"Father," he said. "I heard that it was bad luck to have one's clothes nibbled through by rats. This morning I found on my shirt tooth marks left by rats. My shirt is ruined."

"My good boy, don't believe in nonsense," Cao Cao comforted him. "There is nothing to worry about."

Soon afterwards, the storeroom keeper came to report the rat-bites found in the saddle. Cao Cao just laughed it away.

"My son's shirt was also bitten by the rats. I am not surprised that they went after my saddles too. It's all right. You may go back. Just be more careful in future."

Comment: Cao Chong was a handsome, bright boy. He had a sympathetic heart, too. As a matter of fact he had interceded with his father on dozens of similar occasions for those who had committed an offense under mitigating circumstances. He was Cao Cao's darling boy. Cao Cao had said several times that he wanted Chong to be his successor. Unfortunately Cao Chong died of illness at the age of twelve.

PART IV
LEADERSHIP, MANAGEMENT AND HUMAN RELATIONS

19. THE ART OF MANAGEMENT

Be tolerant, but do not let others take your tolerance for granted; be astute, but make allowance for others. Give away what surplus things you have so as to build up your good will; do not exhaust the good will of others so as to maintain good relationships.

—*Vegetable Roots*

Despite advances in culture, science and technology, human nature has hardly changed since ancient times. I felt this keenly when I was reading Chinese classics on organizational behavior and human resources management. I could not but marvel at the fact that management had already been made a refined art in ancient China. I believe this had to do with China's long tradition of civil administration.

This and the next chapter are a collection of some well-known stories on the topic. The moral in these stories, transcending space and time, seems as relevant to us now as to those who were involved in the story when it took place.

BURNING LETTERS

Cao Cao, the ruler of Wei in the Period of the Three Kingdoms described in Chapter 18, was contending with General Yuan Shao for the control of northern China. He defeated Yuan in a major battle at Guandu (in modern Henan). After his forces captured Yuan's stronghold, his advisor found in the official file secret correspondence between Yuan Shao and many officers in Cao Cao's army who had pledged allegiance to Yuan. The advisor suggested that these officers be arrested and executed for treachery.

Cao Cao thought differently.

"When Yuan Shao was strong, even I was afraid of him. How can I blame others?"

He ordered all the letters be burned and nothing more was said of the matter.

At that time Yuan Shao still controlled large areas in the north. The rivalry for dominance was not over yet. If he started an investigation,

Cao understood, the consequences could be disastrous. Those under investigation might mutiny against him. Burning the letters, on the contrary, would demonstrate his magnanimity and reassure those who had had secret correspondence with General Yuan Shao.

In the end Yuan Shao was crushed by Cao Cao.

Comment: One cannot lead without loyalty. But loyalty is a complex thing with many aspects. It is almost impossible to know without being truly tested.

In so far as everyone loves a winner, to command loyalty, one must deserve it. Loyalty is not necessarily reciprocated. But to expect others to be loyal, act as though they were already loyal.

SELF-DISCIPLINE

Once when his army was passing through a wheat field, Cao Cao issued an order that anyone trampling the crop would be put to death. All the cavalry soldiers got down from the horses to walk. But his own horse ran into the field, causing much damage to the crops. Cao called on his law officer to punish him. But the army could not be without a supreme commander.

"I laid down the rules," Cao said. "If I were not punished, how could I expect others to follow me?"

He cut off his hair with his sword as a punishment on himself and had it displayed to all his soldiers, symbolizing his head.

Comment: A symbol can be a powerful management tool to communicate the culture of an organization and the value of its leadership. Cao Cao used a symbol skillfully to foster the loyalty of his troops by conveying the message that he was a fair and just man and that nobody was above the law in his army.

HUMAN HEAD FOR A LOAN

On another occasion when Cao Cao was engaged in a prolonged campaign, there was a shortage of food supply. Cao asked the commissary what to do. The latter suggested to cut the food ration by using a smaller measure so that the existing supplies could last long enough until new supplies arrived. Cao agreed.

Soon there was much complaint in the army. Soldiers accused Cao of cheating them out of their food. Cao summoned the commissary.

曹操割髮代首

"I want to borrow something from you."

"What do you want?"

"Your head."

"But I've done nothing wrong."

"I know that. But if I don't put you to death, there will be a mutiny. Don't worry. I'll take good care of your family."

Cao announced to the army: "This man stole grain from the army and used a smaller measure for your food rations. Supplies are coming. Please be patient with me." The commissary was executed. The soldiers accepted his explanation and a potential crisis was averted.

Comment: It is worth mentioning here that Cao Cao was a most colorful figure in Chinese history. The current version of the Art of War *by Sun Zi was first edited and annotated by Cao Cao. He wrote a book on war of his own. His generals all studied his book. Unlike his counterparts, Liu Bei and Sun Quan, Cao directed battles himself. In every battle, he gave specific instructions to his generals. Those who followed won victories most of the time. Those who did not were defeated.*

However, if anyone else in his army had smarter ideas on war than his own, Cao would find an excuse to put that person to death.

When he was facing the enemy, Cao always looked calm as though he had no intention to fight. But at critical moments, he would strike with lightning speed and devastating force. He won victories not by luck, but by strategy, by deceiving the enemy, and by varying his tactics on different occasions.

He was a man of keen observation and excellent judgment. It was hard for anyone to hide the truth from him. He would not hesitate to appoint from among surrendered enemy forces capable men to be his generals.

He was thrifty and informal. His life style was plain. Even his wife was dressed simply. But he shared everything with his subordinates. When it came to rewarding someone with merit, he would not think a thousand ounces of gold as too much. But to those without merit, he would not give a penny. If he bore a grudge against his former associates or friends, he would kill that person. He would look at the person, weeping and feeling sorry, but would not allow him to live.

Cao Cao's military and administrative skill, his ruthlessness, his unscrupulousness and his cunning coupled with his literary talent earned him the name of a rogue with many parts. He was at once hated and admired by many

Chinese.

WHEN THE WATER IS TOO CLEAN

Lu Mengzheng was the deputy prime minister under Tai Zong, the second emperor of the Northern Song Dynasty. One day at a ministerial meeting, he happened to be walking past a man who was making a sarcastic remark about him: "Is this greenhorn deputy prime minister?"

Lu pretended that he did not hear anything. A colleague of his who heard it, too, got angry and wanted to find out the man's name and title. But Lu stopped him.

After the meeting, the colleague was still upset because he had not learnt the man's name.

"It's better not to ask," Lu said to him. "If I know his name, I may never forget. If I don't know, I have nothing to vex my mind."

Some time later Lu Mengzheng became the prime minister.

One day the emperor received a confidential report that some officials in the government-owned shipping company were involved in smuggling.

The emperor said to Lu: "There are always people who do that sort of thing. To stop them completely is impossible, as impossible as trying to fill up all the holes in the walls that rats live in. It's not going to be easy. Only the most serious offenders need to be punished. As long as their work is not affected, I'd leave them alone if they take advantage of their position to do a little bit of smuggling on the side. As long as the cargo is being transported safely, I don't intend to probe into the matter."

Lu agreed with Tai Zong.

"If the water is too clean," he added, "there will be no fish. The same is true with humans. If a man is too perceptive, he will probably have few people willing to work for him. If we try too hard to get everything right, things may not get done smoothly. We understand perfectly what these villains are doing, but we'd better tolerate them. In this way they'll have a place for themselves and won't make trouble elsewhere. And because we are able to tolerate, everything functions smoothly. In my opinion, we don't need to make a fuss about this report. We can just give those who are involved in smuggling a warning in private."

Comment: Lu Mengzheng did not really condone such wrong-doings. Implicit in his tolerance of certain cases of infraction of the law is the cost-benefit analysis of law enforcement as well as the recognition of the imperfection of human beings. However lofty the idea of total justice, the benefit of law enforcement, in certain cases, must be weighed against the cost of doing so. When there are only limited resources, society must make an efficient use of them and apply them where we can achieve the most effective results.

Unfortunately those who bent on breaking the law may go through similar exercises and sometimes come to the conclusion that the pay-off is worth the risk.

DELEGATING AUTHORITY

Fu Zijian was appointed governor of Danfu (in modern Shandong) by Duke Ai, the ruler of Lu. Concerned that the duke might listen to slanders of his opponents in court and turn to hinder him in his work, he asked the duke to send two of his aides to go with him to the new post.

All the local officials came to greet Fu when he arrived. Fu told the two aides to make a record. When they were writing, Fu Zijian pulled at their elbows time and again. As a result, the two men could not write properly. Fu then scolded them: "Your handwriting is too poor. You are not fit to do the job."

The two men went back and reported what happened to Duke Ai.

"That's all right," the duke said. "I got his message now. He was asking me not to interfere with his work as I did in the past."

Duke Ai dispatched a messenger to tell Fu Zijian that he had a free hand running the city of Danfu. The message read:

"You have full authority over Danfu. You call the shots. Report to me after five years."

Under Fu Zijian's administration, Danfu enjoyed peace and prosperity.

As governor of Danfu, Fu Zijian did not seem to be specially busy. In fact, he was seen playing the lute everyday. Nevertheless, Danfu was well run.

His successor, Wu Maqi, worked from morning till night. But there seemed to be no end of trouble.

Wu did not know what to do and called on Fu Zijian for advice.

"I heard when you were the governor, you had time to play music and everything was smooth sailing in Danfu. I devote all my time to my job but still things are not going well for me. What was the secret of your success?"

"I trust people and delegate responsibilities to them," Fu replied. "But you prefer to do everything yourself. No wonder you are exhausted, and you still can't do a good job. Make up your mind and learn to delegate. That will make a big difference."

Comment: Just as the duke delegated authority to him, so Fu Zijian delegated authority to his subordinates. He was consistent. He practiced what he believed.

LARGE-MINDEDNESS

Bing Ji started his career as a junior law officer under Emperor Wu of the Han Dynasty. He was eventually appointed prime minister by Emperor Xuan. Bing was a tolerant and easy-going man to work with, for he always carried out his duties in a low-key and self-effacing manner. If any of his subordinates committed an offense, he would not fire him. At most, he would only send that person off on a "long vacation." And he would not check up on him any more.

"When some of your subordinates are sneakily seeking personal gains, how can you, as the prime minister, overlook what they are doing?" one of his guests asked him.

"I am one of the highest ranking officials in the country," said Bing Ji. "If I were to gain a name for investigating the conduct of those who work for me, I would regard it as a disgrace."

So he always tried to cover up his subordinates' faults and weaknesses, but make known their strengths and merits.

His carriage driver was fond of drinking. Sometimes his drinking affected his work. Once he got so drunk that he threw up and made a mess of the Prime Minister's carriage. The personnel manager wanted to fire him. But Bing Ji stopped him.

"You have to forgive him," Bing Ji said to the personnel manager. "To have soiled my carriage is no big deal. But if the man is dismissed because of drinking, I'm afraid he will never be able to get a job anywhere."

The carriage driver came from the border region, and was familiar with the communication system between the border and the capital. One day when he was on the road, he saw a man on horseback carrying a red and white bag, which was a sign that the man was a courier from the border region sent to deliver an important message. He followed the courier to the information office and then learnt from him that the Huns had invaded the provinces of Yunzhong and Dai in the north.

The driver rushed to the prime minister and reported what he had learnt from the courier.

"You'd better check up on those border region officials," he added. "I'm afraid that some of them are too old or just unsuitable for border defense."

Bing Ji thought it was a good idea. He instructed the official in charge to check the record of the border region officials and make a detailed report to him.

Shortly afterwards Emperor Xuan wanted the imperial secretary and the prime minister to discuss border defense with him.

When Emperor Xuan asked Bing Ji about the border region officials, he was able to give a detailed account. But the imperial secretary was caught off guard. He had little information to offer and was reprimanded by the emperor. The emperor thought that Bing Ji was on top of the border situation and was doing an excellent job.

Later Bing Ji remarked, "No one is truly useless. If my driver had not tipped me off in good time, I would have been caught off guard, too."

Comment: One good turn deserves another. Be nice to others. Try to overlook their mistakes and shortcomings as long as you do not condone serious wrong-doings.

THE DOMAIN OF PRIME MINISTER

Once when Bing Ji was riding through the capital, he came upon a scene of street fight. Bodies of the injured and the dead were lying in the streets. But he passed by without saying anything. His aides were astonished.

Going a little further, he saw a man driving an ox. The ox was panting with its tongue sticking out. Bing Ji stopped to ask the man how far he had driven the ox. His aides thought he had lost the sense of proportion, making inquiries into small matters and ignoring more serious ones. One of them said so to his face.

Bing replied, "It's the duty of the magistrate of Chang'an and his officials to deal with street fights and arrest the offenders. All I have to do is to review their performances at the end of the year, decide whether they have done a good job or not, then recommend to the emperor for promotion or demotion. The prime minster does not get involved in handling such municipal matters. It is certainly not appropriate for me to stop in the street to ask questions. By contrast, it's spring and it should not be hot. But if an ox is already gasping after walking a few miles, that may indicate unseasonable weather. Harvest may be affected. I cannot help getting concerned. That's why I stopped to ask the man."

His aides all admired his wisdom and the principles with which he went about performing his duty.

Comment: Sensitivity and a sense of priority are among the essential qualities of effective management.

ECONOMIC WEAPON

Huan, the ruler of Qi, consulted with his prime minister, Guan Zhong, on how to conquer two of his neighboring states, Lu and Liang.

Guan Zhong said: "Both Lu and Liang are producers of silk brocade. I suggest that Your Highness put on clothes made of silk brocade and instruct all government officials to do the same. The Qi people will probably follow suit. At the same time, you must restrict the domestic production of brocade. So we will have to import it from Lu and Liang and they will increase their production for export. Then they'll play into our hands."

Duke Huan immediately began wearing a brocade robe in public. Meantime Guan Zhong placed a large order for this kind of fabrics with the merchants of Lu and Liang, announcing that Qi was willing to pay three thousand ounces of gold for every thousand bolts of this material to meet the popular demand.

The rulers of Lu and Liang were elated and urged their people to stop making other things and increase the production of brocade.

Thirteen months later, Guan Zhong learnt that the people of Lu and Liang were so busy making brocade that they even neglected farming. There was an endless line of wagons transporting the fabrics to Qi.

"Now it's time to conquer them," Guan Zhong told the duke.

"How?"

"Please announce that you will stop wearing anything made of brocade and change to clothes made of fine silk. At the same time, close the borders and cut off the traffic with Lu and Liang."

Duke Huan did what his prime minister suggested because he knew that neither Lu nor Liang made fine silk.

Ten months later, Guan Zhong learnt that the people of these two countries were starving, the governments there had no revenue, for there was no more market for brocade, but grain could not be produced in a short time. The price of grain in Lu and Liang shot up to a hundred times that in Qi. The economy of the two states collapsed.

In two years, sixty percent of the population in Lu and Liang emigrated to Qi. At the end of another year, their rulers were compelled to subject themselves to the rule of Qi.

Comment: Guan Zhong was prime minister of Qi for forty years. He lived about a century before Confucius. He made Qi a superpower in the Spring and Autumn Period in the seventh century B.C.

Guan believed that a sound economy was the basis of everything. In his famous book Guan Zi, *he stated that the first priority in running a country was to make the people rich. When they were well-off, they would feel secure in their community, appreciate their homes, respect officials and refrain from crimes. Otherwise if they were poor, they would not feel secure in their community, not care for their homes, lose respect for the government and would be prone to break the law.*

It is a pity that after Guan Zhong, few Chinese rulers paid much attention to economic development. Some Chinese blamed Confucius for China's economic backwardness. But Confucius stated in no uncertain terms that he would make the people rich first before attempting to teach them. Confucius may not have put forward a comprehensive economic program but holds that a stable livelihood is the precondition for cultivating proper behavior and nurturing virtues.

TREES

Duke Huan noted that the people living in the vicinity of the roadways were poor. They wore shabby clothes, lived in rundown houses and had little income. He asked Guan Zhong if he could change their conditions.

"Let's trim all the trees on the roads," Guan Zhong suggested.

His suggestion was duly carried out. Within a year, the life of those people was visibly improved. They wore better clothes and had new shoes on.

Duke Huan asked to know the reason.

"The trees offered a shade on the roadway," said Guan Zhong. "Before they were trimmed, men and women in the neighborhood often gathered there in the shade gossiping or playing games. Some would even hang in there whole day. Some young people took to shooting birds in the trees. But they should have been working. Now the trees have been trimmed. They no longer have the shade to avoid the hot sun. No more dilly-dallying for them. They have to work and make money. Naturally they are better off than before. That's why I suggested cutting down the trees."

"A good idea!" the duke said.

Comment: What if we substitute trees for the kind of welfare that is high enough to deprive its recipients of the motivation and will to work, but low enough to make them feel underprivileged and cause them to lose dignity?

DRUM BEAT

In 684 B.C., Qi declared war on Lu. A battle was to be fought at Changshao (near modern Laiwu, Shandong Province).

A man named Cao Gui sought an audience with Duke Zhuang, the ruler of Lu. His friend said, "The duke has advisors working on the battle plan, why do you want to get involved?"

"Those people are short-sighted," replied Cao Gui. "They are not up to the job."

When he met the duke, Cao asked: "Your Highness, what do you have to fight the enemy with?"

"I have loyal followers. They support me because I share all I have with them rather than keep it to myself."

"But they are only a small number. The people of the country may not necessarily rally around you."

"When I pray to God, I rely more on my sincerity than on the amount of sacrifice to be offered."

"That much sincerity may not move God. There is no guarantee that he will bless you."

"Even if I cannot review every legal case, I have tried my very best to be fair and reasonable."

"Good! This is the quality that will win the loyalty of the people," said Cao Gui. "You can engage the enemy now. Please let me be your advisor."

The king asked him to ride with him in his own chariot.

When the two armies were lined up at Changshao, Duke Zhuang was about to give orders to beat the drum to signal an attack.

"Wait," Cao Gui stopped him.

Then the army of Qi sounded their drums, the Duke of Lu was ready to respond. But again he was stopped by Cao. The army of Lu was instructed to stand firm and hold their ground.

After the enemy beat their drum for the third time, Cao Gui said, "Now beat the drums!"

In the ensuing battle, Qi's army was defeated and began to retreat.

Duke Zhuang was about to order his troops to pursue the enemy.

"Just a minute," Cao said. He got down the chariot, walked around to examine the wheel-tracks and hoof-prints of the fleeing enemy. Then he stood on the chariot, looking at the enemy in retreat.

"All right. Let's go after them," he said.

The army of Lu pursued the enemy for ten miles, winning an unqualified victory.

When the battle was over, the duke asked Cao Gui to explain his tactics.

"The outcome of a battle depends on the energy and courage of the soldiers. At the first round of drum beats, the fighting instinct was aroused. The enemy was in high spirits. But we held our ground and did not go forward to meet them. At the second round of drum beats, their morale was still high but not as high as before. Again we did not go out to fight. By the time the drums were beat for the third time, their enthusiasm had almost dwindled. But the pent-up emotion made our troops a fierce force. That's why we were able to rout them. Now the Qi army was a formidable one. We had to be wary of any possible ambush even if they were retreating. So I got down to observe the wheel tracks and hoof-prints. When I saw the chaotic state they left behind and their banners thrown all over the place, I was convinced that there was no trick in their retreat. Therefore I gave the word to go after them."

Comment: This is one of the most famous battles in Chinese history. It was also the first piece in classic Chinese that I read when I was a boy of ten.

In the pursuit of many things, there is somehow a certain magic about the first shot. Therefore, ideally, the first should be the best shot. Anything that follows tends to lose that touch of wonder.

20. HUMAN RESOURCES

> Before a man achieves recognition, observe whom he is associated with; when he becomes rich, watch to whom he gives his money; when he has assumed a high position, look at whom he promotes; when he is in difficulty, notice what things he refuses to do; when he is poor, see what he does not accept.
>
> If you know these five aspects about a person, you know who should be appointed as prime minister.
>
> *—Li Ke (5th Century B.C.)*

A FRIGHTENED BIRD

During the Period of the Warring States, when seven states were fighting for supremacy, six of them had lined themselves up in a so-called vertical alliance to confront the menace that came from their common enemy, Qin, the strongest power of the time. In an effort to consolidate the alliance and to strengthen the friendly ties among the member states, the king of Zhao, head of the alliance, sent an envoy, Wei Jia, to Chu.

Wei met with Lord Chunshen, the prime minister of Chu, and asked him whether he had appointed an army general for Chu's forces.

"Yes. Lord Linwu is going to be the commander."

"When I was young," said Wei. "I was fond of archery. If you don't mind, I would like to tell Your Highness a story about archery."

"By all means."

"One day, the king of Wei was accompanied by General Geng Lei on a hunting excursion. General Geng said to the king: 'Your Majesty, I can shoot down a bird with an empty bow.'

"'An empty bow? You mean without an arrow?'

"'Yes, Your Majesty.'

"Moments later, a wild goose came flying from the east. Geng Lei raised his bow, aimed at it without an arrow and pulled the string.

"Twang! The bird fell as though it had been hit by an arrow.

"'This is unbelievable!' the king was astonished. 'How did you do

that?'

"'The bird was already wounded by an arrow before, Your Majesty,' Geng Lei replied.

"'How do you know?'

"'It was flying with difficulty, falling way behind its companions. And its painful calls told me that it was wounded. So I pulled the bowstring, and the twang frightened the bird. The bird thought another arrow was coming in its direction, and made a desperate attempt to dodge it. In doing so, the old wound burst and the bird fell from the sky.'

"Now to come back to what we were discussing," continued Wei Jia. "I understand that Lord Linwu has once been beaten by the army of Qin. He may still have a lingering fear. If I were you, I would not reappoint him to lead Chu's army against Qin."

Comment: Would you appoint Lord Linwu again to fight Qin if you were the ruler of Chu?

WIFELY WISDOM

King Zhuang of Chu often neglected his work for he was fond of hunting. His wife, Lady Fan, had tried to persuade him not to do so, but he turned a deaf ear to her. Then Lady Fan refused to eat the meat of any game the king brought back. Eventually the king gave up hunting.

One day the king came home quite late. Lady Fan wanted to know why.

"I had a most interesting chat in the palace, and did not feel hungry."

"Who were you chatting with?"

"Yu Qiuzi," the king said. Yu was his prime minister.

Lady Fan laughed.

"Why are you laughing?"

"Yu Qiuzi may be competent, but I am not sure whether he is loyal to you."

"What do you mean?"

"Well," said Lady Fan. "I've been with you for eleven years. I often send out people to recruit pretty women to work for you in the palace. I am never jealous of them. Neither am I afraid that they may compete with me for your attention. Now this Yu Qiuzi has been your prime minister for more than ten years. I have never heard him recommend a good person or dismiss an incompetent official. He is blocking the access of capable people to serve in the government. If he knows somebody good but does not recommend, he is not loyal to you. If he does not know any one to recommend, he is not doing his job. So I can only laugh at this man."

When the king told Yu what Lady Fan had said, Yu was at a loss what to say. He soon resigned and recommended Sun Shu'ao to take his place.

The country enjoyed unprecedented prosperity under Sun's administration.

Comment: How many people are there who can cast aside jealousy and their sense of insecurity to recommend somebody more capable than themselves to their superiors? You can tell a man's level of competence by looking at the quality of those who work with him. You can sense a man's level of self-confidence by looking at those he selects to act as his deputies.

RECOMMENDATION

Duke Ping, the ruler of Jin, asked his minister, Qi Huangyang, who would be the most suitable candidate for the governorship of Nanyang.

"Xie Hu will be the ideal one for the position," Qi Huangyang replied.

"But isn't he your arch adversary?" the king wondered.

"Your Majesty asked me who would be the best candidate to run Nanyang," Qi said with a smile. "You did not ask me who my adversary was."

"True. I'll appoint Xie Hu, then."

Xie Hu did a good job running Nanyang.

Some time later the king asked Qi Huangyang to recommend a judge for the court.

"Qi Wu will do the job well."

"But he is your son," the king was surprised. "How can you recommend your own son? What will other people say if they find out?"

"Your Majesty only asked me who would be the most qualified man to sit on the bench. You didn't ask me whether he was my son."

"You are right."

Qi Wu was duly appointed. He worked hard and was fair and reasonable in handling legal cases.

Comment: When Confucius heard of this, he said: "Qi Huangyang made recommendations without prejudice and without fear of being accused of nepotism. He is truly unbiased. In serving his country, he never let personal interest interfere with his work."

DEAD HORSE

King Zhao of Yan wanted to recruit men of talent to work for him. He asked Guo Wei for advice. Guo told him a story.

An ancient king loved horses. He offered a thousand ounces of gold for a horse that could run three hundred miles a day. For three years there was no response. Then a courtier offered to go out and look for such a fast horse. The king gave him a grand sum of money for the purchase. After three months, he came back with the bones of a dead horse that reputedly ran three hundred miles a day when it was alive. He had paid five hundred ounces of gold for the remains of this fast horse. The king was furious.

"I want a live horse. Why did you waste my money on a dead one?!"

"Your Majesty, if people know you are willing to pay five hundred ounces for a dead horse, I am sure you'll find a fast horse very soon."

Indeed, in less than a year somebody presented a fast horse that ran three hundred miles a day.

Guo Wei went on to say: "Now if Your Majesty sincerely wants to attract talented men, you should start with me and appoint me to a senior position. If a man like me is treated well, I'm sure those who are more capable than I am will come to you."

The king built a mansion for Guo Wei and treated him respectfully as though Guo were his tutor. As word spread, many men of talent came to Yan to offer their service to the king.

Comment: Despite the self-serving purpose of Guo Wei, there is some truth in his remark.

THE SCOPE OF DUTY

One evening, Marquis Zhao of Han was drunk. He fell into sleep without taking his clothes off. The official in charge of the crown was afraid that he might catch cold and so put a coat on him. The marquis was pleased when he woke up and saw the coat.

"Who put the coat on me?" he asked the servant.

"The Crown Keeper."

The marquis punished both the official in charge of the crown and the one in charge of the coat. The offense of the latter was negligence of duty and the former overstepping his duty.

"I hate catching a cold," he said. "But overstepping one's duty is worse than a cold. Even if it is a small thing, one should make a distinction between what is your duty and what is not. Even if it is the right thing to do, you should not exceed the scope of your duty. But if something falls within the scope of your duty, even if it is a small thing, you should not leave it to others."

Comment: What about overstepping one's duty in an effort to help others if one has already performed one's own duty?

BALANCE OF POWER

Duke Huan, the ruler of Qi, intended to bestow the title of Lord Uncle on Guan Zhong, his prime minister. He was discussing this with his ministers.

"Those who are opposed to my decision, please stand on the right; those who are in favor, please stand on the left," he said.

Dongguo Ya stood in the middle of the doorway.

"What do you mean?" asked the duke.

"In Your Highness's opinion, is Guan Zhong capable of running the country?"

"Yes, he is."

"Is he decisive enough to carry out a great plan?"

"Sure, he is," the duke confirmed.

"Do you feel safe when he combines his ability with the sweeping power that comes with the new title?"

"I see now," Duke Huan said.

He appointed Xi Peng as interior minister and Guan Zhong as foreign minister so that they could keep a check on each other, and nobody had a monopoly of power.

Comment: Checks and balances are necessary in any organizational structure if abuse of power is to be prevented. In a democracy they are absolutely necessary. But be careful. An organization fraught with built-in checks and balances could be self-defeating in times of crisis when swift action is called for. For too much of them is as bad as too little.

RATS IN A TEMPLE

Duke Huan of Qi asked Guan Zhong, his prime minister, what was the biggest threat to the country.

"It is those who resemble rats in a temple," Guan Zhong replied.

"Explain, please."

"Your Majesty must have seen rats in the walls of a temple. The temple is a sacred place. But if it is infested with rats, there is very little we can do. If we try to smoke them out, we may set the place on fire; if we pour water into the holes in the wall, we may damage the plaster and the paint on the walls.

"Bad men who get close to the ruler are just like those rats. They use their influence to benefit themselves. They take bribes and collude with interest groups to the detriment of the country; they act as agents for foreigners and spy on the ruler; they give favor to those who listen to them and make life difficult for those who don't. All the time the ruler is kept in the dark. These people should be punished, but they have the ear of the ruler. If things are allowed to continue like this, the country will be ruined.

"The bad man who gets close to a ruler also resembles a dog in the wine seller's shop. Let me give you another example.

"There was a man who sells wine. The wine was good and the price reasonable. But he had very few customers. He did not understand why his business was poor and asked his neighbor for advice.

"'You have a fierce dog, don't you?' the neighbor said.

"'But wine is wine, dog is dog. They have nothing to do with each other.'

"'Yes, they do. Whenever customers come to your place, the dog barks at them. The customers are afraid that the dog may bite them, so they go away. If you don't kill your dog, nobody will come and your wine will turn sour.'

"If a king has ministers like rats in the temple or dogs in that man's shop, the whole country will be at risk."

Comment: Men in power, do you have such rats and dogs around you?

RESPONSIBILITY

Emperor Wen of the Han Dynasty had two prime ministers, Zhou Bo being the senior prime minister and Chen Ping, the junior.

One day the emperor asked Zhou Bo how many law suits there were in the country that year.

"I don't know," Zhou said regretfully.

"What is the expenditure and revenue of this year in terms of money and grain?"

"I'm sorry I don't know," Zhou apologized, sweating all over.

The emperor turned to Chen Ping with the same questions.

"There are officials in charge of these matters," Chen replied.

"What officials?" the emperor asked.

"If Your Majesty wants to know the number of law suits, it is for the Ministry of Justice to answer. If you are interested in the amount of money and grain, we can check up with the Treasury and the Ministry of Agriculture."

"If everything is handled by these ministries, then what is your responsibility?" the emperor asked.

"I am honored to be your prime minister. A prime minister's duty is to assist the emperor in governing the country. Externally I manage our relationships with foreign countries; internally I try to make people happy by making sure that officials in various ministries are performing their duties properly."

Emperor Wen was pleased with the answer.

When they got outside, Zhou Bo blamed Chen Ping.

"Why didn't you tell me how to answer such questions beforehand?"

"As prime minister, you should know what your responsibilities are," Chen said with a smile. "If the emperor asked you how many thieves there are in the capital of Chang'an, would you try to answer that?"

Zhou realized he was not as qualified a prime minister as Chen. Not long afterwards he resigned on grounds of ill health, and Chen Ping became the only prime minister.

Comment: What matters is not that we know everything but that we know what relevant information we need for our purpose, and where and how to obtain it.

THE ARMY ETIQUETTE

In 158 B.C., the Huns invaded the northern border of China. To strengthen the border defense, Emperor Wen of the Han Dynasty appointed three generals, Liu Li, Xu Li and Zhou Yafu to three garrisons on the northern border areas.

Once the emperor paid a personal visit to the troops stationed there. The emperor's party could go straight into General Liu Li and General Xu Li's barracks. The generals and soldiers came out on horseback to greet him and see him off.

When they marched to General Zhou's barracks, the royal entourage was stopped at the entrance by soldiers armed with swords and bows and arrows. The emperor's vanguard announced that it was the emperor's party. But the army officer in charge replied: "General Zhou says we take orders only from him."

Soon the emperor arrived; he, too, was not permitted to proceed. He sent a messenger to General Zhou with royal credentials to inform the general that he would like to enter the camp and meet with the officers and soldiers.

Zhou Yafu then ordered that the gate be opened.

"Galloping is not allowed here!" the guards at the gate told the carriage drivers and cavalry soldiers in the royal procession. Therefore the royal party moved slowly into the camp. General Zhou was waiting in front of the headquarters in full uniform and bowed to the emperor.

"Forgive me for not kneeling, Your Majesty," said General Zhou. "A soldier in armor salutes only in a manner in accordance with the military etiquette."

The emperor was impressed. He straightened up and bowed in salute to the army. When he finished the inspection, the emperor sent a messenger to General Zhou saying that he wished to thank him for his trouble, and then departed.

As they went out of General Zhou's garrison, officials of the emperor's entourage were wondering how His Majesty was going to react to the way he had just been received there.

But Emperor Wen said: "Now there is a real general. The other two garrisons were like child's play. No discipline. No rule. They could be taken prisoner at any time if the enemy stage a surprise attack. But with Zhou Yafu, you cannot take a chance."

The emperor went on praising him for a long time.

Comment: General Zhou was later promoted to be the commander-in-chief for the defense of the capital.

If you bend the rules in order to please, you will lose more than you gain.

CALIBRE

Zi Si was Confucius's grandson. When he was serving in Wei, he recommended a person to the duke of Wei.

"I believe Gou Bian has the calibre of a general. He should be given an important position."

The king shook his head.

"Gou Bian may have the ability of a general. But when he was a government official, he once asked his subordinates to donate two eggs each for his personal consumption. I am bothered by that. I cannot appoint such a man a general."

Eggs were a luxury item at the time.

"Your Highness, I'm afraid your judgment of people is a bit too narrow," Zi Si expressed his disagreement. "Sure it is not right to collect eggs from employees for personal use. But when a wise ruler hires somebody, it is just like a carpenter selecting wood. He throws away the bad part of a tree and uses the good part. Even a good tree sometimes has knots and rotten parts. But a good carpenter will not throw it away because of a few holes on it. He throws out only the bad part and makes full use of the good part.

"We are living in an age of war and uncertainty. We need as many talented people as we can get. I am sorry that Your Highness refuses to use someone of outstanding qualities because of a few eggs. Just don't let other countries know about it because it's Wei's shame not to make use of talented people."

Comment: Do not demand perfection. Few people are free from faults. The question is the nature and magnitude of the fault and whether it is relevant.

21. THE PRIME MINISTER

> The noblest is one who has pioneered a moral cause that benefits his generation as well as future generations; the next is one who has performed great services to the people in general; and the next is one whose words enlighten and inspire all others. These are three immortal achievements in life.
>
> —*Zuoqiu Ming's Chronicles*

The name of Yan Ying is familiar to almost every Chinese. A contemporary of Confucius, he was the prime minister of Qi (in modern northern Shandong and southeastern Hebei provinces), under Duke Jing, about 2,500 years ago. I remember that even as a boy, I was fascinated by stories about his wit and humor.

REWARD OR NO REWARD

Before he was appointed prime minister, Yan Ying had been governor of Donge Province. At the end of three years of his administration, protests against him were so loud that they reached the ear of Duke Jing.

The duke intended to relieve Yan Ying of his post as governor of Donge.

"Your Highness," said Yan Ying. "I see my mistakes now. If you allow me to stay on in Donge for another three years, I guarantee I will improve."

Three years later, there was indeed much commendation about Yan Ying. News came round and the duke was pleased. He summoned Yan Ying to the court to be rewarded for his good services done in Donge.

Yan Ying, however, declined this honor.

"When I went to Donge the first time," he said, "I built roads, carried out public works, and cleaned up corruption in the government. Then I incurred the enmity of certain circles. I encouraged frugal living and urged people to respect their parents. I punished criminals. As a result, I made law-breakers hate me. I gave a fair hearing to everyone alike and did not give special consideration to the rich and influential, so I offended them. When those around me asked me for something, I only gave them what was legally permissible. Little wonder they also took offense. There were occasions when I had to entertain my superiors. I did not exceed the limit of the normal standards. They certainly did not like me for that. That was why all those people heaped slanders on me. At last, their vilifying remarks reached the ear of Your Highness.

"Then I changed my way of running the government during the last three years. No more public works. No more control over corruption. No more talk about frugal living. No hard penalty for those who broke the law. Whatever those around me asked for, I granted with a smile. Special consideration was given to the rich and influential. And I treated my superiors with lavish hospitality. As a result, all of them started to say good things of me. And in time you heard them.

"Frankly speaking. I should have been rewarded for what I did in my first three years and be punished for what I did during the last three years. So I do not deserve a reward this time."

The duke was so impressed that he appointed Yan Ying the Prime Minister to help run the country. In three years, Qi became a most prosperous state.

FAMINE RELIEF

There was a famine in Qi. Yan Ying asked Duke Jing's permission to open the state granary to aid the disaster-stricken people. But his request was rejected.

At the same time, the duke was building a new palace for himself. In his capacity of prime minister, Yan Ying secretly instructed the official in charge of the project to double the wages for the workers, expand the scope of the project and slow the pace of the construction work.

The construction was completed after three years during which period people who otherwise would have starved to death were able to obtain relief through working on the project. The duke was also pleased to see the new palace completed. By the time of its completion, the famine was over.

THE HAUGHTY COACHMAN

As prime minister of Qi, Yan Ying had a private coachman. One day the coachman's wife was watching her husband from behind the gate when he went out. Horse whip in hand, the eight-foot-tall coachman was sitting under the canopy in the front of the official carriage, looking so very pompous.

When he returned home, his wife told him that she wanted a divorce. The alarmed coachman demanded to know the reason.

"Look at Yan Ying. Though he is only five feet tall, he has great fame and commands respect throughout the world. Yet he looks gentle and unassuming - not like you! You are eight feet tall. You are nothing but somebody's coachman. But look at the way you put on airs! What is there for you to be so haughty? That is the reason I want to leave you."

The coachman asked his wife to forgive him. Thereafter he began to conduct himself in a humble and earnest manner. Whenever he had a spare moment, he would be engaged in self-study. Yan Ying noticed the change in his coachman. When the coachman told him the truth, Yan Ying was impressed. Later he recommended him to be a government official, for he was aware how a good wife could help and inspire her husband.

REDEEMING A SLAVE

On his way to the state of Jin, Yan Ying saw a man taking a rest by the road with a bundle of firewood beside him.

"What's your name? Why are you cutting the firewood?" asked Yan Ying as he saw the man did not look like a common laborer.

"My name is Yue Shifu. I am an indentured slave because I have to support my family."

Yan Ying took pity on him and redeemed him from his master at the cost of one of the horses of his carriage. He also invited the man to ride with him. When he got home, Yan Ying went straight in without saying a word, leaving the man to wait at the gate. He did not come out for quite a while. Yue Shifu took offense and declared that he was going to break with Yan Ying.

Yan Ying was surprised. "I never knew you," he said to Yue Shifu. "But I redeemed you. Isn't that good enough? Why are you talking about breaking with me?"

"A gentleman may put up with those who do not understand him but expects to be treated as equal by those who know him," Yue replied. "For three years I've been working as a slave. Nobody knew me and nobody cared for me. Since you redeemed me, I thought you were my friend. But you do not treat me like a gentleman. You were not courteous when we were riding in the carriage. I thought you just overlooked your manner. Just now you were outright rude to keep me waiting like this. I'd rather be somebody else's slave than to be treated like a slave by one whom I take for a friend."

Yan Ying quickly apologized and began treating Yue as he would do a guest of honor. Yue Shifu proved to be a man of great ability and integrity.

THE INTERPRETATION OF A DREAM

Duke Jing of Qi fell ill with edema, an excess of body fluid. He was sick for ten days. One night he dreamt that he was beaten by two suns in a battle.

The next morning he told Yan Ying of the dream and asked whether it was not an omen of his death.

"You should consult a dream interpreter," said Yan Ying. "I'll get you one." So he sent for the dream interpreter. When the man came, Yan Ying met him at the entrance of the palace and told him: "Last night the duke had a dream that he was beaten by two suns. He thinks he is going to die. So you are called to tell him the true meaning of the dream."

"I have to go home and consult my book," the dream interpreter said.

"No, it's not necessary," Yan Ying stopped him. "The duke's illness is caused by too much body fluid and in his dream he was defeated by two suns. Body fluid is water, and water represents yin. The sun represents yang, because it is the source of light and heat. One yin cannot win two yangs. So I think the duke will get well soon. You just tell him that."

The dream interpreter explained to the king the way Yan Ying suggested. Three days later, the duke got well. He was ready to reward the dream interpreter handsomely.

"I don't deserve a reward, Your Highness. You should reward Yan Ying, because it was he who told me how to interpret your dream."

Duke Jing sent for Yan Ying, but Yan would not accept the reward either, saying: "Although the interpretation was mine, yet you would not accept it unless a professional dream interpreter tells you so. If I had told you myself, you wouldn't have believed it. So I don't think I can take the credit."

The duke decided to reward both of them.

POWER OF REPARTEE

Yan Ying was less than five feet tall. He was sent to the kingdom of Chu as an envoy. When he arrived at the royal palace, some officials of Chu played a joke on him. They took him to a small door beside the regular entrance of the palace. Yan Ying refused to enter.

"Only when I visit a dog kingdom, I will go through a dog gate. But I am coming to the kingdom of Chu. Shall I enter your country through this door?"

He was therefore led through the front gate.

"Are there so few people in Qi that they have to send you as an envoy?" King Ling of Chu asked when he saw Yan Ying.

"There are so many people in our country and the capital city is so crowded that it looks as though it were raining when people brush sweat drops off their faces."

"Then why did they send you?"

"We have a policy of sending worthy men to worthy countries, more worthy men to more worthy countries and less worthy men to less worthy countries. I am the least worthy of all. That is why I am the right person to be sent to Chu."

At the banquet in honor of Yan Ying, a man in manacles, led by two guards , was walking past the doorway of the dining hall.

"Who is this man?" asked the King of Chu.

"A man from Qi," said one of the guards.

"What has he done?"

"He has committed theft."

The king turned to Yan Ying. "Your people steal. What a shame!"

Yan Ying stood up and replied, "They say orange trees produce sour and dry fruits when they grow in the north but sweet and juicy oranges when they grow in the south. Their leaves are similar but the taste is different. Why so? Because the environment is different. Now the people in Qi do not steal. But when they come here, they have become thieves. Most probably, the environment in Chu is conducive to that kind of behavior."

CONFUCIUS EMBARRASSED

When Confucius was visiting Qi, he called on Duke Jing, but not the prime minister.

"Why are you not willing to see my prime minster?" asked the duke.

"I heard that Yan Ying has served three rulers of Qi," said Confucius. "I am not sure how his loyalty stands. Three rulers must have had three different agendas. How could he serve them with the same loyalty? I do not know whether I can trust him. So I don't want to see him."

Duke Jing told Yan Ying what Confucius had said.

"What?" exclaimed Yan Ying, astonished. "Confucius accused me of being untrustworthy? How could he jump to a conclusion so soon? I used to have high regard for him and his disciples. Now I am not quite so sure that I have judged them correctly. I have served three dukes not because I shifted my loyalty that easily, but because all the three dukes have got one mind and one goal - peace and prosperity. That is why I have been able to carry out my duty with devotion. If I shifted my loyalty so quickly, I could not even work for one duke, to say nothing of working for three."

Yan Ying's remarks spread fast.

"I'm sorry to have offended Yan Ying," Confucius said to the duke, realizing his own misjudgment. "I have been unfair to him. Now Yan Ying has pointed out my fault, he should be my teacher."

So he went straight off to ask Yan Ying to forgive him.

KILLING THREE BIRDS WITH ONE STONE

There were three brave warriors in Qi: Gongsun Jie, Tian Kaijiang and Gu Yezi. They were arrogant and overbearing. Government ministers found them hard to get along with. And Duke Jing was bothered by their behavior.

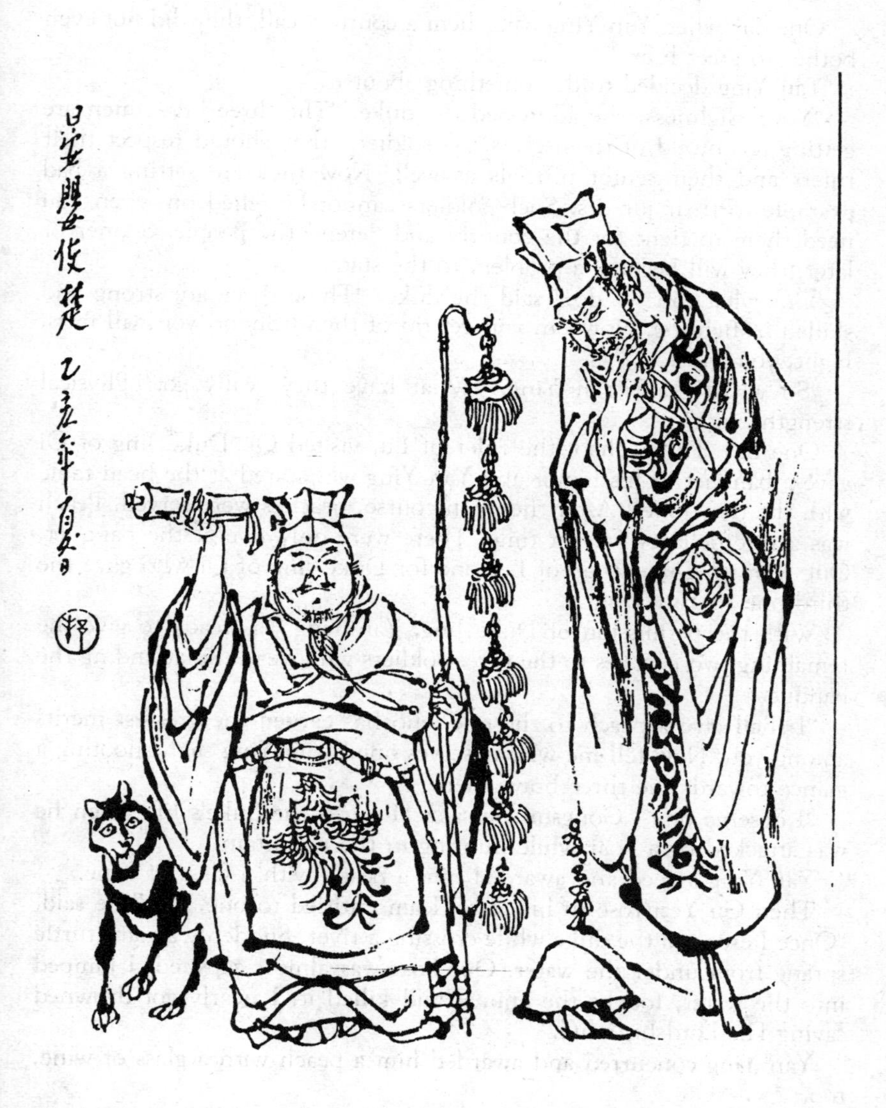

One day when Yan Ying paid them a courtesy call, they did not even bother to greet him.

Yan Ying decided to do something about it.

"Your Highness," he addressed the duke. "The three brave men are getting too proud of themselves. As soldiers, they should respect their rulers and their senior officials as well. Now they are setting a bad example to their juniors. Such soldiers cannot be relied on when you need them to fight for the country and defend the people. Sooner or later, they will become a problem to the state."

"But what can we do?" said the duke. "These three are strong and skilled in fighting. How can you get rid of them? Shoot, you will miss. Fight, you will lose."

"So what?" said Yan Ying. "What have they really got? Physical strength only."

One day, Duke Zhao, the ruler of Lu, visited Qi. Duke Jing of Qi gave a banquet in his honor and Yan Ying was seated at the head table with the two dukes. After the main course, peaches were served. Peach was a rare delicacy at that time. There were only five at the banquet. One went to Duke Zhao of Lu, one for Duke Jing of Qi who gave the third one to Yan Ying.

With the permission of Duke Jing, Yan Ying was ready to give the remaining two peaches to the three soldiers who were also attending the banquet.

"I shall give a peach to the one who has earned the greatest merits among you. Now tell me who deserves one," Yan Ying said, shooting a glance towards the three brave men.

"I deserve one," Gongsun Jie said. "I saved the duke's life when he was attacked by a boar while hunting in the mountain."

Yan Ying agreed and awarded him a peach with a glass of wine.

Then Gu Yezi rose to his feet. "I am entitled to one, too," he said. "Once I escorted the duke while crossing a river. Suddenly a giant turtle sprang from under the water. Our boat was almost capsized. I jumped into the water, fought the animal and killed it. I nearly got drowned saving His Lordship's life."

Yan Ying concurred and awarded him a peach with a glass of wine, too.

At this moment, the last one of the three, Tian Kaijiang, stood up.

"Your Highness, I saved your life twice with my sword when you were attacked by the enemy. Don't you remember?"

"Yes, I do," the duke said. "Your record certainly tops theirs. You have better claim to the peach. But you spoke up too late. Right now I can only offer you some wine and will award you a peach the next year."

Tian Kaijiang was angry. "Killing a boar or a turtle is fine. But I fought the enemy in battles to save the country. Now I can't even have a peach, I'll be a laughing stock in the country."

Instantly, he drew out his sword and killed himself.

Gu Yezi was stunned. "My record does not match up to that of Tian Kaijiang. Now he is dead because I took the peach away from him. I hate what I've done. I would be a coward not to die."

With that, he killed himself with his sword.

Gongsun Jie looked on in consternation. "The three of us are always together. Now that two of us have died, what face have I got to live on?"

He bellowed and fell on his sword too.

Duke Jing ordered a state funeral for the three men.

Comment: Yan Ying was one of the most illustrious politicians in Chinese history. The passage of time has hardly dimmed his brilliance.

After studying biographies of hundreds of politicians from the earliest time in Chinese history to his day, such was his admiration for Yan Ying that the great Chinese historian, Sima Qian (145-90 B.C.), declared that if Yan Ying were alive, he would deem it an honor to serve as his coachman.

Oddly enough, sometimes it appears that our wisdom does not seem to have progressed much since his time.

22. A WILY RABBIT

> Make friends with those who are faithful and sincere. Have no friends who are not your equals. When you have faults, do not fear to correct them.
> —*Confucius*

This is a story about Lord Mengchang, a chivalrous and most remarkable politician, and Feng Huan, his eccentric and sagacious advisor. Lord Mengchang was as famous a prime minister of Qi as was Yan Ying who lived about two hundred years before him. As recounted in the previous chapter, Yan Ying was known for his wit and humor. But Mengchang was known for his generosity.

OUT OF HIDING

Lord Mengchang was a member of the royal family of Qi in the fourth century B.C. His father, a wealthy man, had been prime minister under three kings.

When Lord Mengchang was a child, he was not liked by his father who had more than one wife and more than forty children.

He was born on the fifth day of the fifth month, an unlucky day according to ancient Chinese tradition. His father told his mother to get rid of the boy, but she raised him in secret. When Mengchang grew up, she decided to let him come out of hiding and go to see his father with his brothers.

His father was astonished and not at all pleased to see him.

"Why don't you like me, Father?" Mengchang asked.

"It is said that a boy born on the fifth day of the fifth month will bring disaster to his father if he grows to be as tall as the door, and a girl born on that day will bring trouble to her mother," his father explained.

"What governs a man's fate - Heaven or door?" asked Mengchang.

His father was at a loss what to say.

"Well, if it is governed by Heaven," Mengchang continued, "you have nothing to worry about. If it is governed by a door, you don't have to worry, either, because all you need to do is raise the height of the door so that I will never grow to be tall enough for the door to do you any harm."

His father told him to shut up.

THE MORE THE MERRIER

One day Mengchang asked his father: "What is the son of a son?"

"A grandson."

"What is the grandson of a grandson?"

"A great-great grandson."

"And what is the grandson of a great-great grandson?"

"I don't know," his father said.

"Father, you've been prime minister under three kings. Although you have become a millionaire, the country has not seen much improvement. You don't have capable men working for you. Your ladies and servants all wear clothes of silk and brocade, and their tables are spread with gourmet food and delicacies. But capable men in the country can't even keep body and soul together. It seems odd that you should neglect your work for the government and concern yourself only with how to amass a fortune for your grandsons whom you yourself do not know."

His father was struck. Since then he took a liking to Mengchang and put him in charge of domestic affairs as well as public relations. Gradually more and more men of talent came to work for him. When his father died, Mengchang inherited his title of nobility and hence became Lord Mengchang.

In those days, all aristocrats kept a large number of lodger-guests in their mansions, usually capable men who came from all walks of life to seek fortune under the roofs of noblemen. Lord Mengchang's reputation had attracted several thousand of such men from all over the country. Scholars, soldiers, knights-errant, refugees, and even criminals rallied around him. He treated them generously. Whenever he talked with his lodger-guests, his secretary would sit behind the screen to take notes. Immediately after the guests were gone, gifts would be sent to people whose names had been mentioned by them in their conversation with Lord Mengchang. He treated each one of his lodger-guests in such a way that each thought he was a special friend of Lord Mengchang.

One night when he was having dinner with a few guests, somebody happened to be standing against the light, thus casting a shadow on Lord Mengchang's table. One of the guests who could not see what Lord Mengchang was eating became suspicious that Lord Mengchang was enjoying better dishes than he himself. In a fit of anger, he walked out. But Lord Mengchang stopped him to show that his meal was just the same as everybody else's. The guest felt so ashamed of himself that he committed suicide.

A DOG AND COCK SHOW

It was not uncommon, during the Period of the Warring States, for scholars and officials of one country to take office in another. The state of Qin traditionally had a policy of employing aliens of distinguished abilities. When Lord Mengchang was sent to Qin as an envoy, King Zhao of Qin wanted to appoint him prime minister.

"It's true that Lord Mengchang is a capable man," one of King Zhao's close associates suggested, "but he is also a member of the royal family of Qi. He is bound to put the interests of his own country above anything else. Would it be wise to make him prime minister?"

"Shall I send him back, then?" asked the king.

"By no means," said his associate. "Since he came here, Lord Mengchang has already known too much about our country. You will be taking a great risk if you send him home. Kill him, is my advice."

The king, accordingly, put Lord Mengchang under house arrest. In desperation, Lord Mengchang sent a messenger to the king's favorite concubine, Lady Yan, to ask her for help. Lady Yan agreed to intercede with the king in exchange for a silver fox fur coat that she knew Lord Mengchang had in his possession.

Lord Mengchang did have such a coat. It was a matchless luxury item worth thousands of ounces of gold, but he had already given it to the king of Qin as gift. What was to be done, he was worried. So, he talked with his followers about the matter. But, none of them could come up with any idea until at last a man who used to be a thief spoke up.

"I'll get it back for you."

That night this man, disguised as a dog, slipped into the palace, and carried off the fur coat. When Lady Yan got the coat, she talked the

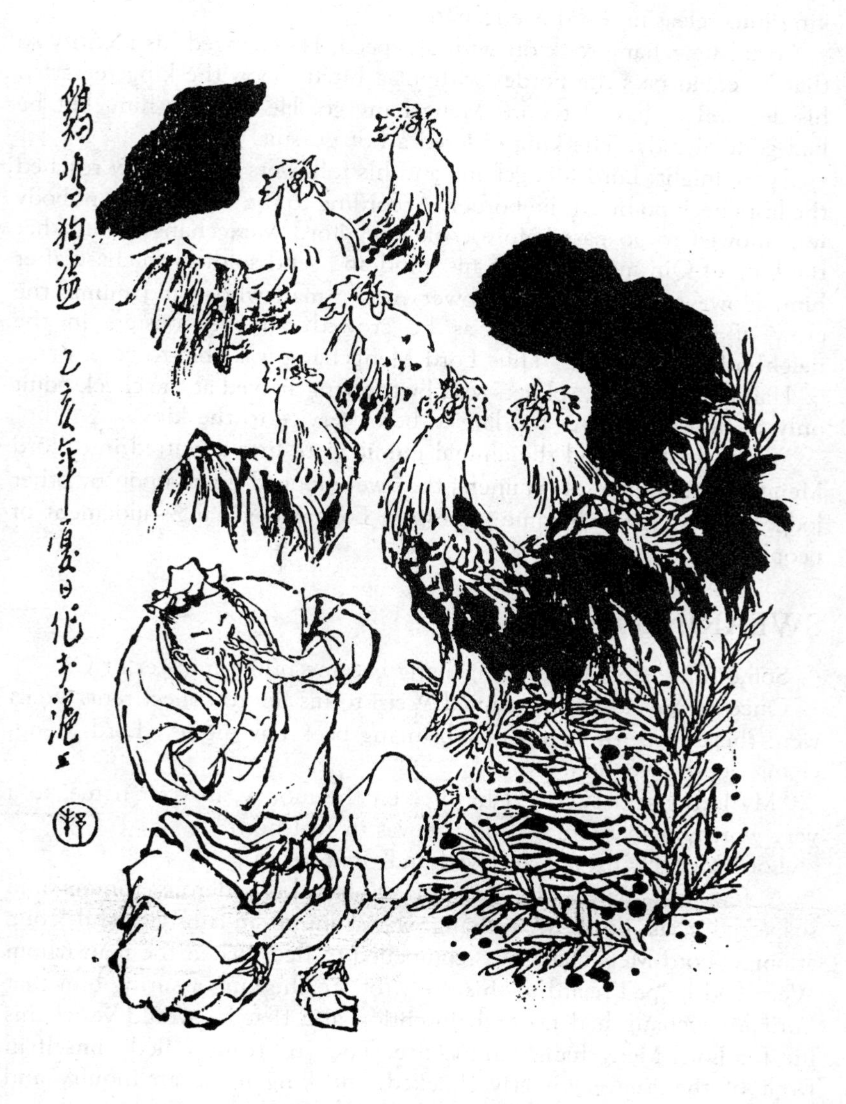
鷄鳴狗盗
乙亥年夏日作于滬上

king into releasing Lord Mengchang.

Lord Mengchang took off with all speed. He changed his identity so that he could pass the border without a hitch. Soon the king regretted his decision to have let Lord Mengchang go. He sent for him, but he had gone already. The king ordered a hot pursuit.

By midnight, Lord Mengchang and his followers had already reached the last check point on the border. According to the regulations, nobody was allowed to go past before cockcrow. Lord Mengchang feared that the king of Qin might change his mind and send soldiers to chase after him. However, among his followers was a man who could mimic the crow of a rooster. As soon as he crowed, all the roosters in the neighborhood followed. Thus Lord Mengchang was able to get away.

Half an hour later, soldiers sent by the king arrived at the check point only to find themselves too late to be of service to the king.

When the thief and the animal mimic were first admitted into Lord Mengchang's retinue of retainers, they were looked down upon by other lodger-guests. Now all came to respect Lord Mengchang's judgment of people.

SWEARING BY DEATH

Some time later, Lord Mengchang became prime minster of Qi.

Once he sent a steward named Weizi to his fief to collect rent. Weizi went there three times without bringing back any money. Lord Mengchang questioned him.

"My lord," said Weizi. "I have given the money, in your name, to a very worthy man there because he was in real need."

Lord Mengchang was annoyed and fired Weizi.

A few years later, the king of Qi heard slanderous rumors and suspected that Lord Mengchang was behind an unsuccessful coup attempt. Lord Mengchang was compelled to flee. When the man whom Weizi had helped heard of this, he wrote to the king assuring him that Lord Mengchang had no such intention and that he would vouch his life for Lord Mengchang's innocence. Then he really killed himself in front of the palace. Greatly shocked, the king made an inquiry and recalled Lord Mengchang to office after his innocence was proved.

SWORD SONG

Feng Huan was a poor man. Upon hearing about Lord Mengchang's hospitality, he asked to be introduced to the lord.

"What are your interests?" Lord Mengchang asked him.

"Nothing special."

"What can you do?"

"Nothing particular."

Lord Mengchang was amused by the answers.

"All right. Be my guest, anyway."

Lord Mengchang had him put in the hostel for new comers. There the guests had only vegetables for meal. Ten days later he asked the warden of the guest houses how Feng Huan was doing.

"He is really poor. He has nothing but a sword. He likes to beat his sword and sing to himself: 'Sword, Sword, let us go home. I have no fish for my meals.'"

The lord then had Feng transferred to a better hostel where fish was served. After a few days, Lord Mengchang asked the warden about Feng Huan again.

"Our guest is still beating his sword. This time he is singing: 'Sword, Sword, let us go home. I have no carriage to ride in.'"

So Lord Mengchang moved Feng to a hostel for the most distinguished guests. A carriage was provided for his use. Five days later he again asked the warden about Feng Huan.

"He is still beating his sword but this time he is singing: 'Sword, Sword, let us go home. I have to provide for my family.'"

All his fellow house guests were put off by Feng, thinking he was insatiable. Only Lord Mengchang did not seem to mind.

"Does he have a family?" he asked.

"His mother."

Lord Mengchang immediately sent food and clothing to his mother and made sure that she was well taken care of. After that Feng stopped singing and stayed for over a year without any more complaint.

BURNING THE BOOKS

As prime minister of Qi, Lord Mengchang retained three thousand lodger-guests. Though his fief in Xue had ten thousand households to provide the revenue, the income was not enough to meet his expenditure. He had to supplement it with interest accrued to the money he lent to citizens in Xue.

That year the debtors were unable to make interest payment due to poor harvest. Lord Mengchang put up a notice asking if anyone who knew accounting would be willing to go to his fief in Xue to collect the debt.

Feng Huan signed his name on the notice.

"Who is this man?" asked the lord. He had forgotten Feng already.

"The man who used to tap his sword and sing his complaints."

"Ah, after all, Mr. Feng is going to do something for me," Lord Mengchang chuckled as he gave him all the loan documents for use.

"Is there anything you want me to buy back, Your Highness?" Feng Huan asked, before departing.

"If you think I need anything in my house."

When he arrived at Xue, Feng Huan managed first to collect one hundred ounces of gold from them. He bought wine and beef and hosted a party. All the debtors were invited no matter whether he could pay or not. Feng asked them to bring their loan documents with them to tally with the documents he had brought with him.

At the party, he approached each debtor to check the loan documents and review his financial status. If the debtor could repay the debt, a repayment schedule was worked out then and there. If the debtor could not, he simply burned the loan documents.

"Lord Mengchang lent you money to help you start or expand your own business," Feng spoke to the gathering of debtors. "The reason he asked for interest is that he has need for it to supplement his expenditure because he has to support so many retainers. Now for those who can pay, we have worked out a payment schedule. And for those who have difficulties, I have burned the loan documents and the debt is cleared. The money you have borrowed will be Lord Mengchang's gifts for you. Let's call it a day and have a good time."

All the people there rose to their feet and gave Feng Huan a standing ovation.

Lord Mengchang was furious that Feng had burned the loan documents. He summoned him.

"Look! What have you done?!" he shouted at Feng. "I've got three thousand mouths to feed, you know. I need the interest income to meet the deficiency. Why did you burn the loan documents? Why did you waste money throwing a party for those who owe me money?"

"If I did not buy wine and meat, I could not have a party. Without a party, I could not know who could afford to pay and who could not," replied Feng. "For those who could, I have worked out a schedule for them to repay the debt. For those who are too poor to pay anything, there is no point in pressing them. You can keep demanding payment for ten years and still get nothing. If you put too much pressure on them, they may simply run away. In that case, you can't get your money back, and they will say you don't care for them at all. Your reputation will be at stake. Burning useless loan documents and forgiving uncollectible debts can only win you greater popularity. You told me to buy whatever you need in your house. You have plenty of valuables in your house. You have fine dogs and horses. And there is no shortage of pretty women. I figured what you need is loyalty from your people. Xue is a small place. Instead of taking care of the people living on your fief, you have exploited them like a merchant. I cancelled the debt in your name and burned the documents in your name. The people there cheered you heartily."

Lord Mengchang was not pleased at all.

"I've had enough," he snapped. "Go back to the hostel!"

THREE BURROWS

One year later, the king stripped Lord Mengchang of his office because he heard that the reputation of Lord Mengchang had outshone his own and that the lord was contemplating grabbing more power for himself.

Lord Mengchang had to return to his home estate in Xue. He was yet thirty miles away from Xue when the residents there, old and young, men and women, all came out to greet him. Mengchang's heart was filled with warmth.

"So this is the loyalty you have bought for me," he remarked, looking at Feng thankfully.

"A wily rabbit has three burrows in order to survive, my Lord," said Feng. "Right now you have barely got one. Let me go to the state of

Liang and I will make the king of Qi restore your status and expand you estate."

Lord Mengchang prepared a carriage and two hundred and fifty ounces of gold for Feng's journey, although he did not quite understand what Feng Huan had in mind.

"It was under Lord Mengchang that Qi has become a superpower," Feng said to King Hui of Liang. "Now he has been removed from his office because the king of Qi has heard malicious rumors. Whoever hires him first will benefit for sure. If he comes to Liang, don't you think his knowledge and experience will be very useful to Your Majesty? If I were you, I would not miss this opportunity."

King Hui dispatched an envoy bringing a hundred carriages and 10,000 ounces of gold as his gift to invite Lord Mengchang to visit Liang.

In the meantime Feng Huan hurried back to advise Lord Mengchang not to accept the invitations and the gift. The envoy of Liang called upon Lord Mengchang three times. Three times Lord Mengchang declined Liang's offer.

—What would become of Qi if Lord Mengchang was driven to work for other countries?

The king of Qi was troubled when he heard the news. Other ministers were also shaken. The king hastened to reappoint Lord Mengchang prime minister, adding another one thousand households to his estate, and awarded him 10,000 ounces of gold, two decorated chariots and a sword. He even wrote a letter of apology saying:

"I see my mistake now. Please come back to your office, though I may not be worthy of your service. Do come back for the sake of our ancestors, if not for me, for I know you love them as deeply as I do."

"You've got two burrows now," Feng said to the lord. "Let's make a third one." He suggested to Lord Mengchang that he take this opportunity to ask the king to move the royal ancestral temple to Xue. This would make his fief a sacred place. No matter what happened, the king of Qi could not very well attack Xue. Moreover, if Xue was invaded by foreign countries, the king of Qi would be compelled to come to Xue's defense.

When the construction of the royal temple in Xue was completed, Feng said to Lord Mengchang: "Now Your Highness have got three burrows. You can feel secure and carefree."

FORGIVE AND FORGET

As Lord Mengchang became prime minister again, those who had left him when he was in trouble came back one by one.

"I always treated these people well," the lord sighed. "That's why I had three thousand retainers. But when I was stripped of my office, they left me without a qualm. What face have they got to come back to me? I feel like spitting in their faces!"

Feng was just getting down the carriage when he heard Lord Mengchang's remarks. He bowed to the lord, and Lord Mengchang bowed back.

"Are you apologizing to me on their behalf?" Lord Mengchang asked.

"No, I was not apologizing for them. I was apologizing for what you said just now."

"I don't quite understand."

"In this world, all creatures die," Feng Huan said. "The rich and powerful are bound to have many friends and the poor have very few. This is not going to change. Have you noticed the shoppers in the marketplace? In the morning they push and jostle to shove their way into the marketplace. But when it gets dark, they turn away from the place. They don't even look back. Not that they like it less in the evening than they like it in the morning, but what they want is not there in the evening. When you lost your position, your guests simply went away for the same reason - they couldn't get what they wanted. There is no need for you to bear grudge against them. I hope you will treat them exactly as you did in the past."

Lord Mengchang bowed again, took his advice and had the names of the five hundred men that he had blacklisted scraped from his record.

Comment: "A wily rabbit always has three burrows" is an immortal saying of Feng Huan. Thanks to his advice, Lord Mengchang was able, in an age of chaos, trickery and treachery, to maintain his position as prime minster of Qi for decades.

Feng Huan's idea was that one should prepare for bad times while fortune was smiling on him and keep a following of grateful people and friends in case one need them some day. This was certainly wise thinking. But Lord Mengchang's hospitality seemed indiscriminate. While he attracted many people to him, truly useful ones were very few. One cannot help wondering whether or not his was the best way to recruit men of distinguished abilities even if he had the income of ten thousand households.

As for Feng Huan, with his outstanding talent and vision, he could probably have done much better than confining himself to the limited circle of Lord Mengchang's, though his loyalty must be admired.

Feng Huan's burning of loan books reminds me of a story told by Jesus in Luke:

There was a rich man whose manager was accused of wasting his possessions. So he called him in and asked him. "What is this I hear about you? Give an account of your management, because you cannot be manager any longer."

The manager said to himself, "What shall I do now? My master is taking away my job. I'm not strong enough to dig, and I'm ashamed to beg -I know what I'll do so that, when I lose my job here, people will welcome me into their houses."

So he called in each one of his master's debtors. He asked the first, "How much do you owe my master?"

"Eight hundred gallon of olive oil," he replied.

The manager told him, "Take your bill, sit down quickly, and make it four hundred."

Then he asked the second, "And how much do you owe?"

"A thousand bushels of wheat," he replied.

He told him, "Take your bill and make it eight hundred."

The master commended the dishonest manager because he had acted shrewdly. For the people of this world are more shrewd in dealing with their own kind than are the people of the light.

Jesus then said: "I tell you, use worldly wealth to gain friends for yourselves, so that when it is gone, you will be welcome into eternal dwellings."

PART V
LOVE, SEX AND SEXUAL HARASSMENT

23. SEXUAL HARASSMENT

In conducting yourself in society, combine firmness with tact; in dealing with people, combine kindness with principle. Forget the favors you did for others, but forget not your own faults. Remember the favors you received, but remember not the injuries others did to you.
—*Vegetable Roots*

Sexual harassment exists everywhere and it has been there since the beginning of history. Only today we have become more conscious of it. The three stories in this chapter are among the most famous ones in Chinese history, all of them having something to do with sexual harassment, though at a time when women were subordinated to men in the patriarchal family and in Chinese society at large, when people took concubinage and the inferior status of women for granted. Apart from the appeal of the stories themselves, I think it intriguing, given today's heightened awareness of sexual harassment, to look back on how the ancient Chinese handled the issue at the time.

A RIBBON-RIPPING BANQUET

This happened some 2,600 years ago.

King Zhuang of Chu was giving a banquet to all his ministers and generals. The queen and all the court ladies were also present. The band played music and toasts were exchanged amid a convivial atmosphere.

The banquet went from afternoon into evening and candles were lit. Radiant with joy, the king asked the beautiful Princess Xu to walk around the hall and pour wine for each of the guests at the table.

In the midst of laughter and tinkling of glasses, a wind suddenly blew out all the candles, and the banquet hall was enveloped in darkness. At this juncture, Princess Xu, who was pouring wine, happened to come near a man who, enticed by her beauty, pulled at her clothes until his fingers nearly touched her breast. Princess Xu was quick enough to stave off the intrusion with one hand, and, with the other, ripped the chin ribbon off the man's hat. A hat was an indispensable part of the costume on such occasions.

The princess immediately ran to the king.

"My Lord," she whispered in agitation. "Just now someone tried to pull off my clothes. I have snatched the chin ribbon off his hat. Please give your order to have the candles lit up right away. I can identify the man easily."

However, instead of summoning the waiters to light up the candles, the king announced: "Come on, everyone! Let's have a good time. Let's not be formal. Let's all take off our hats and rip off the ribbons. Tonight is a special occasion. Let's drink to our hearts' content!"

Only too willing to oblige, everyone present did what the king proposed. When the candles were relit, Princess Xu was unable to identify the person who had harassed her. She was very upset.

When the party was over, the king explained to the princess: "That man must have been a little drunk. It's only natural that he did what he did. You needn't make a fuss to spoil the party. All of them have worked for me in good faith. I wanted them to have a good time."

Three years went by. War broke out between Chu and its neighboring state, Wu. King Zhuang was surrounded by the enemy troops in a battle and was fighting desperately to break out. At this critical moment, one General Tang rushed to his rescue and beat off the enemy at the risk of his own life. He fought so bravely that the king was enabled to snatch victory out of defeat.

Filled with gratitude, the king wanted to reward the general.

"I haven't been especially nice to you, why did you fight so hard for me?" asked the king.

General Tang declined the offer of a reward.

"Your Majesty," he said, "I am the one who harassed Princess Xu at that banquet three years ago. You could have executed me for being rude to your favorite princess but you generously overlooked my fault. From that day on, I've been seeking a chance to demonstrate my gratitude to you."

"I am glad I did not listen to the princess," the king said.

Comment: The king's handling of the situation has long been hailed as a fine example of tolerance and magnanimity of a statesman who had earned the loyalty of his subordinates.

The fact that the general was probably a first-time offender makes it a bit easier for us to agree that the king did act wisely at the time, even without the benefit of hindsight.

If the same thing happens today in a corporate environment, with due respect for the victim's right and personal dignity, it might still be advisable to give the first-time offender a chance to see his own mistake without damaging his career.

SENSE AND SENSIBILITY

The Chinese traditional wedding ceremony had different formalities in different places. But it usually lasted three days.

On the morning of the first day, the bridegroom would go to the bride's house in a palanquin to deliver gifts to his in-laws and to take the bride to home, the bride seated in another palanquin. Having arrived at the bridegroom's home amidst the cacophony of drums, gongs, cymbals and firecrackers, the couple would bow to heaven and earth, bow to the memorial shrine in the ancestral temple, bow to their parents, and bow to the bed when they were conducted to the nuptial chamber. Then they would meet with all the guests. On the second day, the bride would formally greet all her in-laws, especially her father-in-law and mother-in-law and other elderly members of the family. Every time she bowed to an elder, the elder would give her some money wrapped in red paper. On the third day, the bride's family would come to take her back for a day. This was also the occasion when the bridegroom would formally greet his in-laws. On the fourth day, the couple would finally settle down in their new home, the bridegroom's home as a rule.

The wedding ceremony was never complete without boisterous merry-making in the nuptial chamber on the first night of the wedding. Guests were free to poke fun at the bride and the bridegroom, to ask them to sing and dance, or to challenge them to drink as many cups of wine as possible. Some even went to the length of playing pranks on them. It was believed that such merry-making would bring luck to the future husband and wife, the more boisterous, the better.

In the Ming Dynasty, a family in Anjie, Zhejiang Province, was celebrating the wedding of their son. Many guests were present. Amid all the hustle and bustle, a burglar sneaked into the nuptial chamber, hid himself under the huge bed, and waited for a chance to steal some jewelry after the lanterns were extinguished and the young couple went to sleep.

The celebration lasted three days. The nuptial chamber, brightly lit, was particularly busy. People came in to see the new couple, to admire the luxurious decoration, or to bring gifts to them. As a result, the burglar never had a chance to carry out his plan. He was hungry and could no longer hold. Seizing a quiet moment, he slid out from underneath the bed, only to be caught by the bridegroom's servants and taken to the local magistrate without a moment's delay.

"I'm a physician, not a burglar, Your Excellency," he protested. "I am the bride's physician. She asked me to accompany her to the wedding."

He went on to give a detailed account of the bride's family because he overheard all the private conversation between the bride and the bridegroom. He even mentioned that the bride had a certain kind of gynecological condition.

His testimonial convinced the magistrate that he had been wrongly accused. The magistrate decided to subpoena the bride to the court to be cross-examined. However, the newly wed couple asked to be spared. They were terrified at the prospect of having to testify against the burglar in public who knew all the intimate details of the woman's family.

Not totally insensitive of the embarrassment that the trial might give the bride, the magistrate consulted a senior aide of his.

"For a newly wed, my lord, it will be hard on her if she is taken to the court to bear witness against the defendant, no matter what the outcome of the trial is," the aide reasoned. "whether she wins the case or loses, she will be humiliated by the questioning."

"What can we do?"

"I have an idea. If the man had sneaked into the bedroom and was caught the minute he tried to get out from under the bed, as the bride argued, the chances are he can't have actually met the bride face to face, he can't recognize the bride if he sees her. Suppose we let another woman, posing as the bride, appear in court, we'll find out the truth in all probability."

The magistrate agreed that it was an excellent idea. He sought help from a local prostitute and made her put on the bride's wedding dress and come to the courthouse in a nuptial sedan carried by four men. As soon as she appeared before the magistrate, the burglar, standing in the defendant's corner of the courtroom, shouted in anger:

"You did not feel well that day and asked me to come with you to your wedding, didn't you? How could you say I was a burglar?!"

The magistrate broke into laughter and convicted the burglar.

Comment: Under our legal system, rape victims have to appear in court as witness to be cross-examined by lawyers of both the prosecution and the defense. The process, sometimes, is so humiliating and psychologically traumatic that it amounts to, in a way, sexual harassment itself. Even if the victims win, they lose. Maybe we can learn something from the magistrate and his aide.

MEMORY KEPT GREEN

Madame Li, a concubine of Emperor Wu of the Han Dynasty some 2,100 years ago, was beautiful and good at dancing. She had won special favor from the emperor.

Shortly after giving birth to a son, she fell seriously ill and was confined to her deathbed. When the emperor came to see her, she pulled her comforter over her face.

"Your Majesty, I can't let you see me. When I'm gone, please look after my brothers and my son."

"I know you're ill," said the emperor. "But why can't I see your beautiful face? You can ask for whatever you want. You know I won't grudge you anything."

"A woman should not look at her lord when her face is not properly made up," Madame Li replied. "I won't dare to let you see me in my present condition."

"Just one look, please," asked the emperor. "I'll reward you and promote your brothers."

Madame Li was adamant.

"What difference does one glimpse make? Whether or not you take care of my brothers, it's up to you."

"Let me have a look at you!" The emperor was insistent.

Madame Li turned her face to the wall, sobbing. The emperor was so frustrated that he walked out in silence.

"Why didn't you let the emperor look at you? Why on earth should you make him angry?" Madame Li's sisters blamed her for being so stubborn.

"I didn't let him see me because I wanted to make sure that he looks after my brothers. He likes me because he thinks I am pretty. When my beauty is gone, so will be his love. The emperor only knows how I used to look. That is why he misses me so much. Now my illness has destroyed my looks. If he saw me, he would be scared and would probably want to forget me. How can I expect him to cherish my memory and look after my brothers?"

When Madame Li died, the emperor had her buried with the honor accorded to an empress. Missing her deeply, he wrote poems in her memory and had a portrait of her painted in the palace. Later, he promoted all her brothers to high government posts.

Comment: Curiously enough, Madame Li and Greta Garbo seemed to have something in common.

After making a series of romantic movies, Garbo was acknowledged as one of the greatest screen actresses in history. Her classic beauty and memorable performances enchanted millions. But the Swedish-born star quit Hollywood at the age of thirty-five before her youthful beauty was worn. For the next forty-nine years she lived as a recluse.

Although she died in 1990 at the age of eighty-four, the world only remembers her as a beautiful, young actress. And she will remain so forever in the memory of the audience, eternally young, beautiful, exuberant.

24. THE SEX LIFE OF CHINESE EMPERORS

> The company of beautiful women may tempt one into having unrestrained sex. But having unrestrained sex is like chipping away at the root of one's life with an axe. The taste of fine food and good wine may lure one into intemperate drinking. But having intemperate drinking is like taking poison that will cause one's vitals to decay.
>
> —*Mei Cheng (?-140 B.C.)*

In this chapter, we digress from the main theme of the book, wisdom in Chinese history, to take a brief look at a uniquely interesting aspect in history, the sex life of the emperors.

There were more than two hundred emperors in Chinese history from the Qin Dynasty founded in 221 B.C. to the Qing Dynasty ended in 1911. According to a statistical research, only twelve emperors lived up to seventy years or older. The average life of an emperor was forty-three years, excluding unnatural deaths caused by regicide or accident. Yet the average life of a Buddhist priest in history was seventy-seven years. Nearly one-third of the emperors died between the age of 20 and 40; one-third died between 41 and 60. By contrast, almost no Buddhist monk died between 20 and 50. Thirty-three percent of them died when they were 70 to 79 and thirty-one percent lived more than 80 years.

Besides job-related stress, among the probable causes cited as attributable to the big difference is their respective lifestyles, in particular their sex life. Sexual indulgence is believed to be responsible for the short life span of an emperor while abstinence is believed to be the main reason for the longevity of a Buddhist priest.

The Chinese in general, however, do not believe in sexual abstention. Just as the interaction between heaven and earth gives shape to all things, the ancient Chinese held, sexual union between man and woman gives life to all things. The worst violation of filial piety was to have no child, no offspring to carry on the family line.

Procreative function notwithstanding, the ancient Chinese took sex to be a double-edged sword. Done in moderation, the sexual act could enhance the man's vital force by making him absorb the woman's essence and also benefit the woman by bringing her power to full potential. However, excessive sex was considered destructive to health.

Confucius regarded sex as something as needful to humans as food, but he lamented on the debaucheries he had seen of those who were in power, saying that he had never seen a man who was fond of virtues as much as he was fond of women. Indeed, Chinese emperors were notorious for their licentiousness.

As far back as during the Zhou Dynasty (1122-256 B.C.), the king kept a large number of women in the imperial harem. Later emperors were more acquisitive. For instance, in the Jin Dynasty, Emperor Wu (who ruled during 265-290 A.D.) kept nearly ten thousand of women in the palace. In the Tang Dynasty, the golden age in Chinese history, Emperor Ming Huang (who ruled during 712-742 A.D.) retained 40,000 women in the imperial harem.

Of all the women confined in the imperial harem, however, only about one hundred and twenty-two had sex with the emperor, according to the ancient imperial tradition. One of them was of course the empress. All were given ranks. The following shows the ranking and the number of women of each rank who were regular royal sex partners:

empress 1
secondary queens 4
queens of the third rank 9
queens of the fourth rank 27
queens of the fifth rank 81

The empress was the principal wife of the emperor. The four secondary queens enjoyed privileges equivalent to those of the prime minister.

The emperor's sex regime was regulated by the wax and wane of the moon. He slept with all the women on the correct days of the lunar calendar with sequence and frequency based on their ranks. As the moon gradually grew in size from the beginning of the lunar month, the emperor moved his sexual favor from lower-ranking ladies to higher-ranking ladies. When the moon was full, he slept with the empress. Then he moved his favor down the scale. In this way, it was believed, his potency would be enhanced by previous unions with women of lower ranks before he had his intercourse with the empress. Because the emperor symbolized the sun and the empress the moon, they must join each other only when there was a full moon, when there was a perfect harmony between the two cosmic symbols of the male and the female.

Thus the emperor's monthly sex regime was scheduled as follows:

Days 1-9 81 queens of the fifth rank, with 9 of them sharing the emperor's favor each night

Days 10-12 27 queens of the fourth rank, with 9 of them sleeping with the emperor each night

Day 13 9 queens of the third rank

Day 14 4 secondary queens

Days 15-16 the empress

Day 17 4 secondary queens

Day 18 9 queens of the third rank

Days 19-21 27 queens of the fourth rank

Days 22-30 81 queens of the fifth rank

There is no thirty-first day in the lunar calendar. This symmetric system, dated back three thousand years ago during the Zhou Dynasty, was designed, among other things, to maintain certain fairness for the emperor in distributing his favor among his wives.

The office of the Imperial Bed Chamber Affairs supervised the royal sexual relations to ensure that the emperor's sex life adhere to correct rules. To keep track of the increasing number of women the emperor had sex with, the office made meticulous book-keeping. The identity of the royal partner, the date of the copulation, and the signs of pregnancy were carefully recorded by a female official in red ink.

When she led the woman to the Imperial Bed Chamber, the female official put a silver ring on a finger of her right hand. After the woman had sex with the emperor, she changed the ring to her left hand. Once the woman became pregnant, the female official gave her a gold ring to wear.

During the Tang Dynasty, a new method was adopted to avoid confusion and false claim. A woman who had slept with the emperor would receive a stamp mark on her arm. The stamp was treated with certain cinnamon ointment to make it indelible.

However, this rigid sexual protocol was not always strictly followed. For example, Emperor Wu in the Jin Dynasty put several hundred

插竹洒盐乙亥

beautiful women in different mansions. He would tour the imperial harem complex in a chariot drawn by goats. If the goats stopped at a particular residence, he would go inside and spend the night with the court lady there. Consequently all the women vied with each other for the goats' attention. They grew the freshest green grass in front of the gate of their houses and sprayed salt on the grass as spice to entice the animals to stop by.

Ming emperors adopted a multiple choice system of mating. Wooden nameplates were painted green on the top, each bearing a court lady's name written in Chinese ink. At dinner, the eunuch in charge of the Imperial Bed Chamber Affairs would place a dozen or so of these nameplates on a silver tray and present them to the emperor along with the meal. If the emperor felt like making love, he would pick up a nameplate. If he seemed not sure which to choose, the eunuch would make suggestions to him, recommending such and such a lady as looking rather refreshing on that particular day, or dismissing such and such a lady as not being spirited enough and probably not able to satisfy His Majesty that night. Words of the eunuch often carried considerable weight.

Both the chosen lady and the empress would be informed of the arrangement. In fact, it was the empress's duty to make a formal request to the chosen lady to serve the emperor. This was a formality in deference to the authority of the empress.

The chosen one would bathe herself, and let her hair down as a coy way to suggest she was too young to be a partner for the emperor. Two eunuchs would come to summon her and she would strip herself in their full view. They would roll her in a red comforter and carry her on their shoulders to the emperor's bedroom. Except for the empress, all the women had to be carried to the Imperial Bed Chamber in the nude, probably to make sure that no weapon was concealed in her dress. The two eunuchs were also required to strip themselves naked before entering the emperor's bedroom for the same reason. The lady-in-waiting would then help the woman put on a silk sleeping-gown and leave her to wait for the emperor. Sometimes the emperor could not wait; he would make love while the woman was still on the shoulders of the eunuchs.

Only the empress had the right to stay the entire night with the emperor. Lesser wives had to clear out before daybreak. The emperor must stop making love by midnight as he was supposed to get up before dawn to meet with his ministers who would already be waiting for him in the court by this time.

At midnight the eunuch outside the royal bedroom would shout: "Time is up." If the emperor did not respond, he would shout again. If the emperor still did not move after the call was repeated a third time, the eunuch was authorized to enter the bedroom and carry off the lady.

The chief officer of the Imperial Bed Chamber Affairs would then ask the emperor: "Your Majesty, do you want to keep the baby?" If the answer was negative, massage would be administered at certain spots on the woman's abdomen to induce the royal semen to flow out along the vaginal canal. This was said to be an effective contraceptive measure. If the answer was yes, the date and name of the woman would be noted down. From then on, she would receive special treatment to help her bring birth to a child for the royal family.

Some queens, conscious of the duties of their spouse, would rise from the bed of their own accord when time was up. For instance, seeing her husband reluctant to go to the court after a night's joy of sex, a Zhou queen took off her ear-rings and hairpins and knelt before him, saying: "Please punish me. It is my fault that Your Majesty is late for work." The king, ashamed of himself, got up early to work ever since. Her action was hailed as a virtuous example of a good wife.

As eunuchs were in charge of the Imperial Bed Chamber, it is not difficult to understand that a peculiar intimacy existed between the emperor and the eunuchs. In fact, it was the eunuchs who gave the young emperor the first lesson in sex education as the latter literally grew up among them. That is why in some dynasties the eunuchs wielded too much power to the detriment of the imperial rule.

Comment: Under this super-polygamous system, women were reduced to no more than a vessel for emperors to derive sexual pleasure from. Genuine love seemed foreign to these monarchs. Perhaps that is why the love story of Tang Ming Huang and Lady Yang in our next chapter has impressed so many Chinese for so long.

25. SONG OF EVERLASTING SORROW

If there is sincerity in thought, there will be righteousness in the heart; if there is righteousness in the heart, there will be integrity in character; if there is integrity in character, there will be harmony at home; if there is harmony at home, there will be order in the nation; if there is order in the nation, there will be peace in the world.

—*Great Learning*

The Tang Dynasty is one of the longest and most prosperous dynasties in Chinese history. The fatal attraction of Tang Ming Huang, the sixth emperor of Tang, to his daughter-in-law, Lady Yang, the most famous beauty of China, is a poignant story known to almost every Chinese.

A CAPTIVATING BEAUTY

Emperor Ming Huang began his reign in 712 A.D. with great promise. He attended to his duties diligently. He had schools built throughout the country, widened the range of the imperial examinations for selecting civil servants, endowed a library and established a music college known as the Pear Garden. He was a patron of art, music and literature. Poetry, painting, music and performing arts flourished in his days. Merchants, entertainers, artists, monks, scholars, and foreign envoys flocked to the capital of Tang, Chang'an, which was probably the most cosmopolitan city in the world at the time.

However, Ming Huang's family life was not happy. Having repudiated the barren Empress, he lived with a favorite concubine of his for twelve years until she died, leaving him infinitely depressed. He was fifty-six then. He had thirty sons and twenty-nine daughters, none of them seemed able to console him. He had thousands of women in the palace harem, none of them seemed to interest him either.

To lift up his spirits, his chief eunuch called his attention to Lady Yang, wife of his eighteenth son. It was at his son's wedding that Ming Huang first saw his pretty daughter-in-law when she was only sixteen. Now that five years had elapsed, her beauty was in full bloom. Lady

Yang was born in 719 A.D. in Sichuan where her father was a government official. She was brought up by her uncle because her father died when she was yet a small girl. Plump, sensuous and extraordinarily beautiful, she was also gifted in singing, dancing, and playing the lute. Ming Huang was thrilled at the sight of such a stunning beauty.

However, the emperor could not very well take his daughter-in-law openly into his court. So he first arranged for his son to marry another woman. Then he had Lady Yang relinquish her marital status by going into a convent to be a nun, as a gesture symbolic of renouncing all her past relationships.

After a period of waiting, Lady Yang was officially admitted into the court in 740 A.D. and given the title of Imperial Consort.

The emperor used to have his wives flip coins to decide who was to sleep with him. Sometimes he would also let them hold a flower-picking competition in the royal garden. Whoever picked the most beautiful flower would spend the night with him. Then he would release a butterfly he was holding in his hand to see whose flower the butterfly would touch first. The winner would be the next one to sleep with him. But now Lady Yang had come to the palace. Her radiant youth and ravishing beauty cast all the court ladies into the shadow and monopolized the emperor's attention. Ming Huang's favor was heaped on Lady Yang alone.

Both Ming Huang and Lady Yang were music lovers. Sometimes the emperor composed music for court musicians to play while Lady Yang performed the famous Rainbow Feather Dance. The members of the royal family and the musicians of the Pear Garden had formed an orchestra, with the emperor to beat the drum, Lady Yang to play the lute and strike the stone chime. The concert would go on from daybreak to noon. Lady Yang also gave music lessons to other princesses and palace ladies.

Ming Huang started to ignore his duties, skip meetings with his ministers, often went to work late in the morning and, sometimes, even spent a whole day with Lady Yang.

The couple took frequent vacations and would spend most of their time in the Palace of Hot Springs in the suburbs of Chang'an (in modern Lintong, Shaanxi Province). There were sixteen bathing ponds for palace ladies. One special pool, made of marble and decorated with precious

三千寵愛在一身
乙亥夏日
作于滬上

stones and stone carvings, was built for the royal couple to take their daily bath in the bubbling spring water. Ming Huang even asked a well-known artist named Zhou Fang to paint the lovely Lady Yang stepping out of her bath. The painting so pleased the emperor that the artist was asked to draw another picture portraying Ming Huang himself making love to Lady Yang in the company of four other beauties. These are among the first erotic paintings in China.

Lady Yang was not only sexy and voluptuous, but also instinctively able to anticipate the emperor's desires. She knew exactly how to please the emperor. Once when she was watching Ming Huang playing a chess game with his brother, she noticed that the emperor was on the point of losing. So she sent a puppy onto the chessboard to ruin the game, to the delight of her husband.

She was fond of lichee, a sweet, juicy, milk-colored tropical fruit. To gratify her fancy, the emperor dispatched express couriers to get the best kind of lichee for her. Lichee grows in Guangzhou in the south, 600 miles away from the capital, Chang'an, which is in the northwest of China. To preserve the freshness of the fruit, orders were given to officials en route to provide fast relay horses for the couriers so that the mission could be completed in five days.

Lady Yang's sisters, uncles and cousins were all given titles of nobility and generous allowances. Each of them owned magnificent mansions. Lady Yang's three sisters and two brothers were particularly ostentatious. When the Yang families joined together in the streets of Chang'an, the procession resembled a splendid mobile flower show, each household having their own distinguished color. Hairpins, pearls, slippers were strewn along the streets. Fragrance spread over several miles. If they saw a better mansion than theirs in the capital, they would pull down their own houses and build new ones, more splendid and more luxurious.

The Yangs were at once the admiration and envy of the public. A popular song in the days of Emperor Ming Huang ran as follows:

Don't feel sorry if your baby is a girl;
Don't feel happy if your baby is a boy.
A boy may not be a duke,
But a girl can become a royal consort.

Officials vied with one another to curry favor with the Yangs. They brought costly gifts to befriend the Yang family. There were so many of them that the gates of the Yang family mansions became as crowded as the marketplace.

LADY YANG'S TEMPER

Lady Yang was witty, charming, graceful, but not so modest. Her relationship with the emperor was not always smooth-going. An emperor was entitled to make love with more than one woman; so was Emperor Ming Huang. Lady Yang's tendency towards jealousy vexed the emperor. One morning about a year after she arrived at the palace, the emperor, in a fit of anger, expelled Lady Yang out of the palace. But by noon time, the emperor was already missing her. He became easily irritated. He would punish anyone on the slightest provocation. The chief eunuch knew very well what was on the emperor's mind. He suggested food and wine be sent to Lady Yang's residence. Ming Huang immediately agreed. He halved his meal and had it sent to her. That evening lady Yang was brought back. A banquet was held on the following day to celebrate the royal reconciliation, with Lady Yang's sisters giving musical performances for which Ming Huang heaped on them many costly gifts.

A few years later, the same thing happened again. One day the emperor invited several princes to a dinner party. Lady Yang was also present. Prince Ning, the emperor's brother, played a tune on the flute. When the dinner was over and the guests gone, Lady Yang took the flute and played it for a while.

"Why don't you use your own flute?" the emperor teased her. "This one has just been used by Prince Ning. It is still warm with his breath."

"What's wrong with playing somebody else's flute," she retorted. "I heard that somebody's shoes were once stepped on, and Your Majesty didn't mind one bit."

The remark was deliberately made in allusion to what happened at a garden party a few years ago when Ming Huang's then favorite lady was performing a dance and an official accidentally stepped on her shoe and tripped her. She was furious, but Ming Huang dismissed it as nothing.

Knowing that Lady Yang regarded that lady as her rival, the emperor was not amused by the innuendo.

"You have gone too far," said the emperor, annoyed by her jealousy again.

For the second time the emperor expelled her.

In her absence, the emperor again became depressed. Knowing that the separation was hard on him, the chief eunuch came up with an idea.

"Lady Yang has been receiving your favor for so long," he said to Ming Huang. "Even if she deserves to die, she should have a place to die in the palace, not to exhibit her disgrace to the outside world."

The emperor relented, and again sent expensive gifts to Lady Yang.

"All I have was given by the emperor," Lady Yang wept and said to the messenger sent by the emperor. "Only my skin and hair were given by my parents. I have nothing to offer to His Majesty but this small lock of hair as a token of my love and gratitude. Please give it to the emperor and tell him not to worry about me any more." She cut off a strand of her hair and handed it to the messenger.

Ming Huang was alarmed when he saw her hair, thinking Lady Yang was going to commit suicide. That night she was welcomed back to the side of Ming Huang. When he saw her kneeling silently before him in simple dress, the emperor's heart melted. They vowed to love each other forever and ever and never to be separated again, although Lady Yang had never borne Ming Huang a child.

THE TATAR GENERAL

Tang was a gregarious dynasty. There were different races living in China beside the Chinese themselves. Officials were appointed according to their merits, not their ethnic backgrounds. Among them was a Tatar general named An Lushan who was of Persian and Turkish stock. He rose from the ranks because of his bravery and cunning. In addition, he understood six foreign languages.

An Lushan often sent the royal couple exotic gifts, such as a parrot that could talk and sing, and musical instruments made of jade. But what pleased Ming Huang most was an aphrodisiac. The aging monarch used it every time before going to bed with Lady Yang.

An was a big, fat man weighing about 400 pounds. Yet he was an expert in an exotic whirl dance. He often cut a clownish figure in the palace. At first he only knelt before the emperor, not the Crown Prince.

"Why didn't you pay respect to the prince?" asked the emperor.

"I am a Tatar. I only know who the emperor is, but not the prince," replied An, looking genuinely ignorant.

"The prince is the heir to the throne. He will be the future emperor when I am gone." Ming Huang explained.

An Lushan immediately apologized and made obeisance to the prince, saying: "I am sorry. I only know I must serve His Majesty and had no idea that Your Highness would inherit the throne."

The emperor was greatly amused.

When An Lushan saw Ming Huang and Lady Yang, he made a point of bowing to Lady Yang first.

"It's our Tatar custom to greet mother first," he said when the emperor asked to know the reason.

The royal couple were so flattered that they adopted him as their son.

On another occasion, Ming Huang pointed at his big belly and asked: "What's inside there?"

"There is nothing but a big loyal heart, Your Majesty."

Ming Huang liked this seemingly simple, blunt, unsophisticated but loyal Tatar. An Lushan, for his part, tried hard to cultivate such an impression, too.

One day a friend of his told him of a case of gross favoritism in that year's imperial examination. The son of a senior official was given high marks even though he could not read or write. Many people resented it, but no one dared to say anything about it because the examinee's father was a close aide of the emperor. An Lushan, however, raised this issue with Ming Huang who subsequently presided over a re-examination personally. Only a small percentage of the students passed, and the young man in question turned in a blank paper. As a result, the examiner and the young man's father were demoted. And Ming Huang all the more liked the Tatar for his loyalty and straightforwardness.

The emperor had a luxurious mansion built for An Lushan in Chang'an. An was promoted to the highest position ever held by a non-Chinese, put in charge of three military regions in the northern frontier in Fanyang (in modern Hebei Province), a city near Beijing. Virtually one third of Tang's army was under his command. His status as the foster son of the royal couple gave him easy access to the palace, so he moved in and out of the imperial harem freely. Sometimes he had dinner with Lady Yang, and sometimes he even stayed overnight.

Lady Yang did not wear a bra. She designed a low necklined dress to half-expose her lovely bosom as she knew that Ming Huang took a fancy to her shapely breasts. Soon the semi-topless dress became the fashion of the palace.

She was said to have an affair with An Lushan. One day, when making love with her, An scratched and bit her breasts. To cover the bruises, Lady Yang improvised a small red silk apron. Ming Huang's attention was directed to the apron, and suspected nothing at all. The red apron, too, soon became the fashion of all the palace ladies.

On An Lushan's birthday, a big party was held for three days. At the end of the three-day festival, Lady Yang said to An: "My son, it's our custom to bathe a new born baby three days after its birth."

So she removed his clothes, swaddled him in brocade, and then placed him in a sedan-chair to be carried around by the maids in the courtyard for the fun of it. The emperor heard the noise, and came out to watch the parade. Amused by the comic scene, he had a good laugh and gave An a huge amount of gold and silver as the baby's bath money.

THE SCHEMER

Thus, An was able to observe at close range the decadence and corruption of the house of Tang Ming Huang. Being an ambitious man, he began to picture himself taking over the house of Tang and sitting on the throne one day. But there was one man he really feared. That man was Li Linfu, the prime minister.

At first, he did not show much respect to Li. To teach him manners, Li interviewed, in the presence of An, a wealthy financier who held the same rank in the government as An. The financier walked up quickly, bowed very low, and listened very attentively to Li. An took the hint and changed his manners immediately.

The prime minister seemed to have an uncanny way of knowing what An Lushan had in mind. Every time An wanted to say something to Li Linfu, before he opened his mouth, Li would speak up what he had in mind. An was awed. He felt Li could read his mind. When he talked to Li, he would sweat even in winter. Back in his garrison, An always asked his envoy from the capital what Li had said about him. If he heard that Li spoke well of him, he would jump with joy. If Li said: "An

Lushan should examine his behavior," he would tremble with fear. But Li actually liked him and supported him.

When Li died in 752 , Yang Guozhong, cousin of Lady Yang, became the prime minister. In spite of the fact that Yang Guozhong held more than forty official positions and was very powerful because of the family connection, An had no respect for him. In the course of time, a deep rancor developed between them.

Yang Guozhong was an incompetent man, arrogant, overbearing and ruthless. Whoever disagreed with him would either be degraded or dismissed. Moreover, he openly started an incestuous relationship with his widowed cousin, a younger sister of Lady Yang's. The two rode side by side in a carriage up and down the crowded streets. Sometimes they rode horses together and sped them up in the street just for fun. Thus, Yang Guozhong became the most hated politician in the country.

People gnashed their teeth when his name was mentioned. But nobody dared to challenge him except An Lushan. Yang, in turn, often spoke ill of An before Ming Huang. Yang predicted that An sooner or later would betray the royal court.

In fact, news of how An had been secretly storing war horses, grain and weapons kept coming in, but Ming Huang did not believe that An would be plotting against him. After all, he had been so generous to the Tatar.

In 754, Yang Guozhong urged the emperor to summon An to the capital, alleging that An dared not come for fear of his plot being uncovered. In this way Yang hoped to convince the emperor to take actions against An.

When An received the imperial order, he immediately understood its real intent. He came at once and accused Yang of trying to frame him. Yang was outwitted. The emperor comforted An Lushan with a further promotion.

Back to his garrison, An stepped up preparations for his rebellion and a show-down. He had probably intended to wait until after the death of Ming Huang, who had bestowed so many favors on him. But the open hostility of the prime minister precipitated him into action.

Yang, now joined by other officials, repeatedly warned the emperor of An's treacherous intentions. The emperor sent an envoy to An's camp to investigate. An bribed the envoy. When he came back, the envoy gave a glowing report of An's loyalty, and the emperor was taken in again.

However, Yang Guozhong, still suspecting, arrested An's associates in the capital for interrogation. An, in turn, sent in an angry memorandum to denounce Yang. In the meantime, he decided to act while he still had a formidable force under his command. He had a son in the capital who was to marry a princess of the royal family in 755. When Ming Huang sent an invitation to him to attend the wedding, this time he declined.

THE REBELLION

In December 755, An Lushan led an army of 150,000 in revolt, falsely proclaiming that he was ordered by the emperor to put down Yang Guozhong. Ming Huang, having dismissed the news as malicious rumors at first, was now compelled to face the reality. Yang Guozhong was gleeful because events had borne out his predictions. However, he had underestimated the gravity of the situation. The army of Tang had not seen fighting for many years. They were no match for An's well-trained cavalry and infantry. The Tang Dynasty had two capitals, the eastern capital of Luoyang and the western capital of Chang'an. An's troops quickly captured the eastern capital of Luoyang and advanced rapidly toward Chang'an, where the royal court was seated.

The emperor appointed an experienced retired general to lead an army of 200,000 to guard a strategic pass to the east of Chang'an. Due to its geographical advantage, the pass was an impregnable bulwark. So the general adopted a defensive strategy. Everyday a fire was lit on the tower of the fortress to announce that the Tang troops were holding their position. But Yang Guozhong feared that the general had too much power and suspected that his own position could be jeopardized. So he urged the emperor to order the general to attack. The general argued that since An's army came a long way off, what they sought was a quick battle. To engage An Lushan's elite forces in a front attack would be disastrous, given the current condition of the Tang army. But Yang interfered again and forced the general to launch an offensive. As a result, the Tang army was crushed and the general killed.

Three days later, An Lushan overran the strategic pass, and Ming Huang and Lady Yang, accompanied by the Crown Prince and some other senior officials, fled Chang'an.

It was July 756. The emperor and his retinue were on their way to Szechuan in the southwestern direction. At lunch time they reached a suburban town where the local officials had already fled. They were hungry, and Yang Guozhong bought the emperor some cakes. The local residents, having found out who had come, immediately brought out some rice. The members of the royal family grabbed the rice with bare hands and started to eat. There was not enough to go round.

"Your Majesty," an old man came to the emperor and said. "An Lushan has plotted this for a long time. But you were taken in by his flattery. We knew this was going to happen, but you were far away, and we had no access to you. If things had not come to such a terrible state, we would never have been able to see Your Majesty."

"I'm sorry, it's all my fault. But now it's too late," the emperor replied.

THE DEATH OF A BEAUTY

The next day the royal entourage reached a postal station called Mount Mawei (in modern Xingping, Shaanxi Province), about thirty miles to the west of the capital. The imperial guards of 1,500 men, hungry and exhausted, held Yang Guozhong responsible for all this. They wanted to kill him. At that time a group of starving Tibetan emissaries came up and stopped Yang to ask for food. As the soldiers nearby saw this, they accused Yang of plotting against the emperor with foreigners and shot at him with an arrow which only hit the saddle of his horse. Yang got down and ran, but he was overtaken and killed. The soldiers also killed Lady Yang's other relatives who were among the royal entourage.

The mutineers then surrounded the temporary lodging house of the emperor.

"It's my fault that we are in such a miserable state," Ming Huang came out to speak to the crowd. "Yang Guozhong is already dead. I am not going to blame anybody. Please go back now."

But the soldiers refused to leave. There was a throbbing silence.

"What is the matter?" Ming Huang asked his advisor.

"I know what they want," said the army general. "The root cause of the disaster has not been eradicated. They feel it is not appropriate for Lady Yang to be around, Your Majesty."

"But Lady Yang has nothing to do with politics," the emperor protested, as he stood at the entrance leaning on a cane, confronting the mutineers. "She lives in the inner palace with me. I'll take care of the matter myself."

"True she is not guilty," the general urged. "But as the officers and soldiers have killed Yang Guozhong, how can they feel secure if Lady Yang remains at Your Majesty's side? I cannot guarantee your safety, if they don't feel safe. Please decide quickly."

The emperor eventually gave in and broke the news to Lady Yang.

Lady Yang began to cry. Choked with emotion, she could hardly utter a word. Finally she found her voice.

"Your Majesty, I am willing to die for your sake. Take care of yourself. Thank you for everything. I don't deserve all the favors you have bestowed on me. I hope everything goes well for you. Before I die, please let me say my prayers to Buddha." Ming Huang covered his face with his sleeve. He could not bear parting with her.

Lady Yang was led to a Buddhist temple nearby and was given a long silk cord with which she hanged herself on a pear tree in the compound. She was thirty-eight then. Having confirmed her death, the general had her wrapped in purple cloth and buried by the roadside.

It was just at that moment when a shipment of lichee, Lady Yang's favorite delicacy, arrived.

Distraught with grief, Ming Huang abdicated in favor of his son, thus ending his forty-five-year reign.

Two years later, the capital was recaptured. An's rebellion was finally quelled. The collapse of Ming Huang's rule marked the beginning of the decline of the Tang Dynasty, the most glorious one in Chinese history.

On his way back to Chang'an, Ming Huang passed by Mount Mawei. He wanted to have Lady Yang reburied, but an official warned him that reburial might arouse suspicion and fear among those soldiers who executed Yang Guozhong. Though a proper ceremony was denied, Ming Huang secretly ordered to remove her body into a coffin and have it buried somewhere else. When her body was dug out, Ming Huang broke into tears, seeing that her flesh had already decayed, but the perfume sachet buried with her was still intact.

The death of Lady Yang left the old monarch devastated. He had a portrait of Lady Yang placed in the palace and gazed at it day and night, never ceasing to mourn for his dear departed during the remaining six years of his life. He died at the age of seventy-eight.

Ming Huang's passionate undying love for Lady Yang was narrated in *The Song of Everlasting Sorrow* by Bai Juyi, a great poet in the Tang Dynasty. It remains one of the most popular poems in China.

Comment: The story of Lady Yang and Tang Ming Huang captured the imagination of generations of Chinese. The hot springs where Lady Yang took her bath still exist in Xi'an.

Of many things written about Lady Yang, one story is hauntingly provocative.

In the Ming Dynasty, more than seven hundred years later, a scholar paid a visit to the famous hot spring resort in Chang'an, the erstwhile capital of the Tang Dynasty, where Lady Yang had bathed.

When he was taking a bath, he noticed some red spots on a stone in the pool. Then he was told that they were believed to be the stains of the menstrual blood of Lady Yang, and his heart was moved.

That night, a beautiful, plump woman appeared in his hotel room, identifying herself as Lady Yang. She told him that he evoked her spirit when his heart was moved at the sight of the red spots on the stone. Since then the ghost followed him everywhere and showed up every night. He tried to persuade her not to bother him, but she did not oblige. He was so disturbed that he was unable to hold on to a steady job. It was after a long time that the ghost stopped haunting him and the scholar was able to resume his career.

26. PRETTY WOMAN

> Once a prostitute turns over a new leaf, her past is forgiven. But when a good woman lapses from virtue, all her past is forgotten. It is true that the end counts so much more than the beginning.
> —*Vegetable Roots*

Here is another great love story which took place four hundred years ago and has since left generations of Chinese to cheer, to sigh, to condemn and to admire.

In 1592, when General Toyotomi Hideyoshi of Japan, invaded Korea, the king of Korea appealed to China for help. The Ming government of China agreed to send troops there. To partially finance the expedition, a new way of raising money was found. Anyone who could afford to pay could buy a place in the Imperial College in Beijing or Nanjing. Students at the Imperial College stood a better chance to pass the imperial examinations, success at such examinations being a necessary step before one can be appointed to senior government offices.

Li Jia was one of those students who purchased a place in the Imperial College in Beijing. He came from a well-off family in Zhejiang Province in the east of China. His father was a treasurer in the provincial government. In Beijing, Li met a friend, Liu Yuchun, also a native of Zhejiang, studying in the same college. Together they frequented brothels in the city. It was in one of those brothels that Li met a beautiful nineteen-year-old girl called Du Wei.

Du became a prostitute when she was thirteen. Since then she had captivated countless young men who spent their fortunes on her. Li Jia was infatuated, too. Never having seen such a ravishing beauty before, he pursued her passionately. A handsome young man, Li Jia was amiable, generous and attentive. Du Wei took to him. She had long wanted to quit her present profession. Seeing Li was so devoted to her, she wanted to be married to him. The two fell deeply in love. They spent all day and all night together as though they were husband and wife. However, Li could not marry her without the permission of his parents in Zhejiang.

Loving Li, Du Wei refused to see any other client. Li spent lavishly on her. At the sight of money, the brothel mistress was all smiles. A year went by quickly. Li's money was nearly exhausted and he was not as open-handed as he used to be. The brothel mistress began to spurn him. When his father, a strict old man, heard what Li had been doing in Beijing, he ordered him to return home immediately. But Li was head over heels in love with the girl. He was not at all thinking of going home.

Although Li was a poor man now, Du Wei loved him all the more. The brothel mistress told her to stop seeing Li, but she refused. The mistress started to insult Li in order to chase him out, but he ignored her insulting remarks.

"In our profession, we depend on our clients for our livelihood," she said to Du Wei. "The more traffic we generate, the more money we can earn. Now Li has been hanging around here for more than a year. Old clients no longer come, to say nothing of new ones. Soon enough there'll be no smoke in our chimney. What are you going to do?"

"Mr. Li didn't come with empty hands," the girl retorted. "Don't you remember how much money he has spent here?"

"That was quite a while ago. I'm talking about the present. Other girls are earning big money, but you are supporting a pauper. Go and tell that beggar of yours that if he has any decency at all, he must give me some money. Then you can go off with him and I'll get another girl to take your place. Wouldn't that be good for both of us?"

"Do you really mean it?" asked Du Wei.

"Of course I mean it," the old woman said, believing Li had no money at all as he had already pawned his clothes.

"How much do you want him to pay?"

"If it were anybody else, I would ask for a thousand ounces of silver. But I'll only ask a poor devil like him for three hundred. With that I can get another girl. There is one condition, however. He must pay me in three days. Then you may leave straight away. If he does not come with the money, I'll drive him out with my cane. And no one is to blame me!"

"But three days is too short," said Du Wei. "Could you make it ten?"

"The young fool is broke," the old woman thought. "Even if I give him a hundred days, what difference will it make? When I finally get rid of him, I'll put my house under control again, and Du Wei will have nothing to say."

"All right," she told the girl. "I'll give him ten days as you wish. But don't blame me if he fails to pay at the end of the ten days."

That night Du Wei discussed her future with Li.

"I want to marry you, darling," Li said. "But it would cost at least a thousand ounces of silver to get you free. Where can I get all that money?"

"I've spoken to my mistress already. She wants only three hundred, but she demands the money to be paid within ten days. I know you have run out of money. But you must have friends and relatives in the city. Can't you borrow from them? If you can raise the amount, I'll be yours forever."

"My friends and relatives have been giving me the cold shoulder because I spend too much time here. But tomorrow I'll tell them that I want to bid good-bye to them because I'm packing up to leave for home. Then I'll ask them to lend me some money for my travelling expenses. I may be able to collect three hundred this way."

"Do it quickly. I'll be waiting for you."

Li called on these people at once. Although they were pleased to hear that he was going home, no one was willing to help when he mentioned money. They were afraid Li might spend the money on girls again because Li's frequent visits to brothels had damaged his creditability.

Three days went by. All his efforts came to nothing. Li was too ashamed to go back to Du Wei. He went to his fellow student Liu Yuchun and told him the story. Liu shook his head in disbelief.

"Three hundred ounces? That's impossible!" said Liu. "Du Wei is the most famous girl in that quarter; her price must be at least a thousand ounces of silver. Her mistress knows you are broke. They all know you cannot afford the money. But as you are an old customer, they cannot very well kick you out. Once the ten-day deadline is past, you naturally won't have the face to go back. That is their way to get rid of you."

Li was not convinced and kept going from one acquaintance to another trying to raise the money. He stayed at Liu's for the next three days. Du Wei became anxious, now that only four days were left of the ten-day allowance. She sent a boy servant to look for him.

"Mr. Li!" the boy shouted to him when he came across Li in the street. "My mistress is looking for you. Come back right away!"

Li was too ashamed to go back.

"I'm busy today," he said. "I'll come tomorrow."

But the boy grabbed his coat and pulled him along. "You must come with me," he insisted.

When he saw Du Wei, Li sat down without a word.

"What progress have you made?"

"I stayed away because I am too ashamed to come back to you empty-handed," said Li Jia in tear. "I have done my best, but people are just callous."

"Don't let the old woman know," said Du Wei. "Stay here tonight. We'll talk it over."

They had dinner together.

"You really can't get any money at all? What is going to become of me then?"

Li had no answer.

"I have saved a hundred and fifty ounces of silver," Du Wei whispered to him. "Take that. Now you have half of the amount needed, it should be easier to raise the other half. But hurry up. You've got only four days."

She took the cash out from under her mattress. Li was astonished.

He went to see Liu immediately and told him what had happened.

"She must love you very much," Liu said, deeply impressed by Du Wei's sincerity. "You must not let her down. I'll do what I can for you."

"If you can help me, I'll never forget."

Liu went around to all his friends. In two days he borrowed one hundred and fifty ounces of silver.

"I did this not so much for you as for the girl," said Liu, giving Li the money. "I'm touched by her devotion to you."

Li raced to Du Wei's, his heart throbbing with happiness.

When he told her about his fellow student, Liu Yuchun, Du Wei put her hands on her forehead in thankfulness.

They spent the night in great joy. Du Wei got up very early next morning.

"We'll be leaving in the morning," Du Wei said exuberantly. "You'd better decide where we are going. I have borrowed twenty ounces of silver from my friends for our travelling expenses."

Li was delighted that Du Wei had anticipated the need for travelling money. As they were chatting, the brothel mistress knocked on the door. It was the tenth day.

"Today is the deadline," she announced. "Can you pay?"

"I was just going to call on you," Li said, putting the three hundred ounces of silver on the table.

The old woman's face changed color. She was dumbstruck.

"I've been working here for eight years. I must have earned many thousands for you," Du Wei said to the brothel mistress. "Now I'm going to turn a new leaf. Today is the happiest day in my life."

The old woman remained silent for a while. Finally she gathered herself up and weighed the silver. It was the correct amount, no more, no less.

"Well, I suppose I can't keep you," she said. "But if you want to go, go now. You're not to take anything with you except for the clothes you are wearing." With that she pushed them out of the door.

It was late autumn. Du Wei had just got up and was only scantily dressed.

"Wait here. I'll call a sedan-chair for you," Li said.

"Just a minute, I'm going to say good-bye to my colleagues here. They've been awfully nice to me." Du Wei took Li to see other girls and introduced him specially to two who were her best friends.

She washed herself in their lodgings. They brought out gold bracelets, jade hairpins and ear-rings, a brocade petticoat, a decorated girdle and a pair of embroidered shoes to outfit their departing friend. They treated the couple to a dinner and let them stay in their place for the night.

The following day, they gave a big party to celebrate the union of the two lovers. All the prostitutes were invited. They sang and danced, each doing her best to entertain the couple.

The couple stayed overnight in the residence of one of Du Wei's friends.

Du Wei asked Li whether he had made any plan for their travelling.

"My father is already angry with me," said Li. "If he hears that I have married a whore, not only will I suffer, but you will feel his anger, too. I've been thinking for some time, but haven't come up with any solution yet."

"A father loves his son," Du Wei comforted him. "He won't be angry with you for long. Maybe we should not go home straight away. We could make a sightseeing trip to Hangzhou or Suzhou first. Then you can go home alone and ask your relatives and friends to put in a good word for you. Once you have made peace with your father, you can come to take me home. And all will be well."

"That's a good idea," Li agreed.

The two then went to see Liu Yuchun. Du Wei knelt down before Liu to express her gratitude.

"Don't mention it," Liu bowed back and said. "You are a most remarkable lady."

The three of them dined and wined all day. An auspicious date was chosen for the journey.

Along with all the other girls of the brothel, Du Wei's two best friends came to see them off. They gave her a gift-box. "This is from all of us to wish you good luck."

Du Wei accepted it with thanks. She did not open the box, though.

As they reached River Lu, at the northern end of the Grand Canal near Beijing, where they were to take a boat journey down the river, Li started to worry about money again. What little money had been left as he had spent on redeeming his nice clothes from the pawn-shop.

"Don't worry," Du Wei opened the gift box and took out fifty ounces of silver.

It was a pleasant surprise. "Without your help, I could not have made it," Li Jia said, filled with gratitude.

A few days later, they reached Guazhou, a city in northern Jiangsu Province at the intersection of the Grand Canal and the Yangtze River. Most passengers went ashore. Li Jia and Du Wei were due to transfer to another passenger ship. It was mid-winter. The moon was full and the sky serene.

"Since we left Beijing, we've been shut up in the cabin," Li said. "I'm glad we have the boat to ourselves today. Let's have some wine."

"By all means. It's been a while since we had a few laughs."

Li took out a bottle of wine and spread a rug on the deck. They filled each other's glasses and kept drinking until both felt a little tipsy.

"Sing a song for me," said Li. "The first time I saw you, you sang so wonderfully that I fell in love with you then and there. You have the

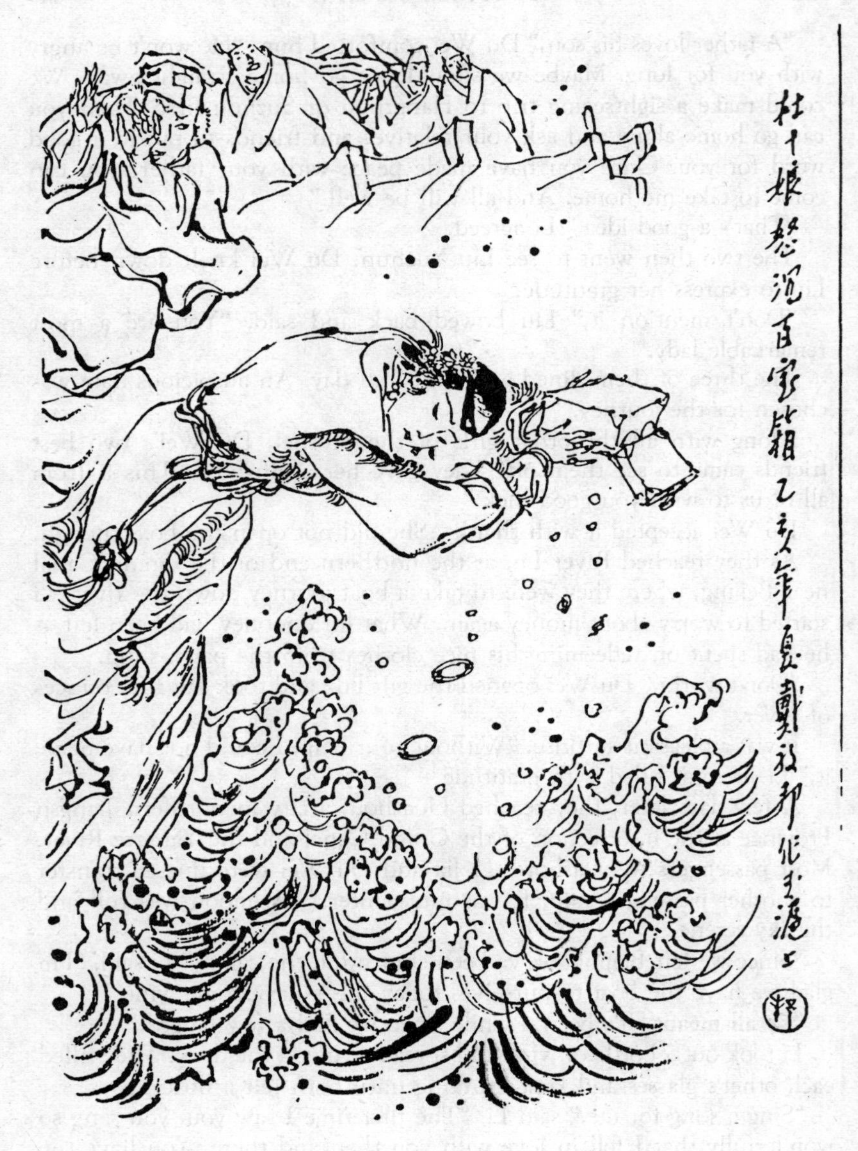
杜十娘怒沉百宝箱
乙亥年夏戴敦邦作于沪上

most beautiful voice in the world. What a lovely night! Look at the moon! Look at the rippling waves! They are so beautiful. Sing a song for me, please."

Du Wei cleared her throat. Tapping her feet on the deck, she sang the Wine Song from a classical play of the Yuan Dynasty. She was filled with happiness.

On a neighboring boat moored at the harbor there was a young man named Sun Fu, who was a student in the Imperial College in Nanjing. He was twenty years of age, and also a rich man's son of the pleasure-bent type. His family had been in the salt business in Yangzhou for generations. A frequenter of brothels, he, too, liked the company of girls.

He was drinking by himself that evening when he heard a woman singing nearby. What a heavenly voice she had! Sun Fu stood up and listened, spellbound. Just when he realized that the voice came from the next boat, the singing stopped.

She could not possibly come from a respectable family, Sun Fu thought, her singing being so professional. How could he get to see her? He kept thinking of the owner of the heavenly voice, unable to go to sleep.

A snowstorm broke out near dawn. All the boats were forced to stay in the harbor. Sun Fu ordered the boatman to pull his boat closer to Li's. He opened the window pretending to watch the snow. Du Wei happened to draw up the curtain of her cabin and he caught a glance of her. He was smitten. He hoped to see her face a second time. But Du Wei never approached the window again. Suddenly an idea occurred to him. Sun also started to sing.

When Li Jia heard the singing from the next boat, he looked out just as Sun Fu had wished.

"Hello!" Sun hastened to greet Li Jia.

The two men introduced each other and found out that they were from the same Imperial College. They soon became friends. Sun invited Li for a drink on shore.

While chatting over wine and food, they quickly turned to the topic of women. They found their mutual experience in brothels interesting.

"I heard a woman's voice singing on your boat last night. Who is that woman?"

"She is Du Wei, a famous prostitute in Beijing," Li was boastful.

"How did you manage to get her?"

Li told him the whole story.

"You must be very happy to bring a beauty home. But what will your family say?" Sun asked.

"I am not too worried about other people," Li said. "The trouble is my father. He is a very strict man."

"What are you going to do?"

"We thought about it. I am going home first. Du Wei will be staying in Suzhou or Hangzhou for a while. I'll ask my relatives and friends to intercede for me with my father. When he is no longer angry, I'll bring Du Wei home."

Sun did not say anything.

"What do you think of the plan?" Li asked.

"We've just met. I don't want to sound intrusive."

"Come on, tell me what you think."

"Well," said Sun. "Your father is a senior government official. I am sure he is concerned about the family reputation. He was angry when he heard you were visiting brothels. Do you think he would let you take a prostitute home? As for your friends and relatives, they probably won't be too helpful in such matters. I'm not at all sure that any one of them is willing to stick his neck out for you. Even if they do, once they know your father is dead against such a marriage, they'll shut up. I don't see any satisfactory solution, to be honest. Right now you can hang around in Suzhou or Hangzhou, but how long can that last? As soon as you run out of money, you'll be stuck."

"Do you have any idea?" asked Li, acutely aware of his financial difficulties.

"I'd better not get involved," said Sun. "We don't really know each other."

"Please help me," Li urged him.

"Women are fickle by nature; prostitutes are particularly so. Since Du Wei is well-known, she must have clients everywhere. She is just using you. Maybe she has another man in the south."

"Oh, no, that's impossible."

"Maybe you are right. But young men in the south are very good at picking up girls. If you leave her by herself, how do you know she would not take up with one or two of them? But you cannot take her straight home either. This is your dilemma."

Li looked troubled.

"The relationship between a father and a son is sacred," Sun went on. "If you hurt your father for the sake of a prostitute, you'll be condemned by everyone. Your mother won't be happy. Your brother will not recognize you, and your friends and relatives will desert you. You'll be a social outcast."

"What should I do?"

"I have some idea that might work out for you, but I'm not sure you'll listen to me."

"I'll be much obliged."

"You've been away for more than a year. You have spent all your money on a prostitute. If you return home empty-handed, you would ruin your chance of inheriting the family fortune, because your father would think you are a spendthrift and not fit to inherit the family fortune. But if you are willing to part with your girlfriend, I'm ready to offer you a thousand ounces of silver. Bring the money home and tell your father that you've been teaching in Beijing. I'm sure he'll be pleased. Think over my offer carefully. Not that I want your girlfriend, I just want to be helpful."

Li was always afraid of his father. Sun's words seemed to offer relief.

"Let me talk to Du Wei first. I can't leave her just like that."

"Talk it over with her. If she really loves you, she will help you."

They drank some more wine and stayed in the wine shop until evening.

Du Wei was preparing the dinner when Li Jia came back. She noticed that he looked as though he had something on his mind. He went to bed without saying a word. Du Wei felt uneasy. As she helped him undress, she asked: "What has happened?"

Li just sighed. She asked again, but he would not talk. She sensed something wrong and could not go to sleep.

In the middle of the night, Li sighed again.

"What is wrong with you? Why can't you trust me?"

Li sat up. He tried several times to speak, but stopped short each time. Tears were streaming down his face.

Du Wei took Li in her arms. "We've known each other for a long time. You've never looked so depressed. We're on a honeymoon trip; you should be happy. Now tell me what is bothering you?"

"You've been nice to me all these days," Li said, finally pulling himself together. "But I have a very strict father. I don't know what is going to happen. I'm afraid he'll kick us out and we'll be homeless. That would be the end of my relation with my family. And our marriage won't be happy, either, in that case. Today I met a friend of mine. He and I talked about it. I felt heart-broken."

"What do you intend to do?" Du Wei was alarmed.

"An insider cannot see things clearly. But my friend Sun Fu helped me put things in perspective. He made a good suggestion. Only I'm afraid you may not agree."

"Who is this Sun Fu? If he has a good suggestion, why should I object?"

"He is a salt merchant and a student in the Imperial College. He heard you singing last night and asked about you. When I told him our story, he offered to help us out. He is willing to give me a thousand ounces of silver for your hand. I can take the money and you will have a home too. But I can't bear to leave you." Li's eyes were filled with tears.

Du Wei gave a strange laugh.

"He must be a really nice gentleman to be so thoughtful," she said, pushing Li aside. "You'll get a thousand ounces of silver, and I'll find another man and stop being a nuisance to you. Sounds a really good plan. Where is the money?"

"Since I have to talk to you first, the money hasn't changed hands yet," said Li, no longer crying.

"Go to him tomorrow morning. A thousand ounces of silver is a lot of money. You mustn't miss this opportunity. I'll go to his boat. Don't let the salt merchant cheat you."

It was beginning to dawn. Du Wei got up to dress herself.

"Today I am seeing an old client off and take a new one in," she said. "It's a big occasion."

She applied her make-up with great care and put on a splendid dress with expensive jewelry. Her fragrance permeated the air. She was radiantly beautiful.

By the time she had finished, it was already early morning. Sun Fu

27. ALIENS OF DISTINGUISHED ABILITIES

Lack of financial resources is not poverty to a nation. Failure to make the best use of its human resources is real poverty.
—*Wei Yuan (1794-1857)*

Ralph Waldo Emerson once said: There is properly no history, only biographies. How truly he had put it. Indeed, most of us are not so much interested in history as in the people who made history, in the individuals: what they thought, what they did and how they did it, for they were the source of wisdom, the agent of change.

Although each of the following chapters can be read by itself, the period covered in Parts VI, VII and VIII is a continuous time span.

It is one of the most important and eventful periods in Chinese history. It begins from the foundation-laying work by four generations prior to the ascension of the First Emperor of the Qin Dynasty, who was famous for the building of the Great Wall, up to the dynasty's rapid collapse after a mere fifteen year-rule over China when it was replaced by one of the longest and greatest dynasties in Chinese history, the Han Dynasty.

Each story depicts some famous men in those tumultuous years—men whose lives were packed with action and whose words sparkled with wisdom.

A RADICAL REFORMER

The Zhou Dynasty, established in the 11th century B.C., became weakened in the late fourth century B.C. after nearly eight hundred years' rule over China. Under the royal court of the Zhou king, there were various states. The state governors, originally members of the royal family, were the king's vassals. In the course of time they became more powerful than the king, the king actually ruling over a domain much smaller than those of some of the princes who exercised absolute power over their respective principalities. Some princes even assumed the title of king.

Later these hereditary rulers fought each other for dominance and beginning from the middle of the fifth century B.C.

China entered a period known as that of the Warring States. Smaller states were annexed by bigger states until there were only seven left. The state of Qin, now the provinces of Shaanxi and Gansu in northwestern China, was the most backward as it was separated from the civilized life of the other six states—Yan, Zhao, Han, Wei, Qi and Chu. Hence, Qin was considered as a barbarian state.

Qin rulers, eager to remedy the situation, adopted a policy to recruit from other states men distinguished for great abilities. Among those recruited, the most famous was Shang Yang.

Shang Yang, a native of Wei, was well-versed in law and political science. He was a senior officer in the employ of the prime minister of Wei. Knowing that Shang Yang was a talented man of great ability, the prime minister had a good mind to recommend Shang to King Hui of Wei. But before he did so, he fell ill.

"Should anything happen to you," said King Hui when he came to see the bed-ridden prime minister, "what am I going to do?"

"Use Shang Yang," said the prime minister. "I know him well. He is extraordinarily gifted and will do immense good to the country."

The king did not say a word.

"If you do not intend to use Shang Yang," the prime minister went on, "you have to kill him. Never let him leave Wei and go to work for other countries."

The king nodded. After he left, the prime minister sent for Shang Yang.

"I have recommended you to the king to succeed me as prime minister," said the prime minister to Shang Yang. "But he didn't listen to me. So, for the interest of the country, I suggested that he kill you lest your talent should be discovered by rulers of other states. Now you'd better leave the country for safety sake."

"If the king did not take your advice to appoint me, why should he listen to you to have me killed?" Shang Yang refused to go.

The king was back in his palace. "I am sorry to see my prime minister so ill," he said to some of the ministers. "He doesn't seem to be in his right mind. Just imagine! He recommended Shang Yang to succeed him as the prime minister!"

After the death of the prime minister, Shang could not find a meaningful job in his own country. Upon learning that King Xiao of

Qin issued a standing invitation to all men of great talent to come to his country, Shang Yang set out for Qin.

King Xiao of Qin had several interviews with Shang Yang. At first, Shang Yang talked in conventional terms about the value of virtue and the ways of the sage kings of the past. But the king was so bored that he dozed off half way through the conversation. He told Shang Yang that he wanted to make a name during his lifetime, not to wait for hundreds of years for his policy to bear fruit. Shang Yang then put forward an ambitious reform program. The king was fascinated. Their conversation continued for several days and Shang Yang was appointed prime minister.

As the prime minister, Shang Yang began to implement a series of unprecedented legal and economic reforms.

Agriculture was encouraged. Peasants were no longer attached to the land of the feudal overlords. They had the right to own, to buy and to sell the land. Land ownership induced migration to uncultivated areas. Government monopoly of basic products like salt and iron discouraged profiteering by traders. To encourage marriage and stimulate migration, a new ruling stipulated that a man with two or more adult sons living with him had to pay a double amount of tax.

To effect a complete break with the past, Shang Yang did away with the old hereditary system and created a new aristocratic hierarchy based only on military merits and contribution of surplus grain to the state.

All the people in Qin were organized into units of every five or ten households to be mutually responsible, and surveillance over each other's conduct was obligatory. If one should fail to report a crime committed by his neighbor, he would have to share the punishment. Even his relatives were held to be equally guilty. And the penalties for breaking the law were cruel. Apart from death, there were various forms of corporal punishment such as cutting off the nose, tattooing the face, branding the forehead, etc. Even littering in the street would mean flogging for the offender.

The king of Qin was concerned that the unprecedented reform program might give rise to controversy. But Shang Yang urged him to stick to what was good for his rule.

"Your Majesty, if you hesitate, you will get nowhere. Do not expect to be popular when you introduce new policies. Ordinary people cling to conventions. Scholars are handicapped by their own learning. They are good enough to perform office duties and maintain the law, but not daring enough to embark on a reform program. The wise make the law, the foolish are ruled by it. The wise change the convention, the foolish are enslaved by it. If we cannot get consensus, we just have to go ahead and carry out the reform, and then enjoy the fruit with the people. History is good only for reference. But we should not be hampered by precedents or lack of precedents, for that matter. As long as what we do is in the best interest of the country, our cause will be vindicated."

His argument convinced the king.

When the new policy was initially announced, Shang Yang was afraid that nobody would take it seriously. He had a wooden pole erected at the south end of the market place in the capital. Then he offered a hundred ounces of gold to anybody who would move it to the north end of the market place. There was no response. People were skeptical. Shang Yang increased the reward to five hundred ounces of gold. A man came up, moved the pole, and walked away with the amount promised. After that the people knew Shang Yang meant what he said.

At the beginning, many people complained about the new measures. The Crown Prince broke the new law. Shang Yang said: "The reform is not working because those at the top are breaking the law." He wanted to punish the prince. But as the heir apparent was not supposed to be punished, Shang Yang punished two of his tutors instead. He ordered to have one's nose cut off and the other's face tattooed. From then on, no one dared to oppose the new law.

As a result of his reform, Qin grew to be a very rich and strong state. The people became obedient; no one dared to commit robbery and theft. Shang Yang held his office as the prime minister for ten years. The king awarded him fifteen towns and the title of Lord Shang. But many aristocrats and members of the royal family hated him bitterly because his reform deprived them of many privileges.

One of his friends foresaw the danger lying ahead of him.

"Beware of the hidden danger!" he warned Shang Yang. "Once the king dies, no one will be able to protect you. All your bodyguards would be useless." He suggested that Shang Yang retire before it was too late. He even advised Shang to return the towns he received from the king and turn his attention to such social welfare as looking after the aged and the orphans.

But Shang turned a deaf ear to his counsel.

Then came the day when King Xiao of Qin died and the Crown Prince came to power. Someone said to the new king: "Isn't it strange that today in Qin everyone talks of the law of Lord Shang. Nobody speaks of Your Majesty's law. It seems that Shang Yang is the supreme ruler of the country, not Your Majesty. When a minister has too much power, the country is in danger. When he is too close to the king, the king's life is in danger. Your Majesty must not forget what he did to your teachers."

The new king, King Hui, had not forgotten the humiliation he had suffered. He issued an arrest warrant charging Shang of sedition.

Shang Yang fled the capital. On his way to the border region, he wanted to put up for the night in a hotel. The hotel manager did not know who he was and refused to accommodate him.

"According to the law of Lord Shang," he said, "I'm going to be punished if I take in anyone without a proper identification paper."

"Now I've become a victim of my own law," said Shang Yang, grief-stricken.

He decided to go to his native country Wei. But Wei would not grant him entry because he had once led an invasion army against Wei and took prisoner his one-time friend, the prince of Wei.

In despair, Shang went back to his fief, and organized an armed resistance. But, being outnumbered, he was killed by the troops sent by the new king of Qin and his whole family were exterminated, also according to the new laws he himself had laid down.

Although Shang Yang was dead, his reform remained in force.

A SUPER DIPLOMAT

As Qin emerged as a formidable power, diplomats became active on the international political arena. Qin's policy of recruiting aliens to work for its government had attracted many talented men of other states to rush to the capital of Qin, seeking for an employment.

A scholar by the name of Su Qin had great aspirations. He made up his mind to be a rich and famous man and the only way to achieve his goal, he thought, was to snatch a place in the international political arena. A native of Luoyang, the capital of the Zhou Dynasty, he made a long journey to the kingdom of Qin, seeing that Qin was the strongest among all the warring states.

He told King Hui of Qin that he could help Qin conquer the world. The king was in no mood to employ any foreigner at the time, having just got rid of Shang Yang. Su submitted ten proposals, but received no response. He used up all his money and had to return home in rags. His family turned a cold shoulder to him. His parents, his sister-in-law, even his wife would not speak to him.

He blamed himself bitterly. But he did not lose heart. He took out all his books and began to concentrate on studying political science and diplomatic strategy. He studied day and night. When he felt sleepy, he would use an awl to jab at himself in the thigh until blood ran down his leg. His hard working spirit has become a household legend in China ever since.

After a year's devoted study, Su Qin was ready to go out again to talk to the rulers of various states into giving him a respectable position. Knowing that the looming threat of Qin was very much on the mind of the kings of six other countries, he formed a brilliant plan of action.

He first went to the ruler of Yan who was trying at the time to ingratiate himself with Qin.

"Your Majesty," he said, "It's true that Yan is enjoying peace and security now. But can you tell why Qin does not wage war on you?"

"I'm willing to hear your opinion, sir," said the king of Yan.

"Qin does not invade Yan," Su Qin continued, "because Zhao is the buffer state that lies between Qin and Yan. I'm astounded to have learnt that Your Majesty, instead of befriending your immediate neighbor Zhao, should turn to please a distant state, Qin. I'm afraid no foreign policy could be more ill-conceived. If Zhao wants to attack Yan, its troops can be in your capital in less than ten days. Can Qin do that? Even if it can, with Zhao's permission to pass through its territory, can it hold on for long by remote control?"

"What am I to do, then?" the king was concerned.

"I suggest Your Majesty join up with Zhao in a vertical alliance against Qin. If the kings of all the six states act in the same way, you will all be safe."

The king of Yan felt that Su Qin's words were like brilliant light flooding in upon his darkness. He immediately provided Su Qin with generous fund for his lobbying activities.

First of all, Su Qin went to Zhao. In Zhao, Su Qin told the king that although Qin hated Zhao most among all the six countries, it was mindful of Han and Wei in the south. If it attacked Zhao, Han and Wei would pose a threat. But if it attacked Han and Wei first, neither was strong enough to stave off Qin. Once these two countries were overrun, Zhao would lie exposed to the danger of invasion by Qin.

"The territories of all the six states put together," argued Su Qin, "are five times larger than Qin's territory; the fighting forces of the six states put together are ten times more powerful than Qin's forces. The best strategy, therefore, was to form a collective security pact against Qin."

The king of Zhao was convinced. He appointed Su prime minister, presented him with ten thousand ounces of gold and asked him to engage in diplomatic activities on behalf of Zhao to help create such an alliance.

Su Qin went to Han as the envoy of Zhao.

"Your majesty is very much mistaken to have tried to appease Qin by yielding your territory to them," said Su Qin at a meeting with the king of Han. "Your territory is limited, but Qin's avarice knows no bounds. In the end you will lose everything, I'm afraid.

"Han is small, but Your Majesty is still the head of a state. What will become of you if you submit yourself to a large country like Qin? Better be the head of a rooster than the rump end of an ox, as the saying goes."

The king of Han was moved. He also put an enormous fund at Su Qin's disposal.

In his conversation with the king of Wei, he denounced those officials as traitors who urged the king to yield to Qin without a fight.

With the support from four countries lined up, Su Qin travelled on to Qi. He used the same argument by pointing out that, with Han and Wei lying between Qin and Qi, Qi had no need for fear. It would be a shame if Qi should consider subordinating itself to Qin. Qi was the second most powerful country among the six. Therefore Qi should back those states which bordered on Qin to stand up to it.

His final stop was Chu in the south, the largest and strongest of the six countries. He told the king: "The greatest enemy of Chu is Qin. The strength of Chu means the weakness of Qin and the weakness of Chu the strength of Qin. There is no room for both of you. Chu is the most powerful and nobody can stand up against you. If you subject yourself to Qin, all the other states will look down upon you and turn to the king of Qin for favor. The best strategy for Chu is to unite with the other five countries in an alliance to isolate Qin. Otherwise Qin will launch a ground-and-naval attack on you. And by then you might find it too late to switch your policy."

Thus the vertical alliance was formed. All passes to Qin were closed. Su Qin was made the prime minister of all the six countries.

On his way to Chu, he passed through his hometown Luoyang. His parents cleaned the house, hired a musical band, prepared a sumptuous banquet and went ten miles outside the city to welcome him. His wife dared not look at him in the face. His sister-in-law crawled before him to apologize.

"Sister, why were you so rude before and so humble now?" Su asked.

"Then you were poor and nobody. Now you are rich and famous."

"Alas! When I was poor, even my parents wouldn't recognize me as their son. Now that I am rich, all the relatives stand in awe. In this world how can one neglect power and wealth?" said Su, sighing.

MAN WITH A SILVERY TONGUE

The state of Zhao became the leader of the anti-Qin alliance. Officials and advisors from the other five countries all gathered in the capital of Zhao to discuss a common strategy against Qin. The king of Qin was disturbed. He began dispatching envoys outfitted with hundreds of thousands of ounces of gold to bribe influential government officials of each of the six states. Those who received the king's gifts became Qin's friends. The king of Qin regarded money thrown away this way as bones thrown to dogs.

"Those who are gathering in Zhao to conceive an attack on Qin are ultimately seeking wealth and fame like a pack of dogs looking for bones," the king remarked to his ministers. "Dogs usually don't fight with each other. Some dogs sleep; some dogs walk around; some dogs keep standing. But if you throw a bone to them, they would all be on their feet, snapping at each other."

The king of Qin believed the power of gold could confuse one's mind and shake one's convictions. He would employ assassins to exterminate anyone who should scorn to be tempted by his gold.

The man behind all this scheme was the king's top counsellor, Zhang Yi, a scholar-diplomat who used to study with Su Qin under one mentor. Now he had become Su Qin's arch rival as far as international politics was concerned.

Like Shang Yang, Zhang was a native of Wei. He was often hard up for he had difficulty in getting a good job. Once he was even suspected of stealing a piece of jade from the residence of the prime minister of Chu and was severely beaten.

"You wouldn't have been humiliated if you hadn't tried to seek favor from the prime minister of Chu," his wife blamed him when he got home.

"Can you see my tongue?" he asked.

"Sure. I can," said his wife with a sneer.

"That's enough. My silvery tongue will bring success to me sooner or later."

Hearing that his good friend and former fellow student Su Qin had become the prime minister of Zhao, he went to see him. However, Su kept him waiting for several days before giving him an interview. At dinner, Zhang Yi was served the same food as that of a servant.

"How come you're in such a wretched state?" asked Su Qin with a sneer. "I certainly can recommend you to my king and make a rich man of you. But, a man with your talent would have gone far long before this. How can I be sure you are worthy of my recommendation?"

Zhang Yi was infuriated at such insulting remarks that came from an old friend. He decided to go to Qin, the most powerful among all the seven warring states.

A fellow traveller by the name Jia was sympathetic with his plight, paid the money he owed the hotel and offered to ride with him. Having arrived at the capital of Qin, Jia bought Zhang Yi a splendid horse-and-carriage and gave him a lot of money so that Zhang could outfit himself nicely before seeking an audience with the king of Qin.

King Hui of Qin was just regretting to have let Su Qin go. So he received Zhang Yi graciously. Zhang Yi proposed to him the strategy of a horizontal league by which to fraternize with the six other states separately in order to play off one against the other, and eventually annex them all. The king was so pleased that he appointed him senior advisor.

Zhang was gloating over his good fortune when his fellow traveller came to bid good-bye to him.

"No, Mr. Jia, don't tell me you're leaving now," said Zhang Yi. "I'm just about to do something to express my gratitude to you. I owe you a lot. Without your help, it would simply be impossible for me to get the job."

"You don't owe me anything," said Jia. "It's your friend Su Qin who instructed me to make your dream come true. All the money came from him. He pretended to treat you badly only because he wanted to spur you to greater things than taking a position in the state of Zhao."

"Please tell my friend I will do anything in my power to assist him, if he needs my help," said Zhang Yi, overwhelmed with gratitude. "In my capacity as a senior advisor to the king, I will never allow Qin to attack Zhao as long as my friend is alive."

This was exactly what Su Qin hoped for. He had just started lobbying heads of various states on behalf of the king of Zhao to form the anti-Qin vertical alliance, and he had already heard that Qin was contemplating an attack on Zhao. He did not want that to happen before the alliance was formed.

"Zhang Yi is more talented than I," Su had said once. "I am just lucky to have got where I am before he gets his place. He has the capability to be the prime minister of Qin."

In two years Zhang Yi became the prime minister of Qin. Although he did dissuade the king of Qin from attacking Zhao, he soon betrayed Su Qin and was bent on sabotaging the vertical alliance.

After Su Qin was assassinated by his political enemies in Qi, Zhang Yi actively went about replacing the vertical alliance with the horizontal league he had proposed in behalf of Qin.

Zhang Yi's diplomatic activities started with a trip to Wei.

"Your Majesty," said Zhang Yi to the king of Wei. "I believe you are aware that yours is a small country. Qin had no quarrel with you. Qin's biggest enemy was Chu. Why not side with Qin and let Qin's troops march across your territory to attack Chu. You know a strong power like Qin can crush a country like yours easily."

The king of Wei was scared into submission. In Han he used the same scare tactics with success.

Zhang Yi's main objective was to drive a wedge between Qi and Chu, the strongest two among the six countries. He promised the king of Chu 100 acres of land if Chu broke with Qi. The offer was tempting enough to make the king of Chu sever ties with Qi. Then Zhang Yi refused to honor his end of the bargain. The king of Chu was so angry that he launched an attack on Qin. But it was too late for him to enlist Qi's help for Qi now sided with Qin, and Chu's army was defeated by the combined forces of Qin and Qi.

Zhang Yi then held out the olive branch to the king of Chu by proposing a marriage between the royal families of Chu and Qin. This was accepted. To further exploit the situation, he turned around and persuaded the king of Qi to cede to Qin a large area of fishing and salt production.

Travelling on to Zhao, Zhang Yi delivered a threatening letter declaring, "Chu and Qin are on good terms. Han and Wei have become protectorates of Qin. And Qi had ceded its fishing and salt resources. Zhao's right arm is virtually cut off. The only way to save Zhao was for the king of Zhao to travel to Qin and meet his counterpart to establish a friendly tie."

As the vertical alliance became no more than a dead letter, it was not too difficult for Zhang Yi to get the king of Yan to yield five cities, as a gesture of good will, to Qin in recognition of Qin's superpower status.

Thus one after another, the six countries were neutralized.

A SPY ENGINEER

The ever-growing threat of Qin made its neighbors feel uneasy. However the king of Han conceived a new idea to deal with the menacing situation. Taking advantage of Qin's willingness to hire foreigners, he sent a spy hydraulic engineer by the name of Zheng Guo, missioning him to induce Qin to embark on large scale public works which would hopefully become a drain on Qin's resources.

The spy engineer proposed to the king of Qin that an eighty mile canal be dug starting from the mountainous region in the west of the country, going along the northern mountain range all the way to the east for the purpose of irrigation. The king accepted his proposal. In the course of the project, the spy's dark intention was uncovered, and was sentenced to death. But the engineer argued: "It's true that I was a spy at the very outset. But now what I am doing will benefit Qin for thousands of years to come, though the project may prolong the existence of Han for a few years."

The king decided to spare his life, and let him continue to supervise the project. The canal was a great success. It irrigated more than half a million acres of land. Therefore the king of Qin named it Canal Zheng Guo after the spy engineer of Han. What used to be arid zones turned into fertile land, and grain crop was increased by many times. The canal enabled Qin to enjoy good harvests year after year.

Although the vertical alliance was resurrected later, the member states lacked the kind of solidarity required to effectively counter Qin's aggression. One by one, they all fell into the hands of Qin.

Comment: The cornerstone of Qin's foreign policy was to make friends with those countries that were distant from Qin and attack those close-by. Thus, according to Qin's policy-makers, every inch of territory gained would be Qin's territory and every foot of territory gained Qin's territory.

The success of Qin's foreign policy was preceded by the success of its domestic reform initiated by Shang Yang. Through his reform, Qin transformed itself, in four generations, from a backward and uncivilized country in the far western part of China into an economic and military superpower. Shang Yang, as an individual, was later discredited for his harshness, but his policy was not.

It was Qin's policy of employing brilliant and ambitious aliens that brought men like Shang Yang to its land in the first place. No country was more eager to attract men of talent from other countries than Qin. The kings of Qin were willing to offer the highest office of the country, the position of prime minister, to a distinguished foreigner. This policy paid off handsomely for Qin.

In that sense, the victory of Qin was the triumph of its employment and immigration policy.

28. A MERCHANT'S INVESTMENT

When a gentleman wants to establish himself, he also helps others to establish themselves. When he wants to be successful himself, he also helps others to succeed. He judges others by what he knows of himself.
—*Confucius*

People from all over the world marvel at the Great Wall of China. It still stands solid and magnificent as when it was erected more than two thousand years ago. It has since become the greatest single testimonial to the enduring civilization of China. But why was it ever built? How was it built? The man who built the Great Wall was King Zheng of Qin who lived about two hundred and fifty years after Confucius's death. But King Zheng was not heir apparent to the throne originally. His story begins with his father Zichu.

Zichu was one of the grandsons of the king of Qin. He was living as a hostage in the state of Zhao (in modern Hebei and Shanxi). During the Period of the Warring States, rulers of various countries often exchanged their family members as hostages to live in neighboring countries so as to prevent possible hostilities among them. Zichu's father was the Crown Prince of Qin who had more than twenty sons. Zichu was the child of one of his concubines who had already died. Even when she was living, she was not her husband's favorite concubine.

Zichu sent as a hostage to Zhao just because his father was not particularly fond of him. Qin and Zhao being on very bad terms with each other, the king of Zhao did not treat Zichu with civility. As he was also ignored by his own father, life as a hostage in Zhao was made all the more miserable for him. He was often hard-pressed for money.

His plight caught the attention of Lü Buwei, a wealthy merchant in Zhao, who saw in Zichu a rare merchandise of a special sort.

"Father," Lü Buwei said to his father, "what is the return on investment in the farming business?"

"Ten times the original investment."

"What is the profit in the jewelry business?"

"A hundred times."

"What if I invest in a future king, Father?"

"My goodness! That will be beyond estimate."

Realizing that the profit derived from inaugurating a king on the throne should last for generations, Lü Buwei set to work. He went to see Zichu.

"Your Highness, I can help you advance your career," Lü said to the royal hostage.

"No joking, please," said the prince with a laugh. "Advance your own career first before you try to help me."

"The advancement of my career depends on the progress of yours," Lü said seriously.

So they sat down for a deep discussion.

"I understand that your grandfather is quite advanced in years," said Lü Buwei. "Your father is the Crown Prince and his favorite concubine is Lady Huayang. Though she herself has no child, she is in a position to appoint an heir apparent to your father. You've been out of touch with your family, living in a foreign country for so long. You have many brothers and your father is not particularly fond of you. When he succeeds to the throne, what chance do you have to be named the Crown Prince?"

"No, not at all," said Zichu. "But what can I do?"

"Money makes the mare go," said Lü Buwei. "I know you're hard up for the time being. Though I am not very rich, I would like to contribute ten thousand ounces of gold to help establish you as the heir apparent to your father. You need money to buy gifts for your relatives in Qin and to make friends here in Zhao."

"If your plan succeeds," Zichu was excited, "I'll share my country with you."

So Lü gave Zichu five thousand ounces of gold as his funds necessary for making friends and influencing people, for popularity was a key factor in political dealings. In the meantime, Lü Buwei himself set out for Qin, as Zichu's emissary, bringing with him gifts worth as much as five thousand ounces of gold.

It was not easy to gain access to Lady Huayang, so Lü managed to strike up a friendship with Lady Huayang's sister by presenting a gift box filled with gold and jewelry.

"My mission here," said Lü Buwei to the royal lady, "is to convey a message from Zichu who is now a hostage in my country. He wants me to bring you, his aunt, and Lady Huayang, his mother, some gifts to express his filial affection, and his longing for his father, the Crown Prince. He lost his own mother when he was yet a child, so Lady Huayang is as dear to his heart as his own mother. He is anxious to have a chance to return home so that he can perform the duties of a son to his mother, although at present he is enjoying great popularity in Zhao."

Lü asked her to present a pile of jewels and ornaments of the worth of five thousand ounces of gold to Lady Huayang.

Lady Huayang was very pleased and became favorably disposed towards Zichu. Lü Buwei visited Lady Huayang's sister again and prompted her to put in a good word to her sister in behalf of Zichu.

So the royal lady said to Lady Huayang: "A pretty woman can win a man's favor. But once beauty fades, the favor will cease and love will vanish, too. Now as the Crown Prince loves you very much even though you have borne him no child, it is high time that you chose from among his sons one who is filial to you and adopted him as your son. Make him the heir apparent. Then you are honored when your husband is alive and you will become the queen dowager when your husband is dead and gone. This is a win-win strategy. Do it now for your own sake. Zichu is a capable young man. As it stands now, he doesn't have the ghost of a chance to be his father's successor. If you adopt him, he will be forever grateful to you and you will enjoy privileges all your life."

Lady Huayang grasped the point. She spoke favorably of Zichu to her husband and expressed her wish to adopt him as her son. Her husband agreed to her request and formally named Zichu as the heir apparent.

The Crown Prince and Lady Huayang asked Lü Buwei to bring back many gifts to Zichu in Zhao as a token of their love for him. They also asked Lü Buwei to be his tutor. Thus Zichu was suddenly shot into prominence from obscurity.

Lü had been living with a beautiful, young dancer, Lady Zhao. One day Zichu came to drink with Lü. One glance at Lady Zhao, and he was captivated, so much so that he asked for her hand. At first Lü was angry at such impudence, but, on second thoughts, he granted the marriage.

Since he had already spent a small fortune on Zichu, he might as well give him the girl. After all, he knew well enough that he himself had a special charm over the girl and the girl would always be loyal to him. Now, as Zichu's wife, she would be in a position to help him place Zichu under his perfect control.

A boy was born to the young couple, and they named him Zheng.

A few years later, Qin attacked Zhao. The king of Zhao wanted to kill Qin's royal hostage. But Lü Buwei paid the border guards twelve thousand ounces of gold to enable Zichu to get back to Qin. His wife, Lady Zhao, and his son, Zheng, went into hiding. Only Lü Buwei knew where they were.

When his grandfather died, Zichu's father succeeded to the throne and Zichu was made the Crown Prince. As his father died only a few days after the coronation, Zichu succeeded to the throne. The king of Zhao was obliged to have Lady Zhao and the young Prince Zheng sent back to Qin. Lü Buwei joined them, too. Soon Lü Buwei was appointed prime minister of Qin and awarded an estate with ten thousand households.

All this happened fifteen years after Lü first spotted Zichu in Zhao.

Zichu ruled only for three years. When he died, his son Prince Zheng became King Zheng of Qin at the age of thirteen. Lü Buwei became the most powerful man in the country, for he was not only the prime minister, but also given the honorable title of "Second Father of the Kingdom".

Despite all the wealth and power in his possession, Lü felt inferior to his counterparts in other countries in terms of scholarship and learning. He had been a merchant, and merchants commanded little respect at that time. Therefore he took upon himself to patronize as many as three thousand scholars and men of letters. He commissioned them to write books in his name. He had the books displayed in public places and declared that a thousand ounces of gold would be awarded to anyone who could add one word in or delete one word from the books. Of course no one was so foolish as to make a try.

Lü Buwei and Lady Zhao had been lovers before he married her to Zichu. After that, they were still lovers. Now as Zichu had died, and the boy king was growing up, their clandestine relationship remained as close as ever before.

Time went by, and the king was nearly twenty. Lü began to feel he needed to be more scrupulous lest the king should find out his secret association with the queen mother. Besides, he was now in his fifties and could not entirely satisfy Lady Zhao sexually. So he started to look out for a substitute to play his part to Lady Zhao. At last he found a man named Lao Ai who had a penis of an enormous size.

He introduced Lao Ai to Lady Zhao, now the Queen Dowager. To enter into the queen's service, Lao Ai had to be a eunuch. All eunuchs had to be castrated. The Queen Dowager bribed the official in charge of castration to make Lao Ai look like a eunuch only by shaving off his beard and eyebrows.

Lady Zhao found great satisfaction in Lao Ai. She showered costly gifts on him and, shortly afterwards, managed to make a marquis of him. Soon enough, Lao Ai became so rich as to own several thousand servant-slaves. Lady Zhao bore him two sons whom she carefully hid away, intending to make one of them king in the event of King Zheng's death.

Their affair went on until King Zheng was twenty when somebody informed him of the secret liaison between his own mother and Lao Ai. What made the king most resentful was the existence of the two sons of Lao.

The king ordered an inquiry to be made. Lao Ai was so terrified that he immediately plotted to stage an attack on the palace when the king was to attend a ceremony to mark his coming of age.

But Lao Ai's plot was uncovered and his armed rebellion quickly put down. The king had Lao Ai and his two sons executed, and the Queen Dowager moved out of the capital. As Lü Buwei was inevitably implicated in the matter, the king wanted to sentence him to death. But, considering that his father, Zichu, would not have been king had it not been for Lü Buwei's help, the king decided not to kill him, but to remove him from office.

After some time the king allowed his mother to come back to the capital for fear of public criticism of his not being a filial son.

Although Lü was no longer a government official, he continued to receive many visitors and foreign envoys and continued to enjoy the income from his estate with ten thousand households. The king was not amused at all. He suspected there might be something afoot.

He sent a letter to Lü to reprimand him, saying:

"For what meritorious services done that you should possess an estate with ten thousand households?—I demand to know.

For what relations between you and the country that you should be called 'Second Father of the Kingdom?'—I want to ask."

He sent Lü into exile to the remotest region of Qin in modern Sichuan. Lü had no more interest in life. On his way to Sichuan, he committed suicide by drinking poisoned wine.

King Zheng was to become the first emperor of the Qin Dynasty.

Comment: Given his background as a merchant, it was remarkable for Lü Buwei to recognize the value of investing in a human. He had vision and was willing to make long term investment.

His investment paid off nearly as perfectly as he had planned. For a period of time, Lü was the most powerful person in the country, second only to the king. His bet seemed a sure win to the end. But he never expected that Zichu should die so early at the age of thirty-two after only three years on the throne. Lü underestimated Prince Zheng and did not seem to have managed the relationship well enough with him. Managing human relation is trickier than managing financial assets. The human heart is a treacherous thing. Human relationship does change.

When he recommended Lao Ai to Lady Zhao, Lü might have thought it was another gamble that might pay off. This time he miscalculated. Perhaps age had dulled his wit as well as his virility. Hence, his total loss of the game.

29. THE ASSASSIN

Wait for the right time to make friends with the good people who can help you; be prudent lest others should be jealous. Choose the right moment to get rid of the wicked who can harm you; be secretive lest the wicked seek for retaliation.

—*Vegetable Roots*

To the wild wailing wind I sigh,
To bid my friend a mournful good-bye
By the chilly water of the Yi River,
Gone is the hero, gone forever.

The above lines are taken from a melancholy song composed by Gao Jianli, a musician, to bid farewell to his great friend, Jing Ke, the assassin.

Jing Ke and Gao Jianli lived in the days when the Zhou Dynasty had already fallen and the Qin Dynasty was about to rule over China.

Towards the late fourth century B.C. real power in China was transferred from the king of Zhou to the rulers of various states. These states brushed the king aside and fought each other for supremacy until there were only seven left. The state of Qin, seated on China's western frontier, gradually gained ascendancy over the other six. In 256 B.C., the Qin forces seized the tiny domain of the Zhou king and ended up the Zhou Dynasty.

Qin was ready to take over other states in a bloody war for dominance.

Our story took place in the year 230 B.C. when the kingdom of Han became the first victim of Qin's war of annexation. Two years later a greater portion of Zhao's domain fell under Qin's rule. As Qin's threat was approaching Yan, the Crown Prince of Yan, Prince Dan, was extremely concerned. Besides, he had also a personal grudge against the King of Qin.

The warring states at that time often exchanged hostages, usually

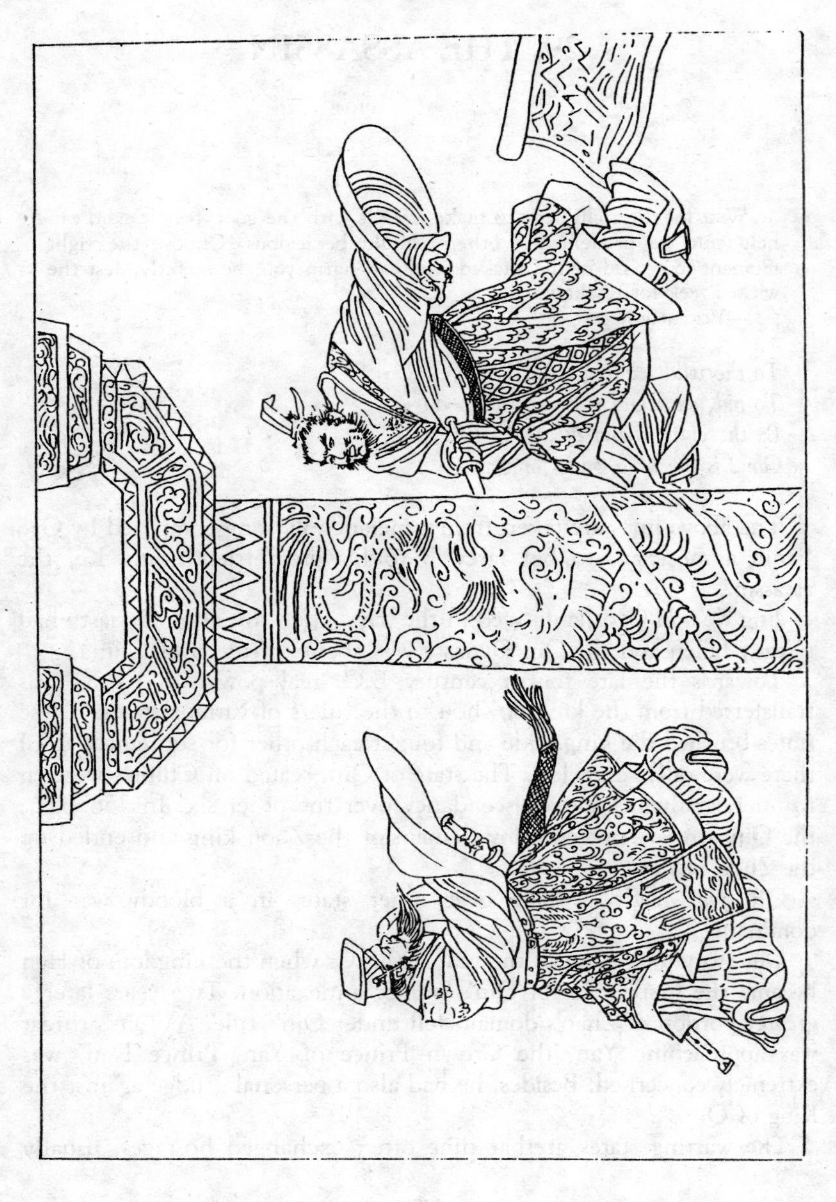

royal family members, to live in another country so as to reduce the likelihood of hostilities. It was a sort of guarantee of non-aggression.

As a child, Prince Dan was made a hostage in Zhao. There he had a playmate by the name of Zheng, the son of the Crown Prince of Qin, who was also a hostage held in Zhao at the time. Young Prince Dan of Yan and young Prince Zheng of Qin struck up a friendship. But when Prince Zheng succeeded to the throne of Qin upon the demise of his father, their friendship came to an end. It so happened that Prince Dan was living temporarily in Qin as a hostage. There Zheng, as the king, treated him shabbily. Prince Dan was bitterly hurt by the betrayal on the part of his boyhood friend. Later he escaped back to Yan.

Prince Dan had a good mind to form an anti-Qin alliance with other states. But such diplomatic activities took time, and the imminent danger called for prompt action. He could not wait. To stop Qin quickly, he decided that the dagger of one assassin could be more effective than an army of a million.

His tutor introduced him to Tian Guang, a nearly sixty-year-old man, who was known for his resourcefulness and courage.

"A stallion can run a thousand miles a day. But in his old age, he cannot even win a race against an ordinary horse," said Tian to the Crown Prince. "What you heard of me is what I was like in my prime. I am no longer my former self now. However, I would like to introduce you to my friend, Jing Ke, who may be able to help you."

Jing Ke was a native of Wei living in Yan. He liked reading and swordplay. He was also fond of drinking. When he and his friend Gao Jianli got drunk, Jing would sing and Gao would play the lute in accompaniment. Carried away by emotion, they would laugh and cry even in the midst of a busy market place, uninhibited as though there were no one around. But, at bottom, Jing Ke was a man of depth, cool-minded and full of brains.

Prince Dan was eager to meet Jing Ke. As Tian Guang was leaving to arrange for the meeting, the prince asked him not to leak out their discussion to any others.

"You may rest assured, Your Highness," said Tian with a laugh.

He called on Jing Ke.

"The prince sought my help. If there is Qin, there will be no Yan. If there is Yan, there should be no Qin. But I am too old to be useful to him, so I recommended you."

"Take me to Prince Dan," said Jing Ke.

"I heard that a man of integrity never acts in a way to cause others to distrust him," Tian went on. "Yet today the prince asked me not to divulge anything he discussed with me because it was state secret. That means he does not trust me. I feel ashamed that I made him feel necessary to tell me so. Go and tell him Tian Guang is dead, so he can rest assured that his secret is safe."

With this, he cut his own throat.

Jing Ke rushed to see the prince and told him what Tian Guang had said. Prince Dan was stupefied.

"Mr. Tian has gone too far," he said in tears, beating his chest in agony. "I asked him not to say anything only because I am too anxious for our plan to succeed. It had never occurred to me that he would kill himself to show me he would never talk."

Prince Dan made a deep bow to Jing Ke.

"Qin's avarice knows no bounds," he said. "It has already seized Han and taken its king prisoner. Now it is attacking Zhao's last remaining stronghold. There can be no doubt that Yan will be the next target. I'm afraid Yan will not be able to hold out even if the entire population is mobilized. But now I have a plan. I want to send a brave man to take the king of Qin hostage and force him to make a vow to give up all the land he has taken from his neighbors. It would be wonderful if the plan works out. If he refuses to do so, he will be killed. Then his death will cause chaos in his country. This would give me time to form an alliance with other states, an alliance like the one we have had before. We did succeed in checking Qin's infernal ambition that time."

Jing Ke was silent.

"This is a momentous decision, Your Highness. I'm afraid I am not equal to the job," he said after a long pause.

Prince Dan kneeled down, earnestly begging him to reconsider. At last Jing Ke agreed to take up the secret assignment.

Prince Dan put Jing Ke up in a luxurious mansion as a guest of honor, entertaining him daily with fine food and wine and showering upon him all sorts of expensive gifts, including numerous beautiful women and splendid chariots. The prince would give him ten times more for whatever he took a fancy for.

Time went by, but Jing Ke showed no sign of action.

Prince Dan grew anxious.

"Qin's army may cross the Yi River any day," said the prince to Jing Ke. "When that happens, I am afraid I may not be able to be hospitable to you even if I wish to."

"I understand the situation even if Your Highness did not tell me," Jing Ke replied. "But to get an audience with the King of Qin, I need something he wants very much as a present. Right now he is offering a reward of ten thousand ounces of gold and an estate of ten thousand households on the head of General Fan Wuqi. If I had General Fan's head and a map of Yan in hand, I think he would be only too delighted to see me, face to face. By that time I can carry out my mission."

General Fan Wuqi was a former high-ranking general in Qin. He fled to Yan after offending the king in a big way. All his family were killed by the king's order. It was Prince Dan who granted him refuge in spite of opposition of his tutor.

"General Fan," said Prince Dan, "came to me in desperation. No other state would admit him. I am a man of honor. I cannot bring myself to do something to betray my friend."

Jing Ke decided to see General Fan himself.

"General Fan, I know what happened to your family. There is a huge price on you, too, dead or alive. Now, what do you intend to do?"

General Fan looked up to the sky and heaved a deep sigh. Tears were streaming down his cheeks.

"My heart is bleeding with grief. But what can I do?"

"Suppose there is a plan that will both avenge you and save Yan."

"Do tell me about it."

"I want to borrow your head to present to the king of Qin. He will surely be pleased to receive me; then I will stab him at close range."

Fan Wuqi rose, bared his arms, and seized his sword in hand.

"Day and night," said the general, "I grit my teeth and beat my chest, thinking of nothing but revenge. Now you have given me the idea."

One slash of the sword, and his head fell off to the ground. His wrathful eyes remained open.

When Prince Dan heard of this, he rushed to the spot, threw himself on the dead body of General Fan and cried for a long time.

The dagger Prince Dan obtained was the sharpest that could be found in the whole kingdom. He had it treated with poison, and tried it on a living person. The moment a trickle of blood appeared on his skin at the first scratch of the blade, the man dropped dead.

Final preparations were now under way for Jing Ke's trip. Prince Dan ordered a young man by the name of Qin Wuyang to go with Jing Ke as his assistant. When only a child of thirteen, Qin Wuyang had killed a big, strong man. Many people feared him. However, Jing Ke preferred to wait for another man to go with him. A few days later, the prince became all the more anxious.

"Time is running out," he said. "You'd better take Qin Wuyang with you."

"But, Your Highness, this is not a boy's job." Jing Ke was not pleased with the prince's suggestion. "I'm the one to go. I'm the one who will not return. I'm only waiting for a friend of mine whom I want to go with."

Prince Dan frowned, knowing that Jing Ke's friend was a knight-errant, and knights-errant, as a rule, were fond of travelling from place to place and there was no telling when the man would turn up.

"We can't wait indefinitely," said the prince.

"If Your Highness insists, I leave today," said Jing Ke.

Thus Jing Ke set out on his journey. It was late autumn. Prince Dan and those who knew about the mission attended the farewell party in white robe and cap as a sign of mourning, knowing fully well that it was a journey of no return. They walked with the assassin and his assistant as far as the Yi River. Sacrifice was offered to the gods and prayers for good speed said. Jing Ke's musician friend, Gao Jianli, played a farewell tune on his lute and Jing Ke joined him in singing. All those present wept, and Jing Ke mounted the carriage, casting no glance behind, not even for once.

When Jing Ke and Qin Wuyang arrived at the capital of Qin, the first thing they did was to bring costly gifts to a close aide of the king, who was only too glad to present them to the court.

"Your Majesty has struck horror into the heart of the king of Yan," said the aide to the king of Qin. "Now he is willing to become your subject and has agreed to pay annual tribute to our court. He dares not come himself, but, out of respect for you, has executed General Fan Wuqi and has sent here his envoy to present Fan's head to you along with a map of Yan."

The king was delighted and ordered a full welcome ceremony to be held in the palace to receive the special envoy from Yan.

Jing Ke arrived at the palace with Qin Wuyang, Jing Ke holding the box that contained General Fan's head and Qin Wuyang carrying the case with the map in it. Step by step the two walked through the hall until they reached the stairs leading to the throne platform. As they came near the king, Qin Wuyang turned pale. He was trembling all over. The Qin officials there noticed it, but Jing Ke turned round and laughed.

"Your Majesty," he apologized to the king. "My assistant is a country boy. He has never seen such grandeur before. Please forgive him."

"That's all right. Please show me Fan Wuqi's head," said the king.

Having identified the head to be genuine, the king asked to see the map.

Jing Ke took the map case from Qin Wuyang, walked up the stairs and presented it to the king. The king opened the case. As the map was unfolded to the end of the roll, a dagger appeared. Jing Ke grabbed the dagger with his right hand, and, with the left, caught the king by the sleeve and struck at the king. The king made a quick jerk and the sleeve was torn off. It was a narrow escape. Now the king was running around a massive pillar on the throne platform. This happened so swiftly that all those present were stunned with horror.

According to the law of the Qin court, no one could go up the throne platform without the king's permission. Even though there were soldiers in the hall, they could not come to the king's rescue. The tension and anxiety of the moment gave the king no chance to utter a single word to call for help. He tried to draw his sword, but it seemed too long to get out of the sheath. Suddenly a courtier shouted, "Push back the sword over your shoulder and draw it from behind!"

Now the king was awakened from his shock, but only to find Jing Ke at close range after him. At this moment, the royal physician threw his medicine bag at Jing Ke. For an instant, Jing Ke was distracted. This gave the king time to breathe. He threw the sword over his shoulder, grasped the hilt and drew the sword from behind his back. Being a good swordsman too, the king turned around and struck Jing Ke fiercely, cutting him through the left thigh. Jing Ke staggered and fell against the pillar that stood on the left side of the platform and hurled the dagger at the king, only to miss him by a hair's breadth. The dagger hit the pillar on the right side of the platform. Now it was the king's turn to attack. His sword fell on Jing Ke eight times. Unable to stand up, Jing Ke leaned against the pillar, his legs sprawling before him. Realizing that he had failed, he laughed and shouted curses at the king.

"I meant to take you alive and force you to return all the land..."

Qin Wuyang darted forth, but was struck down before he made a few steps. The next moment the guards killed Jing Ke. The king fell in a swoon. When he came around, he rewarded the royal physician with two thousand ounces of gold.

This took place in 227 B.C.

The following year, Qin's troops seized the capital of Yan. To save his own skin, the king of Yan killed his son Prince Dan and offered his head to the king of Qin who, five years later, took the king of Yan captive.

In 221 B.C., Qin conquered the last of the six kingdoms and China came to be under the unified rule of Qin. The king of Qin assumed the title of Qin Shi Huang which means the First Emperor of the Qin Dynasty.

As Qin Shi Huang began to hunt out the former associates of Prince Dan and Jing Ke, they all went into hiding. Gao Jianli changed his name, disguised himself as a common laborer and, for a long time, worked as a servant in a wealthy household.

Whenever he heard some guests of the family playing the lute in the hall, he would linger outside, unable to tear himself away. He would comment, "This man played well," or "That man was no good."

One of the servants reported this to the master of the household. The master was curious and summoned Gao to play for his guests. Gao played so well that the master wanted him to join the guests for a drink. So Gao went to his own room, got out his lute and changed to proper dress. When he came back to the hall, everyone was surprised. They sat him at the head table and again asked him to play the lute and sing. His performance so touched them that they were all moved to tears.

Soon Gao's fame reached the First Emperor's ear. A lover of music, the emperor summoned Gao for an audience.

"This is Gao Jianli, Jing Ke's friend!" shouted someone who recognized Gao the moment he came in. But the emperor could not bring himself to kill such a talented musician. He ordered to have Gao's eyes gouged out. After that, Gao was made to play the lute in the court. Every time he played, the emperor applauded, and gradually he allowed Gao to sit near him to perform.

Gao obtained a heavy piece of lead and hid it inside the lute. One day when he was called to play again, he struck at the king with the lute. He missed and was summarily executed. After this incident, Qin Shi Huang never allowed any of the followers of the former kings of the six states to get near him again.

Comment: Prince Dan had probably expected too much to have hoped that Jing Ke would carry off his enemy alive and exact promise from him to return all the land he had taken from other states. Jing Ke, being an intelligent and careful man, had a realistic assessment of the mission from the start. It is not likely that he ever really meant to take the King of Qin as a live hostage. His last words seemed to be only a feeble excuse to console himself as he lay dying.

Jing Ke might have succeeded if he had better swordsmanship or if Prince Dan had waited for Jing Ke's trusty friend to go with him on his mission instead of Qin Wuyang. Failure of a grand scheme can sometimes be traced to the flawed execution of a technical detail.

But would the assassination of the King of Qin have made any difference? Was he a mere agent of forces that pushed Qin to a predetermined victory? Was Qin's victory a historical inevitabilities?

The course of history is inevitable only to the extent that individuals involved have made it so. The role of the individual to shape, change and create history was important then as it is today.

Twelve hundred years after the founding of the Qin Dynasty, Su Xun, a noted scholar of the Song Dynasty in the eleventh century, made some penetrating observations about the failure of the six states that had been annexed by Qin.

He believed that they were destroyed not because their weapons were not sharp or they did not know how to fight. Their failure lay in appeasing Qin. Not that all of them had appeased Qin, but those who had not were destroyed by those who had, because without the assistance of the latter, the former could not stand by themselves.

He pointed out that to appease Qin by giving away territory was like trying to put out fire with firewood. The land of these countries was limited but Qin's greed after territory was insatiable. The more they tried to appease Qin, the more covetous Qin became. Therefore who was to be the victor and who the losers was already a foregone conclusion. Things could only end this way.

Qi never gave away any territory but it never assisted the other five states. Yan and Zhao had their long term strategies. They were able to defend themselves. A small state as it was, Yan was one of the last to fall. It was not until Prince Dan attempted to assassinate the king of Qin that it began to invite trouble upon itself. Zhao fought Qin five times and won three. It was only after its distinguished general Li Mu fell victim to slanderous charges that Zhao failed to hold out.

As Qin's forces were sweeping over China, Zhao and Yan, helplessly isolated, found themselves at the end of their tether. It could be argued that they had done all they could. But suppose Han, Wei and Chu had never tried to appease Qin, suppose Jing Ke had not been sent on assassination mission and suppose great generals had not been purged from power, it would have been hard to say who would win out in the end.

If the territory used to appease Qin had been offered as reward to attract men of outstanding talents throughout the land to help those states against Qin, even if Qin had got them in its jaws, it could never have swallowed them. Admitted that the six states were not as strong as Qin, they could have overcome the aggressor if some of them had not pursued a policy of appeasement, Su concluded.

It seems that Su Xun, though having faulted the assassination attempt, did not believe in any historical inevitability.

30. MIND OVER MATTER

A gentleman does not recommend a person because of his words. Nor does he dismiss good words because of the man.
—*Confucius*

Here are some thought-provoking famous Chinese fables.

THE FOOLISH OLD MAN WHO REMOVED THE MOUNTAINS

The Foolish Old Man of the North Mountain was ninety years old. His house was in the backyard of two huge mountains, each a hundred thousand feet in height and nearly seventy square miles in area. They not only shut off a nice view, but blocked his way so badly that he had to make a detour round them whenever he wanted to go out. Finally he decided to remove the mountains. He called a family meeting.

"Let's remove the mountains," he said to all the members of his family. "Let's chisel away the rocks and level the mountains to the ground."

Everybody in the family agreed except his wife.

"How absurd!" she said. "How can you expect to remove the mountains. You can't even remove a mound. And, besides, where can you put away the mud and rocks chiseled off the mountains?"

"We'll throw them into the East China Sea," others in the family replied in unison.

So the old man, followed by his sons and grandsons, began to break the rocks and dig the soil with chisels and spades. The mud and the broken rocks were placed in baskets and pans and then carried to the sea shore everyday. A seven-year-old boy, their neighbor's son, also came to join them.

One day on his way to work, the Foolish Old Man was stopped by the Wise Old Man of the River Bend.

"Be more sensible, my friend," said the Wise Old Man with a scornful

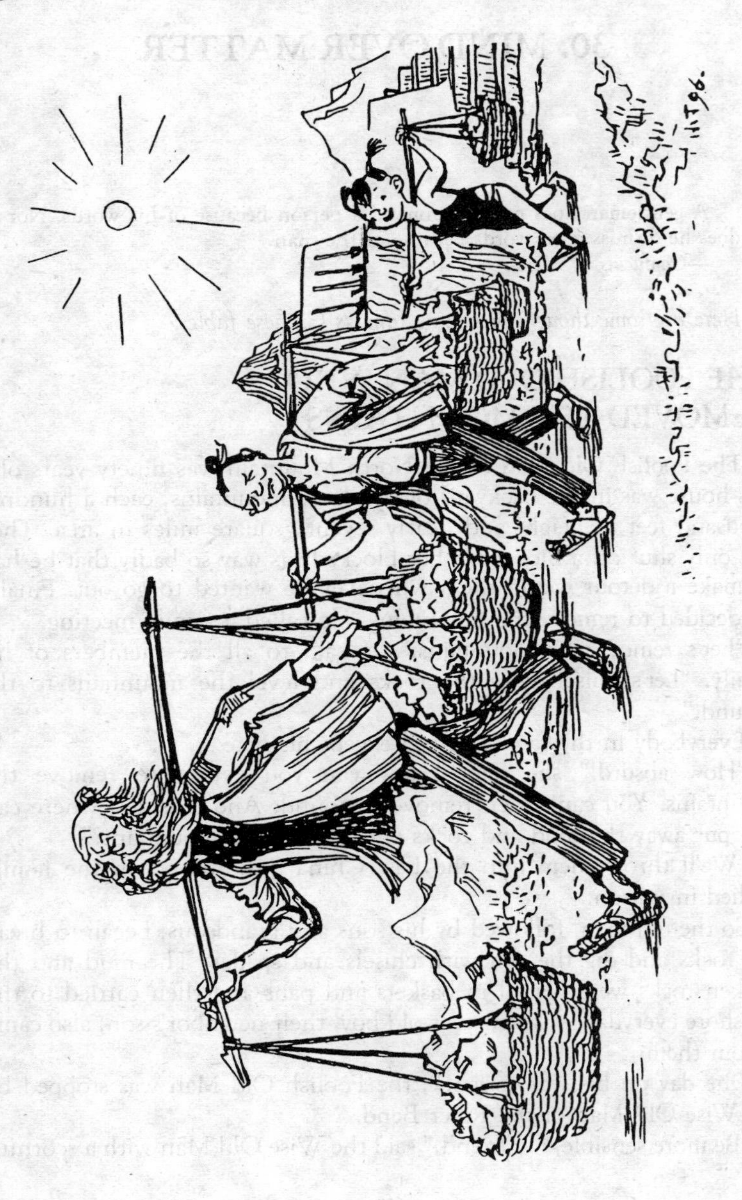

twist of the lips. "You're over ninety. Even a stone on the mountain is too heavy for you to carry-let alone the vast mass of mud and rocks!"

"I'm afraid you're too short-sighted," said the Foolish Old Man with a sigh. "Don't you see that when I die, there will be my children to carry on the work? When they die, they have their children and grandchildren. And those grandchildren will have their children and grandchildren. My family line will carry on forever, but the mountains will not grow any bigger. Why can't we remove them?"

The Wise Old Man raised his eyebrows, not knowing what to say.

Their conversation was overheard by God. He was moved and sent down two angels to carry the mountains somewhere else.

Comment: Faith can remove mountains. But this story somehow reminds me of the mountain of the accumulated national debt of the U.S. Wouldn't it be wonderful if it could be removed this way, too? But, would God be moved to lend a helping hand as the mountain is of our own making and it keeps growing all the time? Worse still, this ever-growing mountain is to be left for our children and grandchildren to deal with.

A NATIVE OF YAN

An old man, who was born in the state of Yan but grew up in the state of Chu, was on his journey back to his native country. While passing through the state of Jin on their way, some fellow travellers tried to play a joke on him.

"This is the capital of Yan," they said to him as they pointed to the city ahead of them.

The old man's countenance immediately turned solemn. There was the deep longing for sweet, sweet home.

"This is the temple of your native town," they pointed to a temple when they were in the city.

The old man heaved a deep sigh.

"This used to be your father's house," they pointed to a house.

Tears welled up in the old man's eyes.

"This is your father's grave," they said, pointing to a mound.

The old man began to weep. His companions were amused and burst into laughter.

"We were just teasing you," they said. "Don't you see we're still in

Jin?"

The man was embarrassed. When he did reach Yan, the sight of the capital, the temple of his village, and his father's house and grave could no longer stir deep feelings in him.

Comment: *Somehow the psychological implications of this story are disturbing.*

THE MISSING AXE

A man had lost his axe. He suspected that it had been stolen by his neighbor's son. He looked at him closely. The boy walked like a thief, looked liked a thief, and talked like a thief. A few days later, the man found his axe while he was cutting wood in the valley.

The next day when he saw the boy, the boy walked, looked and talked like any other child.

Comment: *Don't we all sometimes behave like the man who lost his axe?*

THE EASIEST

An artist was doing some work for the king of Qi.

"What is the hardest thing to draw?" the king asked.

"Things like dogs, horses, and so on."

"What is the easiest thing, then?"

"Ghosts and devils."

The artist is not supposed to make the slightest distortion in drawing a dog or a horse, because everybody has seen dogs and horses. But it is easy to draw a ghost or a devil because nobody has seen ghosts or devils.

Comment: *Be careful with those who claim to be knowledgeable about something which you are totally unfamiliar with. Do not trust any artist who can only draw ghosts but not a dog or a horse.*

THE POWER OF HEARSAY

Zeng Shen was one of Confucius's favorite disciples. When he was visiting a place called Fei, somebody of his same name killed a man in a violent quarrel.

A neighbor of his rushed to Zeng's mother and told her that her son committed a murder.

"My son could never do such a thing," she replied confidently and went on weaving.

Before long, another man came to her and said: "Your son has killed a man."

She continued weaving as though nothing had happened.

But when a third person came and repeated to her the same story, she lost her confidence and fled the house in fright.

Comment: Would you be persuaded to believe such a rumor about your child, or your parent? Why?

FAITH

Fan Zihua, a rich and powerful man in the state of Jin, was a good friend of the king. Although he held no office in the imperial court, he was more influential than many of the high-ranking government ministers. He retained many men of different professional skills in his mansions than there were in the imperial court. In those days men of distinction generally retained a large host of lodger-guests at home, a host of scholars, consultants, and warriors, most of them fortune seekers.

One day two of Fan Zihua's lodger-guests went on a trip out of town. They put up for the night in a small inn run by an old farmer named Shangqiu Kai. At the dinner table, the two men began chatting about their benefactor, Fan Zihua.

"I think," said one, "there is no one more influential now than His Lordship. He can turn a rich man into a poor man and a poor man into a rich man overnight."

"And he can," said the other, "ruin anyone or save anyone from ruin if it pleases him to do so."

The innkeeper Shangqiu Kai overheard their conversation and made up his mind to give up his business and apply to Fan Zihua to be one of his lodger-guests. After all, what was the point of keeping this inn business any more since it had not brought him any profit? He was such a poor man that he needed a change badly.

Before he got permission to meet Fan Zihua, a number of Fan's lodger-guests came to see him. As they all came from noble families, the sight of a shabbily dressed old man with a wrinkled, weather-beaten face irked them. They began to poke fun at him. They jostled against him, pushed and shoved him around, and showered insulting remarks on him. To all this, Shangqiu Kai bore up calmly.

Then they took him to a high terrace.

"A hundred ounces of gold for anyone who dares to jump down!" someone shouted to him.

Without any hesitation, Shangqiu Kai leaped and landed himself on the ground like a bird.

The crowd was not surprised, thinking it was just good luck.

"There's a precious pearl down the river bend. Dive in and get it!" another one said to Shangqiu Kai, pointing a finger at a deep bend of a river nearby.

Instantly Shangqiu Kai dived into the water and came up with the precious pearl.

For the first time everyone began to think more favorably of the old farmer. Fan Zihua heard the news and put Shangqiu Kai on his lodger-guest payroll, giving him meat to eat and silk garments to wear like those who came from noble families.

Not long afterwards, a fire broke out in Fan's warehouse.

"If you go in and save my stock of brocade," said Fan Zihua to Shangqiu Kai, "I'll reward you handsomely."

Shangqiu Kai dashed in and came out with the brocade. He was neither burned nor hurt.

Now there came a marked change in the attitude of those who had bullied him. They were remorseful.

"Mr. Shangqiu," they came up to apologize, "we are all blind fools. Please forgive us. We played tricks on you. We insulted you. Now we've come to realize that you must be an immortal. No ordinary man can perform such superhuman feats as you did. Please let us share your secret."

"But there is no secret to talk about," said Shangqiu Kai. "Truth to tell, even I myself did not know how I did it. However, there is one thing I can tell you. That is, I believed with all my heart what you said was true. So I was obsessed by just one thought - I must do all that was in my power to do. At that moment, nothing else in the world mattered. I forgot what was good for me and what was bad for me. That was why nothing stood in my way. But now that you have told me that you lied, that you were really making fun of me, I can no longer perform what you call superhuman feat. You have intimidated me. I have worries and suspicions now. When I recall how I narrowly escaped from being burned or drowned, I cannot help feeling scared. I was indeed lucky. Shall I ever dare to get near water and fire again? No, because I have lost faith."

From then on, Fan Zihua's men never dared to insult a poor man. They even made a point of getting down from their carriages to greet the street beggars, if they saw one, with a deep bow.

Comment: When Confucius heard the story, he said to his disciples: "A man with absolute faith can move heaven and earth. He can move the spirits. He can go through the universe and nothing would stand in his way. Do you think all he can do is to defy dangers like fire and water and still survive? Shangqiu Kai was able to make his mind overcome matter even when his mind believed a lie. Just think how much more you and I can achieve when we have faith in the truth. Keep this in mind, young men."

PART VII
THE END, THE MEANS AND THE GOLDEN MEAN

31. THE BUILDER AND THE DESTROYER

The king is the boat. The people are the water. The water can support the boat, and also overturn the boat.

—*Xunzi (313-238 B.C.)*

In 221 B.C., after seventeen years of war of annexation, King Zheng of Qin subjugated six other states and expanded his kingdom to entire China. The Qin Dynasty was thus inaugurated. The king issued a proclamation: I am Qin Shi Huang, the First Sovereign Emperor. My successors will be called the Second Emperor, the Third Emperor and so on for thousands and thousands of generations to come.

The name China, in fact, is derived from the dynastic title of Qin. This marked a turning point in the history of China. The Qin empire stretched from Korea to Vietnam, from the valley of the Yellow River to the coast of the East China Sea. Qin Shi Huang was then thirty-nine.

What was he going to do to perpetuate his empire? We shall see.

BIRTH PANGS OF A UNIFIED COUNTRY

Qin Shi Huang ruled with an iron hand. The first order he issued was to confiscate all the weapons in the hands of the people. He had them melted down and cast into twelve giant bronze statues to be placed in the palace, each weighing 120 metric tons.

Under the auspices of his prime minister Li Si, who succeeded Lü Buwei (see Chapter 28), a series of policies of far-reaching significance were carried out. Measures and weights were standardized to replace the hitherto irregularities used in different states. The axles of the wheels of carts and wagons, which used to have different lengths in different states in the past, were to have one uniform size. Different styles of writing used in various states were reduced to one. The Qin coinage was issued as the standard currency throughout the empire.

The fall of the preceding dynasty, the Zhou House, was actually due to the fact that the kings of Zhou had given fiefs to their sons and the relatives of the royal family whose descendants eventually fought each other so fiercely for supremacy that, as a result, the Zhou Dynasty was greatly weakened by these warring states. Therefore Li Si easily persuaded Qin Shi Huang to give monetary rewards for all meritorious services done instead of awarding territories to his sons and other members of the royal family.

All the boundaries of the old states were demolished. China was divided into thirty-six administrative districts under officials Qin Shi Huang appointed. To weaken the influence of the one hundred and twenty thousand wealthy families of old aristocracy from all six former states, the emperor uprooted them from their homes and forced them to move to the capital of Qin, the city of Xianyang, which was in the vicinity of present-day Xi'an, Shaanxi Province.

Qin Shi Huang found the capital too crowded and the old palaces too small. So a huge new palace complex consisting of two hundred and seventy chambers were ordered to be built. The front palace, Epang, alone, had a capacity of 10,000 people. Stone was quarried from the north, timber transported from the south. More than half a million forced laborers were put to work on the project.

Public works on a national road system were under way, too. Tree-lined roads, fifty-feet wide, were constructed, fanning out from the capital in all directions, totalling some 4,700 miles.

THE MASTERMIND

The mastermind behind the unification program was Li Si, the prime minister. A native of Chu, Li had worked as a petty clerk in the government. One day he saw some rats eating filth in the toilet of his office. He noticed how they would scurry off at the approach of a man or a dog. However, in the granary, Li noticed, the rats did not seem to be scared of humans or dogs and they kept on eating the grain, even in the presence of the granary keeper. Li concluded that a man was not unlike the rats in so far as his ability was concerned. It depended on what position he placed himself in.

By the time Li finished his studies, he decided that Chu did not offer him great prospects. Of all the warring states, Qin was the strongest and its king the most ambitious. And Qin was recruiting aliens to work for its government. Li Si felt that Qin held out the best opportunities for his career. He believed in grabbing the tide of chance at its flood. So he set out westward for Qin.

Li had a broad vision of a unified China. He urged the king of Qin to conquer the other six countries and merge them under one government. As his proposal met with the hearty approval of the king, he was made the prime minister of Qin. Li also advocated dictatorship, a state ruled by an absolute king and draconian laws.

Qin always had a policy of employing aliens of distinguished merits and abilities. But after the discovery of the plot of Lao Ai and the fall of Lü Buwei as described in the previous chapter, the king ordered the expulsion of all foreigners, Li Si among them. Li Si hastened to write a petition to the king, citing historical examples of achievements made by foreigners for Qin. He successfully argued that many widely used products were not made in Qin. Likewise many men of talent, though not brought up in Qin, could be trusted to work loyally for Qin. If they were driven away, Qin's enemies would be strengthened whereas Qin would be weakened. Mount Tai does not reject additional soil and is therefore able to attain greatness. A great ocean does not discriminate rivers that run into it and so is able to attain depth. No king who expels people of talent can expect to remain powerful. After reading Li Si's petition, the king of Qin changed his mind and Li was able to keep his position.

At the suggestion of Li Si, Qin was prepared to attack Han. The king of Han sent an envoy, Han Feizi, to Qin, to negotiate peace. Han Feizi was an aristocrat of his country and a distinguished scholar. The king of Qin was delighted to make his acquaintance, for he had read a book by Han Feizi which had so impressed him that he declared: "If I could meet its author, I should die without regret."

In his book, Han Feizi eloquently argued for harsh laws and ruthless dictatorship. But his advice was not accepted by the king of Han.

His arrival made Li Si uneasy even though his political view was essentially similar to that of Li Si. Li Si knew that Han Feizi was a more talented man than he himself, for they had been fellow students at one time. Now he became terribly jealous of Han Feizi. He told the king of Qin that since Han Feizi was a prince of Han, he naturally was working for the interest of Han, notwithstanding the fact that his political view was in line with Qin's policy.

"If you let him go back, you will be making a big mistake," Li warned the king. "The best thing to do is to get rid of him now."

The king ordered to put Han Feizi under house arrest, and Li Si secretly sent poison to him, pressing him to commit suicide. Han Feizi sought to have one more conversation with the king of Qin, but he was given no chance. Later when the king regretted his decision of putting Han Feizi under custody and ordered his release, Han had already killed himself.

For the next twenty years, Li worked with the king and eventually brought about the realization of his ambitious scheme, the unification of China.

MASS MURDER

During the Zhou Dynasty and the Period of Warring States, political and academic ideas were debated openly and writings on various subjects flourished. Qin Shi Huang was afraid that freedom of speech might pose a threat to the stability of his rule. Acting on the advice of Prime Minister Li Si, he ordered that all classics, including literature, philosophy, and history, together with official records of the former six states be collected and burned except for books in the imperial archives and books on medicine, agriculture and astrology. Those who failed to burn up their books or surrender them to the authorities within thirty days would have their faces tattooed and sent to do hard labor at the Great Wall. Those who gathered together to discuss classical works or tried to discredit the present regime by comparing it to the past would all be sentenced to death.

But the burning was far from complete. For instance, Confucius' *Analects* survived the scourge, having been stowed away in the walls of the house of Confucius by his descendants of the eighth generation.

Four hundred and sixty dissident intellectuals were rounded up in the capital and buried alive, as they were found guilty of libeling the emperor. Many more were banished to frontier regions. However, the emperor's eldest son, Fusu, was opposed to such measures.

"We have just established our rule," he said to his father. "People have not settled down yet. If you put so many intellectuals to death, you may throw the country into panic. Please reconsider your decision,

Father."

Qin Shi Huang was displeased. He sent Fusu to the northern frontier to join General Meng Tian to supervise the construction of the Great Wall where the army was stationed.

After the killing of intellectuals, a giant meteorite fell to the earth. Somebody inscribed on it: "After the death of the First Emperor, the Qin empire will be divided." An investigation was made. When no suspects were found, the emperor ordered to have the meteorite smashed and the entire population in the vicinity of the fallen meteorite slaughtered.

THE GREAT WALL

Qin Shi Huang was superstitious and terrified of death, especially after the attempts made on his life by Jing Ke and Gao Jianli. No fewer than three hundred astrologers were employed by the royal court to watch the stars. But all they did was flatter the emperor.

Qin Shi Huang ordered alchemists to work on the elixir of immortality for him. In the third year of the new dynasty, he sent an expedition of twenty ships off the coast of Shandong to look for immortals, said to be living on the islands in the East China Sea. The expedition never returned. Legend says that it landed on Japan and the three thousand young men and women on those ships became the first settlers of Japan. They landed near a place which is the city of Kumano today, and there still exists the tomb of the leader of the expedition, Xu Fu, in the city of Shingu nearby.

Qin Shi Huang worked hard. He read one hundred twenty pound official reports written on bulky bamboo tablets everyday. From time to time, he made inspection tours in the country.

A third attempt was made on his life when Qin Shi Huang was travelling in Henan. The royal procession was ambushed by a man who aimed at the emperor's carriage a 60 kilogram iron hammer which only hit another carriage by mistake. The emperor was outraged. A nationwide search was launched, but nothing turned up.

When on a tour in central and eastern China, the emperor sailed down the Yangtze River to Hunan to worship a goddess in a temple on the mountain. A strong wind blew up, nearly capsizing his ship. He was

so mad that he ordered all the trees on the mountain be cut down.

A fortune-teller told the emperor that Qin would be destroyed by the Hu, which was the Chinese name in those days for the nomadic tribe of the Huns. Qin Shi Huang ordered General Meng Tian to lead an army of 300,000 to attack the Huns, and to build a big strong barricade, known as the Great Wall, to prevent invasion from them. The construction was to link up the existing northern frontier walls built by various former states before the unification of China.

The wall was four men tall and two chariots wide. On the ramparts, watchtowers were built at regular distances from which, in the event of an enemy invasion, the sentries would send smoke signals to put the border defense on the alert. At less frequent intervals, garrison towers were built to station troops and store weapons and provisions. The Great Wall was not built on flat land but over high mountains and deep valleys. Snaking its way 1,900 miles from the northwestern frontier of China to the East China Sea, the Great Wall was also the longest cemetery in the world. More than a quarter of a million people, mostly forced laborers, died and were buried there during the four year construction.

HOUSE OF DEATH

The emperor fell ill and died in 210 B.C. when he was only fifty. He was buried in the palatial mausoleum at Mount Li, twenty-five miles east of Xi'an, the present-day capital of Shaanxi Province. The construction of his tomb was started shortly after he became the king of Qin at the age of thirteen when Qin was still one of the seven warring kingdoms. It was not finished until just two years before he died. More than seven hundred thousand laborers from all over China had been conscripted to work on the subterranean project, the scale of which equalled to that of the Great Wall.

The roof of the underground palace was studded with precious stones like stars in the sky. Underneath, the Yellow River and the Yangtze River were reproduced in quicksilver and made to flow mechanically. Countless treasures filled the tomb. Huge candles of whale fat were burning night and day. Automatic crossbows were installed which would catapult arrows at any intruder.

Altogether it took thirty-six years to finish the enormous tomb. When it was done, all entrances were blocked so that none of the workmen or craftsmen could get out alive to disclose its location and the treasures inside. Qin Shi Huang's successor, the Second Emperor ordered all the childless women of the imperial harem be buried with his father. Then trees were planted on the mausoleum to make it look like a hill.

In 1974, thousands of life size pottery army men were excavated at the foot of Mount Li near the site of Qin Shi Huang's tomb. They were lined up in battle formation with archers and spearmen in the vanguard, followed by chariots carrying army commanders, with foot soldiers holding huge swords standing behind. These magnificent pieces of terra cotta sculpture soon became known as the eighth wonder of the world. They were modelled on living men so that no two faces were alike.

However, the tomb itself has yet to be excavated.

Comment: The Qin Dynasty is the first totalitarian regime in China. It is also the shortest one in history. For more than a hundred years Qin Shi Huang and his predecessors had striven painstakingly to convert Qin from a backward and underdeveloped country into the strongest of all the warring states in China. It finally succeeded in bringing to its knees the other six countries.

But after the epoch-making victory, Qin Shi Huang began to push through sweeping and convulsive changes through brutal force. He wanted to destroy the old order with one stroke and stamp out the memory of the past by burning books and slaughtering dissidents.

As we are going to see in the next chapters, the whole country erupted like a volcano once he passed from the scene. The dynasty which he had hoped to last ten thousand years came to a violent end in less than four years after his death. It takes so little trouble and so short a period to destroy something that took so much and so long to build. The quick disintegration of the Qin regime is a fitting end for someone who had totally disregarded moral values and the interests of the people in the pursuit of his ambitious plan and violated the golden rule of moderation in the change process. Qin Shi Huang failed to recognize that the power to win victory was not the same as the power to maintain it. He has remained a symbol of evil and oppression in Chinese history.

32. WHEN A DEER IS A HORSE

The miscalculation of a moment may become the regret of a lifetime.
—*Chinese proverb*

Qin Shi Huang died after ruling a unified China with an iron hand for twelve years. The death of a strong man always seems to set the stage for chaos, conspiracy and change. The realignment of forces seen and the release of forces unforeseen often trigger a chain of events that may lead to an outcome totally unexpected by the quick and the dead.

SUCCESSION INTRIGUE

In 210 B.C., the emperor fell ill on his fifth inspection tour. When his condition deteriorated, he dictated a letter to his eldest son, Prince Fusu, asking him to come back immediately for the funeral and to succeed to the throne. But he died before the letter was dispatched.

Only very few of the royal entourage knew about the death of Qin Shi Huang, among them Prime Minister Li Si, Chief Eunuch Zhao Gao and Prince Huhai, the emperor's youngest son, who was tutored by Zhao Gao.

Zhao Gao was specially anxious now that the Emperor was dead. If he should dispatch the Emperor's letter to call back Prince Fusu to attend the funeral and succeed to the throne, what would become of himself? For one thing, Fusu and General Meng Tian were great friends. And Zhao Gao had a grudge against the Meng family, because he had once been sentenced to death by General Meng Tian's brother on account of a serious crime. But the First Emperor pardoned him. Fusu's ascension to the throne would certainly jeopardize his position.

He went to Prince Huhai.

"When your brother comes back, he will be the next emperor. Your father died without giving you any estate to live on."

"My father probably knew what he was doing," replied Prince Huhai.

"Think it over," said the eunuch. "Right now the power of the empire

rests with you and me and Li Si. Together we are in a position to control the life and death of everyone. Make your choice now! Do you want to control others or be controlled by others? There is a world of difference between the two alternatives."

"We cannot remove my brother," said Huhai. "It is against the wish of my father. The world would rise against me if I did that."

"Why should you be concerned with such niceties and ignore what really is important?" Zhao Gao continued. "History is not without examples of a son killing his father or a minister killing a monarch in order to be the king. If you do not take decisive action, you'll regret forever."

Huhai was tempted by the prospects of being the emperor. "But is it appropriate to bring up the subject with the prime minister now when my father's body has not even been buried yet?"

"We have to act quickly. I am going to see the prime minister right away."

Zhao Gao told Li Si that the last letter of the late emperor was in the hands of Prince Huhai.

"At present," he said, "only you and I know the content of the letter. We can decide who the next emperor will be. What is your opinion?"

"How can you talk like this?" Li Si was shocked. "We should not debate what the late emperor had already decided on."

"Think about it," Zhao Gao was prepared. "How do you compare yourself with General Meng Tian? Are you more capable than he is? Do you have a better reputation than his? Do you have a greater trust from Prince Fusu than he has?"

"I am not perfect. I believe General Meng Tian excels me in every respect," Li Si admitted.

"I've been in the palace for more than twenty years," said Zhao Gao. "I have never seen a new emperor reappoint the same person who served under his predecessor. When Prince Fusu becomes the new emperor, I'm sure he'll ask General Meng to be the prime minister. And you have to retire to your village. I have taught Prince Huhai for many years. He is kind, sincere, and respectful to elders. He is most qualified for the throne."

"I can only obey the late emperor," Li Si answered. "I leave my fate to Heaven. I am of a humble origin. I owe everything to the late emperor. It was he who made me prime minister, my rank second to none but the emperor. He was the benefactor of all my family. How can I turn to betray him?"

"A wise man does not follow rules," said Zhao Gao. "When times change, he changes. The destiny of the empire is in the hands of Prince Huhai now. If you listen to me, you will keep your position. Your aristocratic title will be passed on to your children. Otherwise you will regret for the rest of your life. Your fate is in your own hands."

Li Si felt like an animal at bay. What was he going to do? He knew he did not have the courage to commit suicide. In this age of uncertainty, he could rely on nobody. To promise his collaboration was the only way out.

FRATRICIDE

Soon an envoy was sent to where Prince Fusu and General Meng Tian were stationed. The envoy handed them a forged letter written in the name of the Emperor. The letter accused Fusu of lacking filial devotion and General Meng of disloyalty. Both were ordered to take their own lives. So, Fusu was ready to kill himself. Meng Tian, suspecting a plot, tried to stop him.

"His Majesty is on a tour now," said Meng Tian who was Qin Shi Huang's most trusted general. "He has not appointed a crown prince yet. He put me in charge of 300,000 soldiers to defend the northern border and made you the supervisor. Why are you so ready to kill yourself just because somebody claims he is the envoy from the emperor? How do you know it is not a trick? Please send a request for confirmation."

Fusu did not question the authenticity of the letter. "When my father wants me to die, what more instruction can I ask for?" he said as he grabbed his sword and killed himself in front of Huhai's envoy.

General Meng refused to commit suicide but allowed himself to be taken prisoner.

As the news of the emperor's death was kept from the public, Zhao Gao had the corpse of the emperor placed in the royal coach. Meals were delivered to the royal coach as usual. It was August 210 B.C. The weather was hot and the dead body began to decompose. To cover the stench, wagon-loads of salted fish were bought. No one had any suspicion; no one dared to raise a question.

Qin Shi Huang's death was not announced until Prince Fusu's suicide had been confirmed. The royal procession returned to the capital city of Xianyang. Huhai became the Second Emperor. Fearing opposition, he had his twelve brothers and ten sisters all killed. One of his brothers intended to flee, but as he was afraid that his family would not be spared, he wrote to the Second Emperor that he was willing to die with his father, the late emperor, and asked to be buried with him. Huhai was so pleased that he immediately granted a hundred ounces of gold for his brother's funeral expenses.

At the suggestion of Zhao Gao, Huhai made new laws harsh enough to prevent anyone who still valued his own life from trying to make the slightest trouble.

Now Huhai sent an envoy to the prison, ordering General Meng Tian to commit suicide by drinking poison.

"My family has served the country for three generations," said General Meng. "I am in command of a great army. Even though I am now in prison, I have the power to start a revolt if I want it. But as I have not forgotten the trust placed in me by the late emperor and I do not want to disgrace the name of my forefathers, I choose to die with honor, and die an innocent man. I believe the new emperor must have been under the influence of some treacherous man so that he should have willed me to meet my end like this. I want to entreat you to convey a message to His Majesty. Please tell him that I hope he would wake up and guard against evil men."

"I am an officer of the law, General," the envoy replied. "I dare not report what you have said to His Majesty."

Reflecting on his past before his death, General Meng seemed to have somehow become environmentally conscious.

"I see now," he sighed. "In building the Great Wall from Lintao in the west to Liaodong in the east, it is impossible that I have not cut through the veins of the earth. Indeed I have committed a crime punishable only by death."

THE END OF LI SI

The first anti-Qin shot was fired just three months after Huhai came to power. In August 209 B.C., a detachment of forced laborers was ordered to march from Henan to a station post in Hebei. Heavy rain hindered them from reaching their destination in time, and the penalty for being late was death. If they ran away and got captured, they would also die. Driven to desperation, a squad leader named Chen Sheng rallied around him nine hundred fellow laborers into a rebel force against the Qin regime. The whole country echoed vigorously. Dissatisfied members of the old regimes of the six states overthrown by Qin Shi Huang rose in revolt like a tidal wave sweeping over the empire, their troops hundreds of thousands strong. One after another, the six state became virtually independent of Qin's rule.

At the death of Qin Shi Huang, Epang Palace was still incomplete. The Second Emperor ordered to have construction resumed. More laborers were conscripted when there were not even enough farmers to work in the field. The land taxes, poll taxes, and sales taxes exceeded two-thirds of a household income. The burden on the people became intolerable.

Knowing the rebellion, fueled by widespread popular discontent, was threatening the stability of the regime, Prime Minister Li Si asked the emperor to halt the construction of Epang Palace and cut the taxes and stop the public works.

"Do you know what is wonderful about being an emperor?" retorted the twenty-one-year-old emperor, utterly callous to the sufferings of the people. "It is to be able to do whatever he desires. Life in this world lasts only an instant. Now as I have the entire country at my disposal, I should follow my own inclinations and enjoy myself to the fullest extent until my life comes to a natural end."

Zhao Gao had many enemies in the court and Li Si was potentially his most powerful adversary. Zhao decided to block his enemies' access to the Second Emperor.

"The late emperor had governed the country for many years," he suggested to Huhai. "He could easily spot mistakes of his ministers. You are young. You'd better not rush to any decision at your meetings with your ministers. If you make a mistake, it will reflect badly on you. And you should not make yourself too readily accessible. Your absence can underscore your authority. If a minister has something to say, he can send in a memorandum first. We will jointly make a decision after careful deliberation."

Huhai was only too glad to take the advice.

Li Si was not at all pleased about this. Each time he asked for audience, Zhao Gao promised Li that he would let him know when the emperor was free. Then Zhao Gao would send for Li Si at a moment when the emperor was frolicking with court ladies. This happened several times until Huhai got annoyed.

"He never comes when I am free," he growled. "He always wants to report something when I don't want to be disturbed. Does he have any respect for me? Does he want to embarrass me?"

"Yes, it is just a little getting out of hand," Zhao Gao chimed in. "He is part of the coup that has made you emperor. Apparently he expects more from Your Majesty than merely keeping his position as prime minister. Rumors say that rebellion was particularly rampant where his elder son was governor because he condoned them. Instead of suppressing the rebellion, his son was said to be exchanging correspondence with the rebels. And outside the palace, the prime minister wields more power than Your Majesty. I am the only person that makes him think twice before doing anything. If I were gone, he would do whatever he likes with Your Majesty."

Huhai instructed Zhao to look into the matter. Li Si, in turn, accused Zhao of corruption, deceit and subversion. But the emperor was prejudiced in favor of Zhao, and Li Si was thrown into prison. Investigations found no evidence against Li. In fact, Li's son was killed by the rebels, but Zhao Gao suppressed the report.

Li Si was tortured and flogged hundreds of times during the interrogation. Unable to endure the ordeal, he falsely pleaded guilty. Still hoping that Huhai might change his mind and release him, he wrote a letter to the Second Emperor reminding him of his more than thirty years' service to the country and his numerous achievements. The letter, however, was detained by Zhao Gao. Zhao sent his own people, disguised as the emperor's investigators, to visit Li. During their visit, Li Si retracted his earlier confession and stated the truth. But as soon as he did that, he was tortured more severely. After a few days, Zhao Gao sent some more people, pretending to be the emperor's personal aides, to see Li. Again Li pleaded not guilty, and again he was cruelly beaten.

This repeated several times. When a real envoy sent by the Second

Emperor came to question him, Li Si thought the same thing was going to happen again and dared not tell the truth. He was forced to sign a written confession and thus convicted of high treason.

On his way to the execution ground, Li looked at his younger son who was walking by his side and said:

"Do you still remember the days when we went out hunting rabbits with our yellow dog in the wilderness of our hometown? How I wish we could do that again!"

At this, the father and the son burst into tears. Li Si was cut in two at the waist and all the members of his family were publicly executed. It took place in the second year after the death of Qin Shi Huang.

A DEER FOR A HORSE

Upon his death, Zhao Gao was made prime minister. In the meantime, the rebel forces grew rapidly in strength. The Qin army was steadily losing ground. When a most prestigious senior general of the Qin army, who was deeply distrustful of Zhao Gao, switched sides to the rebels, it was obvious that the Qin empire was tottering.

The Second Emperor was upset when a courier came to report the advance of the rebel forces toward Xianyang, the capital of Qin. The courier was therefore thrown into prison. The next courier knew better than to tell the truth. He falsely reported that the rebel force was just a handful of bandits and they had all been captured by local authorities. The news pleased the emperor.

Zhao Gao began to have secret communication with the rebel forces which were fast approaching the capital. He believed he could enhance his standing with the rebels after the fall of Qin if he took a timely step to remove Huhai, the symbol of the hated regime.

One day Zhao Gao presented a deer to the emperor, calling it a horse.

"No, it is not a horse, Prime Minister," the emperor laughed. "It's a deer."

"It is a horse," Zhao Gao insisted. Then he turned to all the ministers present. "Tell His Majesty whether it is a deer or a horse!" he said, looking very serious.

Most of those present admitted that it was a horse, and the emperor was alarmed thinking something must have gone wrong with himself.

Zhao secretly threw into prison those who had dared to tell the emperor it was a deer. After this episode, nobody dared to oppose Zhao Gao any more. Zhao was ready for his next move.

Seventeen days after he presented the deer to the emperor, Yan Le, his son-in-law and the commander-in-chief of the garrison forces in the capital, took orders from him, led a regiment of a thousand soldiers and charged into the palace. Some imperial guards tried to stop the intruders but were easily overpowered. Huhai shouted for help, but nobody came. Only one old eunuch followed him as he retreated into the inner chamber.

"Why didn't you tell me about all this beforehand?" Huhai asked the old eunuch.

"I am alive because I did not speak out," said the old man. "If I had told you the truth, I wouldn't have lived to see this day."

At that moment Yan Le came up.

"The whole country is against you," he said.

"I want to see the prime minister."

"No, you can't."

"If you want to remove me from the throne, I'm willing to be a governor of a province."

"That's out of the question."

"Then let me retire with an estate of ten thousand households."

This request was turned down, too.

"Let me live with my wife and family as a commoner, then."

"I am here on the order of the prime minister to execute you on behalf of the country," declared Yan Le. "You may have many requests, but they are none of my business."

He motioned his men to move forward. Before they got him, the Second Emperor drew out his sword and killed himself.

Although Zhao Gao would like to enthrone himself, he thought it would be wiser for him to help the rebels topple the imperial house of Qin and then have them appoint him the ruler. Therefore he decided, for the time being, to allow Zi Ying, son of Fusu, to succeed to the throne.

"The title of 'emperor' should be abolished," he told Zi Ying. "Qin Shi Huang was called emperor because he ruled the entire empire. Now the six states he had conquered are independent, so the new ruler should be called king again."

Before receiving the royal seal from Zhao Gao at the ancestral temple, Zi Ying had to go through a five-day fast in accordance with the imperial tradition. At the end of the fast, Zi Ying pretended ill. Messengers sent by Zhao Gao were repeatedly turned back. Finally Zhao Gao went to see Zi Ying in his residence. Hardly had he uttered a word when guards hidden behind the door dashed forward and hacked him to death.

Forty-six days later, the rebel forces seized the capital of Qin. With a rope round the neck and the imperial seal in hand, Zi Ying drove out in a plain carriage with white horses and surrendered himself to the enemy.

It was 206 B.C., fifteen years after the establishment of the Qin Dynasty.

Comment: Li Si rose to preeminence from a humble background through sheer determination, talent and ruthlessness. He played a key role in the establishment of the Qin empire and in formulating many of the policies adopted by the First Emperor, good policies as well as bad policies.

In politics, nothing stays stable. There is no permanent ally or permanent enemy but only permanent interest. Li Si's assessment of power dynamics in the court after the death of the First Emperor seemed to have failed him.

His preoccupation of self-interest blinded him from correctly judging Zhao Gao, whose character Li should have plenty of opportunities to see through first-hand. In the end, he fell victim to the intrigues of somebody who was obviously much less competent in many respects than himself. That was his tragedy.

33. SHORT AND SWEET

It is easier to be known by the outside world than to really know yourself inside; it is easier to make others believe you have a clear conscience than to convince yourself you have never done a thing in your life to be ashamed of.

—*Vegetable Roots*

SHIELD AND SPEAR

A man was selling shields and spears in the market.

"My shields are the toughest in the world," he told his customers. "No spear can ever penetrate them."

Then he held up a spear.

"My spears are so sharp that it can cut through anything," he said.

"What if you use your spear to attack your shield?" asked a customer.

The man did not know what to say, and everyone there had a good laugh.

Comment: Hence self-contradiction in Chinese is called a spear-and-shield talk.

LOST HORSE

A man lived with his father on the northern frontier of China. One day his horse ran away to the nomads across the border. His neighbors came to express their sympathy.

"How do you know it isn't a blessing?" said his father.

Several months later, his horse returned with a magnificent nomad stallion. Friends and neighbors gathered to admire the stallion and congratulate him.

"What makes you feel so sure this isn't a disaster?" asked his father.

The son took a fancy to the nomad stallion. A few days later, he broke his leg while riding it. Everyone came to console him.

"How do you know for sure that it's necessarily a bad thing?" asked his father again.

A month later, the nomads invaded China, and every able-bodied

man had to go to war. The Chinese lost nine out of every ten men in the border conflict. His son did not go because of the bad condition of his leg.

Comment: Blessings can become disasters, and disasters may turn into blessings. This is a classic story epitomizing the unpredictable nature and possibly cyclical pattern of changes in life.

DOUBLE STANDARDS

A man living in the state of Chu had two wives. His neighbor tried to flirt with the elder one but was rebuffed. He then made advance to the younger one who was willing enough to make love with him.

Not long afterwards, the husband of the two wives died.

"Which one of his two wives would you like to marry?" a friend of the neighbor inquired.

"The elder one," the neighbor replied.

"But she rejected you, didn't she?" the friend was surprised. "Why not take the younger one?"

"When it is another man's wife, you wish her to be easy of approach. But if she is my own wife, I wouldn't want her to be that nice to other men."

Comment: Strangely, double standards here do not seem so offensive.

TRUTH AND TRUST

Heavy rain damaged a corner in the wall of a wealthy man's mansion in the state of Song.

"You'd better have it repaired as soon as possible," his neighbor warned him. "Otherwise burglars may get into your house."

His son said the same thing to him a little while later.

That night some burglar really got into the house and made away with many valuables. The rich man thought his son was very smart to have cautioned him in advance, and he praised his son. But he suspected his neighbor might have had something to do with the theft.

Comment: Often the messenger is more important than the message. Before we try to put our message across, we must first gain the trust of those we try to convince even though our message is sacred truth.

SELF-CONSCIOUSNESS

Yang Zi was staying in an inn where there were two waitresses. The innkeeper seemed to like the homely looking one better than the pretty one.

Yang Zi asked him why. The innkeeper said: "The pretty one is proud, because she always thinks herself so pretty. But I don't think much of her looks. The homely looking one is conscious of her own looks, and is therefore humble and gentle. So I don't notice her looks."

"Remember this," said Yang Zi to his students. "Act nobly but do not think that you are doing something noble, and you will be welcome everywhere."

Comment: What if the pretty one were also humble and gentle? Wouldn't she be perfect then?

MEDITATION

A man could not go to sleep at night. He went to see a monk for advice. The monk told him: "You work too hard. You worry too much. Try to forget your work and detach yourself mentally from all the cares and responsibilities of life. Relax for a while. Meditation will help."

The man went home and sat quietly on a couch for a few days. His insomnia gradually improved. On the third day he told his wife: "Meditation is a good thing. Otherwise I wouldn't have remembered that our neighbor nearly cheated us out of ten liters of wheat. Let me remind him."

Comment: Let's hope that was not the only thing that meditation helped to bring to his mind.

DUTCH COURAGE

A man feared his wife.

"Go to a wine shop, get drunk, and then go home and beat up your wife," his friend advised him.

So, the henpecked husband took a few drinks and gave his wife a sound beating, feeling great to have got the upper hand over her.

Then he sobered up. His wife asked him why he had changed his usual, gentle manner so suddenly. The man said he could not remember anything. Now his wife started to beat him, and he was scared into admitting that he had followed the suggestion of a friend. His wife beat him all the more fiercely, saying: "Your friend is nobody, but you are a scholar. Don't you have your own judgment? You deserve to be punished for listening to others."

Comment: A coward will sooner or later betray himself and his friends.

A HELPING HAND

A man in the state of Song was worried, thinking that the young plants in his field were growing too slowly. To help them grow faster, he decided to give the seedlings a hand by pulling them, one by one, upward a little. At the end of the day, he was exhausted.

"I am tired," he told his family when he came home. "All day I've been helping the plants to grow."

His son hurried to the field and found all the seedlings had withered.

Comment: Some of today's parents, believing it desirable to help their children become mature faster, have thrust them, before their time, into the adult world with all its pressure, conflicts, problems and hypocrisy. And the result is: More children are found to have high anxiety levels and learning problems today.

PART VIII
APTITUDE, ATTITUDE AND DESTINY

34. DINNER AT HONGMEN

He who succeeds is hailed as a hero; he who fails is condemned as a villain.

—*A Dream of Red Mansions*

There have been fifteen dynasties in Chinese history. Some dynasties were more eventful than others. I found that the most interesting periods in history were those between the decline of an old dynasty and the rise of a new dynasty. These periods gave birth to great men whose talents were brought into full swing by fate and whose wisdom demonstrated to its best advantage by circumstances. Great men come out of great conflict.

As this is a storybook of wisdom in Chinese history, it is impossible to cover all dynastic transitions. Therefore, I have limited myself to the most significant ones in Chinese history. I found the events and personalities connected with the changes of four dynasties to be most fascinating. They are Qin, Han, Ming and Qing.

The rise and fall of the Qin Dynasty has already been described in the previous chapters. Now I will try to portray the rivalry for supremacy between Xiang Yu, the most famous war hero in Chinese history, and another great man, Liu Pang at the close of the Qin Dynasty. The stories of these two supermen are known to every Chinese household. The highlights of their dramatic bid for power are represented in the following four chapters including some of the most intriguing episodes in Chinese history.

A BORN WARRIOR

A year after the death of the First Emperor of Qin, when his son the Second Emperor was on the throne, a rebellion led by a farmhand, Chen Sheng, broke out. The rebel forces captured a number of important cities, but before long they were put down by the troops of Qin under the command of an able general, Zhang Han. However, uprisings flared up everywhere in the country. Royalists of the six old states also took arms against the despotic rule of Qin. The strongest among them was one led by Xiang Liang and his nephew Xiang Yu of the former state

of Chu in eastern China.

Having lost his parents in his early years, Xiang Yu was brought up by his uncle Xiang Liang. Six feet tall and very strong, Xiang Yu was held in awe by all the young men in his hometown. His family had been in military service for generations in the state of Chu. As a young man, Xiang Yu was not interested in studying calligraphy which was a requirement of traditional education. He practiced swordsmanship but did not keep up. His uncle, being a well-respected local official in the city of Suzhou (a part of the former state of Chu), was very much annoyed with him.

"Calligraphy is only good for writing down people's names, and swordsmanship is useful only for fighting with one man," said Xiang Yu to his uncle. "Neither is worth the trouble of learning. What I really want to learn is how to fight tens of thousands of men."

His uncle then began teaching him military science and the art of war. Xiang Yu was very interested, but as soon as he had a grasp of the general principles, he did not want to go deeper.

One day Xiang Yu caught a glimpse of the magnificent royal procession passing through his town when Qin Shi Huang, the First Emperor of Qin, was on an inspection tour.

"This man—I want to take his place!" Xiang Yu blurted out.

"Shut up. We'll get killed if they heard us." His uncle quickly raised a hand to cover his mouth.

In the wake of Chen Sheng's rebellion, the Xiangs rebelled too. They killed the local governor and took over his army of 8,000 men. Pretty soon it expanded to sixty thousand. A seventy year old man by the name of Fan Tseng who was well-versed in military strategy also came to join them. Fan proposed to Xiang Liang that to boost his popular appeal, he had to look out for a descendant of the late king of Chu and make him king. Therefore a search was made and a grandson of the late king was found and installed as the king of Chu.

Having scored a series of victories over the army of Qin, Xiang Liang grew arrogant and began to underestimate the enemy.

"Pride goes before a fall," his advisor Song Yi said to him. "If you are conceited because you have won a few battles, your soldiers will become lax, too, and defeat will follow. Now as the enemy is reinforced, please be very careful."

Xiang Liang did not pay much attention to Song Yi. In a subsequent major confrontation with the Qin army, he was killed by Qin's able general, Zhang Han.

The Qin army then turned to launch an offensive against Zhao which was also a rebellious state. Zhao appealed to Chu for help. The new king of Chu appointed Song Yi commander-in-chief and Xiang Yu the second commander to lead the army of Chu to Zhao's rescue.

For more than a month, Song Yi held back. Xiang Yu urged him to attack.

"Qin is attacking Zhao," said Song Yi. "If Qin wins the battle, its army will be exhausted, we can beat them easily. If Qin is defeated, our victory is assured when we commit our forces. The best thing to do now is to let Qin and Zhao fight it out first. I may not be as skilled as you are in using the weapon, but I believe I am a better strategist."

In a not too subtle reference to Xiang Yu, Song Yi issued an order declaring: "He who is as fierce as a tiger, as stubborn as a sheep and as greedy as a wolf, and refuses to obey orders, will be executed."

Xiang Yu was not amused. The weather had turned rainy and raw, and the soldiers were cold and hungry.

"We should be attacking the enemy now," Xiang Yu told the soldiers. "But we are sitting here doing nothing. We don't have enough food and clothing, but General Song Yi wants us to wait. Zhao is no match to Qin; its army is new. If Zhao is defeated, Qin will become even stronger than it is now. The king of Chu put Song Yi in charge of the army, but what is he doing?"

The next morning Xiang Yu killed Song in the name of the king of Chu. Nobody dared to challenge him. The king of Chu was briefed on the incident by Xiang's envoy and was obliged to make Xiang Yu take Song's place as the commander-in-chief.

Xiang Yu immediately took his troops across the river for the state of Zhao. The moment he got to the other side of the river, he ordered to have all the boats scuttled. Each soldier was only allowed to carry with him no more than three days' food, making it clear that they must either win or die, for there was no turning back.

Xiang Yu's men fought so fearlessly that one soldier of Chu could match ten soldiers of Qin. The Chu forces won nine successive battles and the Qin troops were devastated. Rebel troops of other states that came to join forces with Chu were awe-stricken, for they had never seen such a great hero like Xiang Yu. When Xiang Yu called a meeting to celebrate the victory, all the generals of these states knelt down, not daring to look up. Xiang Yu became the undisputed supreme commander of all the anti-Qin forces.

To avoid clashing with Xiang Yu's troops head-on, General Zhang Han of Qin was forced to retreat several times. His move was questioned by the Second Emperor of Qin. At that time, the power of the Qin government was in the hands of Zhao Gao, the chief eunuch who had always been jealous of General Zhang's military exploits. When General Zhang Han's envoy sought to explain the situation to him, Zhao Gao refused to see him. Zhao's distrust made Zhang uneasy.

Zhang Han decided to secretly contact Xiang Yu, trying to negotiate a deal for himself. Before any agreement was reached, Xiang engaged his forces in a major battle and soundly beat Zhang Han's forces.

Taking with him over two hundred thousand men, Zhang Han surrendered and Xiang appointed him to a senior position in the Chu army.

Most of the soldiers of the anti-Qin allied forces were formerly conscript laborers in Qin. They had been maltreated by the soldiers of Qin. Now that 200,000 Qin soldiers had surrendered, it was a good chance for them to have their revenge. So they abused them, they beat them. Humiliated, the Qin soldiers complained that General Zhang Han had tricked them into capitulation and they were concerned about what was going to become of their families in Qin when the news of their surrender got to the ear of the Second Emperor.

Their conversation was overheard by Xiang Yu's men.

"The Qin army did not surrender willingly," Xiang told his generals at a military meeting. "There are so many of them. Once we fight our way to Qin, I don't know whether they will be as obedient then as they are now."

That night Xiang Yu ordered to have all the 200,000 soldiers of the Qin army massacred when they were sleeping except General Zhang Han and his close associates.

Battle after battle, Xiang Yu's army carried the day. When they were approaching the capital of Qin, Xianyang, word came that the strategic pass leading to the city had already been blocked by another rebel force led by Liu Pang and that the king of Qin had already given himself up to Liu Pang. Xiang Yu was infuriated.

A VILLAGE CHIEF

Liu Bang was once under the command of Xiang Yu's uncle Xiang Liang. He was from Pei, a county in the state of Chu (in modern Jiangsu), the state of Chu being the native place of the Xiangs, too.

As the head of a village in Pei, Liu Bang was known to be kindhearted, generous, resourceful, willing to help others and fond of women and wine. He often bought his drinks on credit. The liquor store owner never asked him to pay up, believing Liu to be an unusual man.

Once when he was performing official duties in Xianyang, the capital of Qin, he happened to see the First Emperor riding in his royal carriage. Gazing at the pomp and grandeur of the procession, Liu Bang muttered to himself.

"Why, this, and only this, is the kind of life for a man to live."

One day the governor of Pei held a dinner party in honor of a distinguished guest named Lü. Local celebrities all attended, bringing with them contributions in the form of money. Xiao He, the governor's secretary, announced that those whose contributions were less than ten ounces of gold could only be seated outside the main hall. Liu had brought in nothing but he wrote on his card: "I contribute a hundred."

When Mr. Lü saw the card, he came out to greet Liu. Lü was good at physiognomy. He was struck by Liu's looks and invited him to sit at the head table.

"I can tell fortune by reading faces," said Mr. Lü to Liu Bang when the dinner was over. "I've seen so many faces, but no one has got such features as yours. You will go far. I would like you to marry my daughter."

Lü's wife was angry at his proposal.

"You always say you love your daughter," she said. "When the governor of Pei asked for her hand, you turned him down. How can you give her to a humble village head like Liu Bang?"

"This is not something you can understand." Lü did not elaborate.

In due course, Liu Bang married Lü's daughter. She bore him two children, a boy and a girl.

One day when Madame Liu was working in the field with her children, an old man came along to ask for some water to drink. Seeing he was hungry, Madame Liu gave him some food, too.

"Madam, you are going to be a most honored lady in the world," said the man, looking at her closely.

"Thank you for your kind words," said Madame Liu. "Please examine my two children, too."

"You will be honored because of this boy," said the man, pointing to the boy.

He also predicted that her daughter would become a very honored lady too.

Moments later, Liu Bang came home. When his wife told him what the old man had said, he immediately ran out and overtook him.

"The lady and the children all have noble looks like you, but you have a majesty beyond description," said the old man.

"Your words are encouraging," said Liu Bang. "I will never forget you if I turn out to be as lucky as you have predicted."

In his capacity as a village head, Liu had to escort laborers to Mount Li to work on the construction of the emperor's huge tomb. On their way many of them ran away. Liu concluded that by the time he reached the destination, he would have no one left to escort. So he simply set them free.

"You are free now. I am also my own now," Liu Bang announced.

About a dozen of young men decided to follow him. At that time, Chen Sheng's rebellion broke out. Liu Bang rebelled, too. His followers soon grew to several hundred strong. They killed the governor of Pei and made Liu Bang his successor. Soon Liu led them to join Xiang Liang, who generously put five thousand men and ten generals under his command.

Liu fought shoulder to shoulder with Xiang Yu. After his uncle Xiang Liang was killed in battle, Xiang Yu demanded that the new king of Chu allow him to go westward and attack the capital of Qin. The king balked because he felt that Xiang Yu was too violent and too much bent on revenge and killing. As the people of Qin had suffered enough already, it would be easy to conquer Qin if a more tolerant and gentle person like Liu Bang were sent.

Therefore Xiang Yu was ordered to help the besieged Zhao in the north, and Liu Bang was ordered to spearhead his forces to attack Qin's capital. In his westward advance, Liu Bang prohibited his troops from looting or mistreating prisoners of war and promised leniency to those who surrendered. This lessened the morale of the Qin army.

In the Qin court, the Second Emperor was murdered by his most favorite eunuch minister, Zhao Gao, who now sent an envoy to Liu Bang suggesting that they divide Qin. Liu suspected it was a ruse, but nevertheless, he started negotiation with some other generals of the Qin army. While the bargaining was still in progress, Liu launched a surprise attack and broke the enemy's defense line.

In November 207 B.C., Liu Bang entered Xianyang. The young king of Qin, Ziying, heir to the Second Emperor, surrendered.

When one of his officers suggested that Ziying be executed, Liu Bang said: "I was sent here because the king of Chu believed I would exercise mercy. Now as the king of Qin has surrendered, killing him would bring bad luck."

He then called a meeting with local community leaders.

"I am here to save you, not to harm you," he announced. "Do not be afraid. All officials will please remain on your posts as usual." He told them that all the laws of Qin would be abolished. He only wanted to establish with all of them a three-point code to the effect that those who kill would be executed and those who assault others or steal would be punished according to the nature of their offense. He sent men to all towns and villages to make the new code known. Overjoyed, the people brought out meat, wine and food to greet Liu's army.

Upon entering the palace, Liu Bang was tempted by the luxury and splendor of the Qin court—all the treasures, beautiful court ladies, etc. He wanted to move into the palace.

"No, my lord," said Zhang Liang, his top advisor. "You are here because Qin lost the support of the people. You should stick to your plain lifestyle. You will end up like the Qin emperors if you want to indulge yourself in pleasure the moment you enter the palace."

So Liu ordered all the imperial treasuries be sealed and he himself stayed away from the palace—from its luxury and pretty court ladies.

A NARROW ESCAPE

Xiang Yu was mad that Liu Bang entered the capital of Qin ahead of him.

"My lord," said his top advisor Fan Zeng, "Liu Bang used to be fond of women and money. But this time he has not touched either. He is playing the stoic. What for? Isn't it clear enough that he has bigger ambition? Exterminate him, is my advice! It's easy, for the balance of power is in our favor."

Xiang Yu had a force of 400,000 strong, stationed in Hongmen (a place near modern Lintong, Shaanxi Province)—four times the number of men Liu Bang had. So, he decided to launch an immediate attack on Liu Bang's camp.

Working with Xiang Yu was his uncle Xiang Bo who was a friend of Zhang Liang, Liu Bang's top advisor. Zhang had once saved his life when he got involved in a murder case. Now as Xiang Yu was to launch his attack on Liu Bang the next day, Xiang Bo rushed to Liu Bang's camp to urge Zhang Liang to escape. But Zhang felt it was not right to desert Liu at such a critical moment. So he went in at once and briefed Liu on the imminent danger. Panic-stricken, Liu came out to meet Xiang Bo at once and treated him to a grand dinner.

"Since I entered Xianyang," he explained to Xiang Bo. "I haven't laid my hands on anything, because I've been waiting for Xiang Yu to come and decide on what ought to be done. I sent guards to the pass because I want to make sure nobody else could enter. How would I dare to betray Xiang Yu? Please convey my sincere message to him."

Xiang Bo advised Liu Bang to come to Hongmen the next day and apologize to Xiang Yu in person.

The next morning Liu Bang came to Xiang Yu's headquarters, accompanied by Zhang Liang and Fan Kuai who was his bodyguard. Xiang was pleased enough to accept his apologies and hosted a banquet for him.

During the dinner, Fan Zeng signalled three times to Xiang Yu to kill Liu Bang, but Xiang Yu refused to take the cue from him. Fan Zeng left the banquet hall to get help from Xiang Yu's cousin, Xiang Zhuang, an excellent swordsman.

"The general is too soft-hearted," he said to Xiang Zhuang. "You go inside and toast a drink to Liu Bang. Then ask permission to perform a sword dance and kill him on the spot. If we don't kill him today, we'll all end up as his prisoners one day."

Xiang Zhuang went in, toasted to Liu Bang and offered to entertain the guests with a sword dance. Xiang Bo, whose sympathy was with Liu Bang rather than his own nephew, saw through the design and rose to join Xiang Zhuang. Actually he was shielding Liu Bang all the time so that Xiang Zhuang could not get near his target.

Zhang Liang hurried out to get Liu's bodyguard, Fan Kuai, who immediately barged into the banquet tent. As he did so, he knocked down the guards at the entrance. Spear and shield in hand, he rushed to Liu's side, and stared at Xiang Yu fiercely.

Xiang Yu was startled and rose to get his weapon.

"Who is this man?" he asked.

"He's Liu Bang's bodyguard," Zhang Liang answered.

Fan Kuai's overpowering stature impressed Xiang Yu favorably. Xiang Yu offered him a glass of wine and a pig's leg.

Fan Kuai put the leg on the shield and cut the meat with his sword.

"Fine man! Want some wine?" Xiang Yu asked as Fan began to eat.

"I won't run away from wine just as I won't run away from the jaws of death," bellowed Fan Kuai. "We are on the same side fighting Qin. As Lord Liu Bang entered Xianyang first, he could have assumed the title of king, but he did not touch anything in the Qin palace because he was waiting for you to take over. But what have you rewarded him? You intend to kill him! What difference is there between you and Qin Shi Huang?!"

Xiang Yu did not respond; he just asked Fan Kuai to sit down.

Liu Bang rose, saying he needed to use the latrine. Fan Kuai and Zhang Liang followed him out. Liu Bang never came back to the banquet for he had taken a shortcut back to his camp. Zhang Liang stayed behind and told Xiang Yu that Liu Bang was too drunk to say good-bye to him. On behalf of Liu, Zhang presented an exquisite pair of jade discs, a very precious gift at the time, to Xiang Yu and a pair of jade wine cups to Fan Zeng. Xiang Yu accepted the gift, but Fan Zeng threw the cups on the floor and smashed them with his sword.

"What a fool my lord is!" Fan Zeng said, exasperated. "Sooner or later Liu Bang is going to strike and we will all become his prisoners."

Xiang Yu marched straight into Xianyang in the spring of 206 B.C. He immediately killed the young king of Qin whose life Liu Bang had spared, took captive all the women in the palace and set the Epang Palace on fire. The fire burned for three months.

As the supreme commander of all the rebel forces, Xiang Yu proceeded to divide China into nineteen kingdoms. Without a qualm, he himself took the lion's share and reestablished the kingdom of Chu around his home base. Eighteen other meritorious generals were given land and inaugurated as kings, Liu Bang among them. Still distrustful of Liu, Xiang Yu sent him to a remote mountainous region called Han Zhong (in modern Sichuan) and conferred on him the title of king of Han. Three defected Qin generals including Zhang Han were given territories so close to Han Zhong that they could keep an eye on Liu Bang.

Liu Bang was on his way to his fief in Sichuan. At the suggestion of Zhang Liang, he ordered to have the suspension roadway completely burnt, a roadway formerly built on the gorge leading to the mountainous area of Sichuan. He had it burnt apparently to show Xiang Yu that he had no intention to come back, while the real purpose was to prevent Xiang Yu from chasing after him.

Xiang Yu did send an army after Liu Bang at Fan Zeng's suggestion, but it was too late, for the roadway had already been burnt out.

Xiang Yu had a grudge against the king of Chu who had allowed Liu Bang to enter Xianyang first. Now he had won the war, he had no use for the king. He had the king murdered and he himself assumed the title of the king of Chu.

Comment: There is no denying the fact that it was Xiang Yu's forces that broke the back of the Qin empire. While his gallantry was matched by his savage killing, his selective but wrongly-placed leniency was nothing but folly.

Xiang Yu slaughtered 200,000 soldiers of the Qin army who had already surrendered to him. He executed the last emperor of the Qin Dynasty who had already thrown himself at his mercy. And he murdered the king of Chu whom he had installed himself but found to be inconvenient.

For all his ruthlessness and treachery, he gave Liu Bang, out of all his potential rivals, the benefit of the doubt and let him go scot free from the Hongmen banquet against the advice of his own senior counsellor. Inconsistency is not necessarily a bad trait. But in the case of Xiang Yu, his inconsistent sense of honor proved to be very costly.

35. TWO INTERVIEWS

Neither make small use of great talents, nor make big use of small talents.
—Xiao Yi (508-554)

Behind every great person are always great people who help him. In his strife for the control of China, Liu Bang was aided by other great men who, like Liu, had ambitions quite different from those of ordinary people. These men had enormous self-pride but were also capable of exercising unusual self-control. The path of their rise to prominence was anything but conventional.

THE EDUCATION OF A YOUNG ELITE

Liu Bang, now instituted as king of Han, awarded Zhang Liang a thousand ounces of gold and two bags of pearl. Zhang gave all of them to Xiang Bo to whom Liu also sent large amounts of gifts of his own.

Zhang Liang came from a wealthy family in Han. His father had been the prime minister of the former state of Han, in modern Henan and Shanxi (not to be confused with Han Zhong in Sichuan where Liu Bang was made king of Han). It was the first of the six states trampled on by Qin's army of conquest. Bent on revenge, Zhang Liang hired an assassin to throw a big iron hammer at the First Emperor when the latter was on an inspection tour. But the hammer missed its target. After that, Zhang Liang went into hiding under a false name.

One day when he was walking on a bridge in Xiapi (in modern Jiangsu), Zhang Liang ran into an elderly man.

"Get me my shoe, young man," said the old man, having deliberately dropped one of his shoes under the bridge.

The rudeness of the old man astonished Zhang. He wanted to hit him, but managed to control his temper, went down the bridge and picked up the shoe.

"Put it on for me," said the old man.

Zhang decided not to argue with him. He bent down and put it on for him. The old man left without a word of thanks. Zhang was stunned.

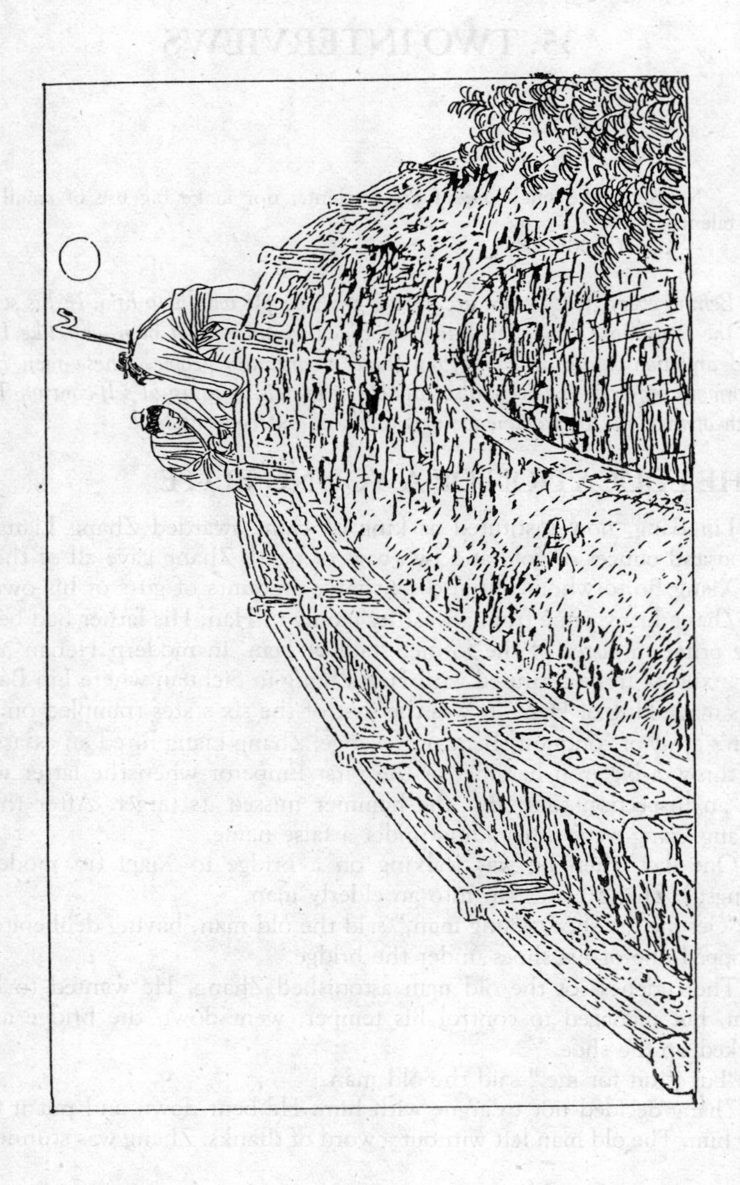

But the old man did not go far before he turned back.

"All right, young man, you are teachable. Meet me here at daybreak in five days."

"I will," Zhang Liang answered, still confused, though.

Five days later Zhang Liang went to the bridge at daybreak only to find that the old man was already there.

"You made an appointment with an old man and you are late," said the man, obviously not pleased. "Come here again five days from today."

The old man left without another word.

Five days later, Zhang got up at four o'clock in the morning and hurried to the bridge, but the old man was there waiting for him again.

"You are late again. Come again in five days."

This time Zhang Liang went there before midnight. A short while later, the old man appeared.

"That's better," he said, with a smile.

He took out a book from his pocket and gave it to Zhang.

"Read this carefully and you will be the teacher of kings. In ten years, the world will change and you are going to have a great career." The old man turned round and left.

It was an ancient book on the art of war. Zhang Liang began to make a deep study of it.

Ten years later Chen Sheng rose up in rebellion against Qin. Zhang Liang gathered several hundred followers, ready to join Chen Sheng when he met with Liu Bang who invited him to join his forces and appointed Zhang his senior officer.

Zhang Liang often explained to Liu Bang what he had learned from the book. Liu Bang showed a quick grasp and frequently adopted Zhang Liang's ideas. When Zhang tried to explain the same thing to others, none could understand. Zhang thought Liu was gifted and decided to work for him.

THE PROMOTION OF A FOOT SOLDIER

Shortly after Liu Bang was nominated as the king of Han by Xiang Yu, a foot soldier named Han Xin left Xiang Yu's camp to join Liu Bang. He was to reverse the course of the wheel of fortune for Liu.

When Han Xin was young, he could not find a job. He had lived on other people's hospitality or charity for a long time. He had been fed by the head of his village until the hostess refused to give him any food.

One day he was fishing by a river. An old woman who was washing clothes for a living took pity on him and provided him regular meals for nearly a month until she had finished her laundry work.

Han Xin was grateful. "Someday I will pay back your kindness," he said to her.

The old woman was offended. "You are not a child. What a shame you're unable to support yourself. I gave you food because I saw you starving, not because I expect anything from you."

In his neighborhood there were some hoodlum-butchers. They often made fun of Han Xin. One day, a young butcher said to him: "You are tall and stout, and you always carry a sword with you. But I bet you are a coward at heart. If you have the guts, kill me with your sword. If not, crawl between my legs."

Han Xin stared at him for a moment, then bent down and crawled between the man's legs. Everyone in the marketplace laughed at him.

Han Xin got a chance to join Xiang Yu's army and was given a job as a guard. A number of times he asked to see Xiang Yu, trying to offer his advice on military strategy. But Xiang Yu took no heed of him. So he came to Liu Bang's camp and was appointed a receptionist.

Once he happened to be involved in a crime and sentenced to death along with thirteen other offenders. All the thirteen co-offenders were executed before him. When it came to his turn, he shouted at the army officer.

"Why kill a brave man at a time when your king wants to conquer the world?"

The officer was struck by his words. A close look at the culprit convinced him that Han Xin was not a common man. He set him free and took him to see Liu Bang. Liu Bang was not specially impressed, but appointed him a commissary officer. In his capacity as commissary officer, Han Xin had access to the prime minister, Xiao He. Chatting with Han Xin for a few times convinced the prime minister that Han was a man of extraordinary abilities.

Disappointed that even Xiao He failed to persuade Liu Bang to give him a better chance, Han Xin made up his mind to desert Liu Bang and to seek for a chance elsewhere. As soon as Xiao He learned of it, he set forth to chase Han Xin back. He was in such a hurry that he did not inform Liu Bang.

Mistakenly thinking that his prime minister had run away, Liu Bang was so shocked that he felt as though he had lost his right arm. A few days later, Xiao He came back.

"Why did you run away?" Liu Bang demanded, happy and angry at the same time.

"How would I dare to run away? I was after somebody who had run away."

"Who?"

"Han Xin."

"He is not the only one who deserted. Why didn't you run after all of them?"

"Other men are no big deal. But Han Xin has no equal in the whole country," Xiao He explained. "If you are content with what you have now, then you do not need Han Xin. But if you want to conquer the world, Han Xin is the only person who can help you to realize your goal. It all depends on what you want."

"Of course I want to expand my kingdom to the east. How can I stay in this miserable corner forever?"

"Well, if that's the case, you'll have to use Han Xin. Now that I've brought him back, you'll have to make him stay."

"All right. I'll make a general of him for your sake," said Liu Bang.

"The rank of a general is not good enough if you want him to stay."

"Then I'll name him a marshall."

"That's better," Xiao He was pleased.

Liu Bang was about to send for Han Xin, but Xiao He stopped him.

"Do it properly," said Xiao He. "A marshall is not appointed this way. Xiang Yu lost him because he didn't respect him. Choose a good date, build an alter, go fasting for a few days before you hold the ceremony."

All the generals in the army were excited at the news that a marshall was to be inaugurated. Every one thought himself the most likely candidate. But when they saw Han Xin, their heart sank.

"The prime minister spoke highly of you," Liu Bang said to Han Xin after the ceremony. "What advice do you have for me?"

Han Xin thanked Liu for the honor.

"I believe Your Majesty intends to expand to the east and take over the country. Is that so?"

"Yes."

"In your estimate, how do you compare with your arch rival Xiang Yu in military strength?"

After a long pause, Liu admitted he was not Xiang Yu's equal.

"I thought as much. I have worked with him. When he gets angry, he can make a thousand men tremble. But he does not trust others. Even though he has brilliant men among his staff, he does not know how to make good use of them. So, his courage is no more than the courage of one single man.

"It is true Xiang Yu is courteous and thoughtful. If a soldier falls ill, he will share with him his own meal and weep in sympathy. But when somebody deserves a reward, he would grudge him the rank and land he deserves. He gave the best land to his personal favorites. That has caused much resentment among his men.

"Moreover, he is unable to exercise self-control and is overly bent on killing. People follow him not out of love but out of fear. If Your Majesty adopt a different policy, employ talented people and reward them properly, the world is yours for the taking."

Han Xin's observations greatly pleased Liu Bang. He wished he had known Han Xin earlier than this.

Han Xin's first move was to rebuild the roadway leading to the territories held by the three former Qin generals. Anyone with common sense knew it would take years to complete the 100 mile long roadwork. Therefore the three generals were not concerned at all.

But the reconstruction itself was a ruse. Han Xin's troops were already marching along a forgotten path over the mountains. With lightning speed, they swooped on the three generals' troops, wiped them out and took control of their three fiefs.

Besides Liu Bang, there were, among the seventeen kings, others who resented Xiang Yu for not being fair in distributing the territories, having awarded the best regions to his own ministers and generals and giving less desirable lands to the descendants of the six former kingdoms.

By this time, three of the seventeen kings had already been eliminated by Han Xin, two had surrendered and five became Liu Bang's allies.

The following spring Liu Bang declared war on Xiang Yu. It was just one year after the dinner at Hongmen.

Comment: "If you had a piece of beautiful jade, would you put it away in a box, or try to sell it at the best price?" One day Confucius's disciple Zigong asked the Master.

"Of course, I would sell it. Of course, I would. I myself am ready for the right offer, you know," Confucius replied.

If a man has a talent and cannot use it, he is doomed to fail. Naturally, all men of great talent are looking for opportunities to realize their potential. Some of them may not be good at marketing themselves and few of them are perfect. A true leader understands the importance of seeking these people out and letting them bring their ability to full play.

36. FAREWELL, MY CONCUBINE

A gentleman should adhere to the Golden Mean. For the Creator does not like extremes. Those who go to extremes will lose one way or the other. At the end of extremity comes change.

—*Vegetable Roots*

There are those who share weal and woe, those who are friends in prosperity but not in adversity, and those who hold together in hard times but fall apart in better days.

In the face of victory over the despotic Qin, Xiang Yu had to confront a new challenge: the distribution of gains. The essence of such distribution was equity, a fair share of the trophy for each person who had fought hard to overthrow Qin. No one can command loyalty from his followers without being fair. And without the loyalty of his followers no one can assume leadership.

THE BATTLE OF YINGYANG

As the supreme leader of all the combined forces that had brought down the Qin Dynasty, Xiang Yu divided China into nineteen kingdoms. Having inaugurated himself king of Chu, he made Pengcheng (a city in present-day Jiangsu) the capital of his kingdom. Among the remaining eighteen kings, quite a few thought Xiang Yu was not fair in distributing the territories to them. It was impossible for Xiang Yu to exercise absolute control over all of them. Some revolted. Others went over to Liu Bang, the king of Han, who had declared war on Xiang Yu and was fighting his way eastward toward Pengcheng from his fiefdom in Sichuan.

At that time, Xiang Yu was in Qi (in modern Shandong), trying to put down a disaffected general who rose in rebellion because he felt he did not get his portion of the spoils fairly.

Liu Bang's army of 560,000 overran Xiang Yu's capital, Pengcheng, without much difficulty. They took possession of all the treasures in the city. The celebration feast lasted for half a month.

Outraged, Xiang Yu turned back with an elite force of 30,000 men.

In the ensuing battle, 100,000 of Liu's troops were killed and another 100,000 drowned while retreating to River Sui (in modern Anhui), because there were no boats. Dead bodies blocked the flow of the river. Liu Bang had to run for life until he was joined by his remaining forces in Yingyang (in modern Henan). Xiang captured Liu's father and wife, and pursued Liu all the way to Yingyang.

For more than a year, Yingyang was under siege. Xiang cut off the supply route. Liu asked for peace talks. Xiang was about to oblige when Fan Zeng dissuaded him.

"If you don't crush him now, you'll regret forever." The same advice which Xiang Yu had ignored at the Hongmen banquet. This time, however, it took effect, and Xiang stepped up his attack.

The food in Yingyang was running short. At this time, Chen Ping, an advisor of Liu Bang, made a suggestion that eventually saved Liu's life and turned the tables upon Xiang Yu.

Chen Ping used to work for Xiang Yu as a senior officer. He defected to Liu Bang when Xiang Yu was about to kill him for having lost a stronghold to Liu Bang.

As he was crossing the Yellow River on his way to join Liu, the boatman thought he was a well-to-do army officer carrying valuables with him. He looked at Chen Ping intensely. Chen Ping sensed a murderous intent in the boatman's eyes. So, he took off all his clothes and offered to help the boatman row the boat.

Seeing Chen Ping naked, the boatman realized that he had nothing valuable on him and gave up the idea of killing him.

Chen was introduced to Liu Bang by a friend. After the interview, Liu offered him the same rank as he had in the Chu army. Later he was promoted to be a lieutenant general under Han Xin, the commander-in-chief. Other officers thought it was not fair that a new comer should rise so rapidly.

"Chen Ping is handsome, but is he talented?" someone questioned.

"We heard he had an affair with his sister-in-law at home," another complained.

"He has switched sides a couple of times."

"When he was in Xiang Yu's army, he accepted bribes."

Others echoed.

Liu Bang summoned the person who had recommended Chen Ping. "I recommend him on account of his abilities, not his moral character," Chen's friend replied. "Moral conduct of an individual is not too useful in war. I know Chen Ping is good at formulating strategies and devising ingenious plans. The only criteria to judge him is whether his ideas work. Why should you doubt his ability because he slept with his sister-in-law or took bribes?"

Liu Bang was not totally convinced.

"You have switched sides several times," he asked Chen Ping. "How do I know you won't do it again?"

"Xiang Yu doesn't trust other people except his own family. He is not willing to take advice even though he has superb military strategists around him. I came here to join you because I heard you place your trust in good counsels. If you find my ideas good, please use them. If not, I am prepared to leave."

Liu Bang decided to let him stay.

Now Chen Ping asked Liu Bang to give him forty thousand ounces of gold to carry out intelligence activities behind the enemy line. Liu not only gave him the money, but also told him that he did not need to account for the use of the fund. Chen Ping sent a number of special agents to spread rumors among Xiang Yu's generals and top advisors, including Fan Zeng—rumors bad enough to create dissension between Xiang Yu and his immediate circle. Chen, a former associate of Xiang Yu, knew that Xiang Yu was credulous and could easily fall a victim to rumors.

When the rumors reached Xiang Yu, he indeed became suspicious. He dispatched an envoy to the Han camp to fish for more information. The envoy was given a red carpet reception. Chen Ping came out to greet him on behalf of Liu Bang. A sumptuous dinner was prepared. But when he saw the envoy, Chen pretended to be surprised.

"I thought you were sent here by Mr. Fan Zeng," said Chen Ping. "But you are not."

All the nice dishes were abruptly removed, and the envoy was served a rather frugal meal instead. After the envoy reported how he had been treated, Xiang Yu started to suspect the loyalty of his seventy-year-old advisor and refused to listen to him any more. When Fan Zeng learnt that Xiang Yu doubted his loyalty, he resigned in disgust. He died on his way home. It was only after the death of Fan Zeng that Xiang Yu realized that he had been tricked.

The removal of Fan Zeng was exactly what Chen Ping wanted. He then suggested that two thousand women be let out of the besieged city at night, to be followed by a man disguised as Liu Bang.

Xiang Yu's troops were ready to storm the city when there came an announcement from Liu Bang's camp: "Our food has run out. The king of Han is coming out to surrender."

At this moment, Liu Bang's double, who was actually a trusted general, came out, sitting in the royal carriage with its distinctive yellow canopy and feather pennants. When the truth was uncovered, Xiang Yu was so exasperated that he had Liu Bang's impersonator burnt alive. But by then Liu Bang had already escaped beyond his reach.

THE GENIUS OF HAN XIN

The defeat of Liu Bang caused some kings, who had earlier joined him in his cause against Xiang Yu, to defect and switch their allegiance to Xiang Yu. While regrouping his remaining forces, Liu Bang ordered Han Xin to crush those who had defected.

Han Xin carried out his task with flying colors.

In one battle, Han Xin's troops were outnumbered by ten to one, but he ordered them to draw up with their backs against a river. When the enemy general heard of this, he laughed and took Han Xin for a poor commander to have put his troops in such a hopeless position. But precisely because there was no retreat, Han Xin's men were invincible. They had to fight particularly hard.

When the fighting was going on, Han Xin had secretly dispatched his cavalrymen to the nearly empty enemy camps to tear down their black banners and raised the red flags of the Han army in their place. Unable to defeat Han Xin as they had hoped, the enemy were ready to retire when, on their way back, suddenly they saw the red flags of the Han army on top of their camps. Thinking that Han Xin had overrun their headquarters, the enemy troops went panic. As a result, they were smashed completely.

In another battle, Han Xin was fighting with an experienced general sent by Xiang Yu. The two armies confronted each other across a river. Han Xin ordered his men to make ten thousand sandbags to form a dam to block the flow of the upper stream of the river. So the river became shallow enough for the soldiers to wade through.

The next day, he led half of his army across the river to the attack. But after some initial fighting, they pretended to be defeated, and quickly retreated to their side of the river. Xiang Yu's general never had a high opinion of Han Xin. He ordered a full pursuit. When they were crossing the river, Han ordered his soldiers to remove the sandbags. The water came rushing down, sweeping away the enemy soldiers who were wading in the middle of the river. Those who had made to the shore were beaten by Han Xin's forces closing in from all sides. With the swift current cutting their way back, they had no retreat. As a result, all 200,000 of Xiang Yu's men were annihilated.

This victory had shaken Xiang Yu, for it had deprived him of his military superiority. The strengths of Liu Bang and Xiang Yu's forces were more or less equal now.

They were at a standoff in Guangwu (a place in modern Henan).

As Liu Bang's father was a captive in Xiang Yu's camp, Xiang threatened to kill him to force Liu Bang to surrender. But Xiang Bo, his uncle, intervened.

"As Liu Bang has set his mind to conquer the world, he will hardly be bothered about the safety of a family member. Killing his father would gain you nothing. And you don't know how things will turn out in the end."

The old man's life was thus spared.

After a long stalemate, Xiang Yu sent words to Liu Bang: "The world has no peace for years only because of the two of us. I would like to engage you in a one-to-one combat to settle our dispute once for all."

Liu scorned the challenge with a laugh. "I prefer a battle of wits than a trial of physical strength."

In a subsequent shouting match with Xiang across the two hundred feet wide Guangwu Gorge, Liu ran a litany of accusations of Xiang: his killing of 200,000 war prisoners of Qin, the unwarranted burning of the Epang Palace, the unfair division of territories and the murder of the king of Chu.

Xiang ordered his soldiers to shoot, seriously wounding Liu in the chest. After he was hit, Liu grabbed his foot and cried: "The rascal hit my toe." For fear of throwing panic into his army, he toured the army camp to reassure them that he was all right before going away to have his wound treated and recuperate.

Xiang Yu had extended his forces too far. Their supply lines were being harassed continuously by the guerrilla tactics of a disaffected general in the north. Xiang Yu was compelled to throw in more troops to deal with the guerrillas. Before he left for the north, he warned his three generals not to fight even if they were challenged to. He asked them to wait and assured them that he would be back in fifteen days.

Day after day Liu's soldiers hurled insults across the river at Xiang Yu's troops until his generals could no longer hold their temper. They ignored Xiang Yu's warning and launched a full-scale offensive. When their troops were half way across the river, Liu Bang's army attacked. As their troops were almost wiped out, the three Chu generals committed suicide, being unable to face Xiang Yu ever again. Liu Bang's troops charged into Xiang Yu's headquarters and captured all the treasures they found in there.

By now Xiang Yu's army was exhausted. Their food supply was running short. On the contrary, Liu Bang's army was well-fed and strong. Xiao He was doing a good job of managing logistical support in the rear.

Earlier when Liu Bang occupied the palace of Qin in Xianyang for a brief period of time, Xiao He took possession of all the official records and maps which had been kept by the Qin government. From these data, Xiao He got valuable information on strategically important military locations, population distribution, the number of households, the general income level, local products, and the grievances of the people of the entire country. Thus he was able to better address to the concerns of the people and to better coordinate logistical supplies and personnel replenishment in support of Liu Bang's war efforts.

Liu Bang seized the opportunity to make peace with Xiang Yu. The two agreed to divide China into two parts, making the Hong Canal, southeast of Yingyang (in modern Henan) the demarcation line. All the territories to the west of the Hong Canal would belong to Liu and those to the east of the canal to Xiang. As part of the peace accord, Liu's wife and father were released from captivity.

Liu Bang was ready to move to the west of the Hong Canal in accordance with the peace treaty. However, Zhang Liang and Chen Ping thought differently.

"We have already got a half of the country and the support of other kings who are opposed to Xiang Yu. His army is tired; his doom is sealed. This is the best time to finish him off. Don't let such a good opportunity slip."

Liu took their advice. Two months later, he scrapped the peace agreement and launched a full scale attack.

CHANCE OF A LIFETIME

Earlier when Liu Bang was hemmed by Xiang Yu in Yingyang, his allies in Qi (modern Shandong) deserted him to join Xiang Yu. Liu sent Han Xin to deal with them. Having made a conquest of Qi, Han Xin sent an envoy to Liu asking to be made the acting king of Qi.

Liu was furious after reading Han Xin's letter.

"What?!" he shouted angrily. "I am fighting for my very survival. Day and night I am anxiously waiting for him to come to my rescue. But he sets his mind to be a king!"

Sitting by his side, Zhang Liang and Chen Ping simultaneously stepped on Liu's feet to stop him.

"We are in a terrible fix," whispered Zhang Liang to him. "We cannot realistically stop him to be a king. Better make him a king than risk trouble."

Liu understood immediately.

"A real man should be a real king," he said to Han Xin's envoy. "Why an acting king? I now name Han Xin king of Qi."

Liang was sent to confirm the appointment of Han Xin as the king of Qi and to bring back some of his troops.

Xiang Yu also chose this moment to send an envoy to Han Xin trying to persuade him to join his side. But Han Xin refused.

"When I was serving Xiang Yu," he said to Xiang Yu's envoy, "he never listened to my advice. My position was just a guard. So I came over to Liu Bang. He made me a marshall commanding thirty thousand men. Why should I switch sides now?"

A man by the name of Kuai Tong saw the matter in a different light.

He came to see Han Xin. Pretending he understood physiognomy, he predicted that Han's physical features indicated a greatness beyond description.

"How so?" Han demanded.

"At present Liu Bang and Xiang Yu are fighting for supremacy. Xiang is stronger than Liu militarily, but Liu has the strategic and geographical advantages. Neither has got the upper hand over his opponent. In fact, the balance of power is in your hands. If you help Liu, Liu will win. Likewise, if you help Xiang, Xiang will win. The best course of action in your interest is to keep good ties with both sides. But don't let either of them win. Then you can divide the country into three and become their peer. You are a brilliant commander. You have the best army. The country has seen too much fighting. Nobody wants war. If you appeal for a cease fire, I'm sure everyone will listen to you. You'll have the chance of a lifetime before you. You'll be a king. If you miss it, you will regret."

"No, it's just not right," said Han Xin. "Liu Bang has been nice to me. He gave me everything I asked for. I can't betray him."

"You think he is your friend. I'm afraid you are very much mistaken. Liu is an unscrupulous man. Remember what happened to the two great ministers Fan Li and Wen Zhong under the king of Yue during the Period of the Warring States? They helped the king of Yue to restore his kingdom from the hands of the king of Wu. After victory, Fan Li was wise enough to have made his escape. But Wen Zhong stayed on in his post until he was forced to commit suicide. The old saying goes, when there are no more wild hares left to be hunted, the hunting dogs are bound to be killed. You have done so much for Liu. No one has got a record that can compare with yours. No reward is too great for you. Liu Bang must be afraid of you. When he discovers that your reputation is overshadowing his, would he feel easy? But if you go to Xiang Yu, he won't trust you either."

Han Xin thanked Kuai Tong for his advice and promised to think it over.

A few days later, Kuai tried to make the same point again.

"If you are content with being a subordinate to others, you'll lose a god-send chance. Be decisive. Vacillation leads to failure. If one has the wisdom to foresee a good chance but fails to seize it because he lacks determination, he will end in failure. If a man of courage does not act, he is no better than an ordinary man who acts. The real meaning of life lies in action. Opportunities are easy to let go, but hard to seize. The same chance never comes twice. Please reconsider."

But in the end, Han Xin rejected the idea of going independent.

FAREWELL, MY CONCUBINE

Liu Bang's treacherous action infuriated Xiang. He countered Liu's attack with vengeance. However, after scoring some initial victories, the supply problem caught up with him again. Meanwhile Han Xin had left Qi to join Liu Bang in Gaixia, a place in southern Anhui, for a decisive showdown with Xiang Yu.

Han Xin divided the 300,000 men under his command into ten regiments to form a tight ring. He led one of them to challenge Xiang to battle. As soon as Xiang Yu came out to fight, Han started to retreat, trying to lure Xiang into a ring of encirclement. Xiang Yu's other generals cautioned him against a possible trick. But Xiang was so roused that no one could stop him. He chased Han Xin relentlessly until he got into the trap. Han's army inflicted heavy casualties on Xiang Yu. Xiang had had an army of a hundred thousand men at the beginning of the battle. Now he had only twenty thousand left.

Xiang Yu had to draw back to Gaixia.

At night, to his astonishment, he heard human voices coming from all directions to his camp—voices singing songs of Chu, songs of his native land.

How come that my countrymen are here in Gaixia singing in Liu Bang's camps? Could it be that Liu Bang has taken them captives? Has Liu Bang already overrun my homeland? He wondered, overcome by dismay.

As the sound of music swept over all of Xiang Yu's camps, the morale of the troops began to crumble. Overnight, desertion had reduced the remaining soldiers to less than a thousand.

Xiang Yu was in low spirits. He could not sleep. He came out of the tent to have a drink. With him was his beautiful concubine, Lady Yu, who followed him everywhere. She was the sister of a general under Xiang Yu. Holding her in his arm, Xiang composed an impromptu song.

My strength can move mountains;
My ambition conquers the world.
But times are against me;
My horse can run no more.
O My fair lady,
What will become of thee?

Lady Yu joined him in singing. As they were singing, tears streamed down their faces. All of Xiang Yu's associates who were present wept too. They turned their eyes away, unable to look at the couple.

Xiang Yu's generals urged him to go before the enemy should start their new offensive the next day.

"Take care of yourself, darling," Xiang Yu said to Lady Yu. "I have to break out before the enemy get hold of me. If I am not destined to die, we will meet again."

"If you leave, where am I to go?"

"Don't worry. Liu Bang won't harm you. You know you are a very pretty woman."

"I want to be with you wherever you go, my dear," Lady Yu was crying. "Even if I die, my spirit will accompany you to your homeland."

"But we are surrounded. I am not sure myself if I can break out. It would be impossible for a woman to make it, sweetheart."

Lady Yu turned to Xiang's attendant.

"Give me your sword," she said. "I want to disguise myself as a soldier to follow him."

Xiang Yu took down his own sword and gave it to Lady Yu.

"All right. Follow me then," he said.

"You've always been sweet, very sweet to me, my dear," said Lady Yu as she held the sword in her hand. "I haven't got a chance to requite all your love. Please don't worry about me any more."

One slash with the sword at her own throat and she fell on the ground. Xiang almost fell from his horse.

When Liu Bang discovered that Xiang Yu had broken through the encirclement, he dispatched five thousand men on a hot pursuit.

Xiang Yu had only about eight hundred men. And they got lost soon, because an old farmer misdirected them to a marsh land where they got bogged down in the quagmire. Xiang Yu knew they were tricked. Then the Han army overtook them. When they got out of the marshes, Xiang

Yu had only twenty-eight men left.

"In eight years, I have fought more than seventy battles and I have never lost a single one," he said to them emotionally. "But now I'm hemmed in here because Heaven is against me. Before I die I promise to win three victories for your sake. I am going to kill the enemy commander, break the enemy line and knock down their flag. Then you will understand. Not that I am not a good fighter, but Heaven is not on my side."

He organized his men in four groups to charge in four directions against several cordons of the surrounding enemy. The Han troops scattered in panic.

"Watch me kill an enemy general for you," he shouted to his men.

His men charged forward. Xiang killed one commander of the Han army, then divided his men into three groups. The Han army also divided themselves into three groups. A fierce battle followed. Scores of Han soldiers were killed. Xiang Yu lost only two men in breaking the siege.

"How's that?" He asked.

"Just as you promised." All his men bowed in admiration.

As they reached the River Wu in eastern Anhui, there was only one boat there. Its owner, a village head, was waiting for them.

"Please get on quickly," he urged Xiang Yu. "This is the only boat here. Liu Bang's army won't be able to catch up with you. There are several hundred thousand people across the river. They will welcome you."

"Heaven is against me," Xiang Yu said with a bitter smile. "What good is there to cross the river? I once led eight thousand young men crossing the river from the other side. Now I am coming back alone. Even if the elders welcome me, how could I face them?"

He pulled the horse over and said to the village head. "This horse has been with me for five years. It can run three hundred miles a day. I don't want to kill it. You can have it."

At this moment. Liu Bang's troops closed in. A hand to hand combat ensued. Xiang Yu killed several hundred of them and got himself wounded in a dozen places. Suddenly he recognized a former friend of his among the enemy.

"I heard Liu Bang offered a thousand ounces of gold for my head,"

Xiang Yu shouted to his friend, noticing that the latter was too ashamed to look at him. "Let me do you a favor for old times' sake."

With these words, he cut his own throat. He was thirty-three then.

Comment: This is one of the best examples of psychological warfare in history: the power of music at its apex. Even if Xiang Yu still had a fighting chance to survive and stage a come-back eventually, his will to fight on seemed to have been crushed. The loss of will power sealed his fate.

37. A VICTOR'S REFLECTIONS

He who respects others will not be insulted; he who is tolerant will win popular support; he who acts in good faith will be trusted by others; he who is diligent will succeed in his undertakings; he who is generous will make others work hard for him.
—*Confucius*

In spite of the fact that Xiang Yu, reputedly the greatest war hero in China, commanded an invincible fighting force, he was eventually defeated by Liu Bang. Indeed, just as Liu Bang himself had acknowledged, he succeeded because he knew how to make full use of talented men like Zhang Liang, Han Xin, Xiao He and Chen Ping, and how to pull them together. On the contrary, Xiang Yu had got only one wise man, Fan Zeng, around him, but did not know how to use him.

Liu and Xiang had embarked upon an undertaking of such magnitude that it is not surprising that the collective wisdom of Liu Bang and his associates prevailed over the individualistic heroism of Xiang Yu. It was a case of teamwork outperforming virtuoso solo.

A NEW EPOCH

Liu Bang became the first emperor of the Han Dynasty. He changed the name of the capital of the Qin Dynasty, Xianyang, to Chang'an which means eternal peace. A general amnesty was proclaimed to celebrate his victory. He personally presided over the burial service for Xiang Yu. He did not punish any of Xiang Yu's family and made Xiang Bo, Xiang Yu's uncle who saved him at the banquet at Hongmen, a marquis.

At the celebration dinner party, Liu asked his ministers why he was able to win the four year war in the end. Someone offered an explanation.

"Sire, I make bold to point out that as far as mannerisms are concerned, Your Majesty are not as gentle as Xiang Yu. He hardly ever insulted his subordinates, hot-tempered as he was. But Your Majesty are generous and willing to share. You reward those who have earned military merits handsomely. On the contrary, Xiang Yu did not reward his men according to their merits, and never shared with them the land and the valuables he had captured from the enemy. And he was jealous of talent. That is why he has lost."

"Yes. But you are only partially right," Liu said. "In formulating strategies and judging things thousands of miles away, I am not as good as Zhang Liang; in leading a million men to beat the enemy in the battlefield, I am not as good as Han Xin; and in running the government and maintaining the logistical support, I am not as good as Xiao He. These three men have extraordinary talents and I am able to use them. That is why I have won. Xiang Yu had only Fan Zeng, but he did not know how to use him. That is why he has lost."

Most of Liu's generals and ministers were of humble origin and poor education. They had no manners. When drunk, they became rude and boisterous. Sometimes they would even slash the pillar in the palace with their swords. Liu Bang was bothered.

A Confucian scholar by the name of Shu Suntong suggested to Liu that he could be of help.

"We may not be very useful in war," Shu said, knowing that Confucian scholars were not Liu's favorites. "But when the fighting is over, we are useful. I can get some scholars to draw up a code of court etiquette."

"Wouldn't it be too difficult to follow?" Liu was interested.

"Different times have different requirements. The old code is probably too elaborate. I'll create a new one for our purpose."

"It must be something that I can learn," Liu cautioned.

Shu Suntong, who had once served under the Second Emperor of Qin and also under Xiang Yu, gathered about a hundred scholars. They devised a new set of rules for court ceremonies and a new costume code, and rehearsed the rituals in an open field in the suburbs of the capital for more than a month. Then Shu asked Liu Bang to be present to watch the scholars at drill.

"Very good, I can do that easily," Liu said, pleased with the performance.

Then he ordered all the ministers and officials to take part in a rehearsal directed by Shu Suntong.

The new palace was completed. A grand opening ceremony was held in October 200 B.C.

At daybreak, all the officials lined up outside the palace in the order of their ranks. They were led by the master of ceremony through the gate inside. Chariots and cavalrymen, guards and foot soldiers were all standing at attention. In the palace hall and under the fluttering, colorful banners, military officers were standing on the west side and civilian officials on the east.

When Liu Bang appeared, all the senior officials came forward to offer salutations in turn. The salute to the emperor was followed by a banquet. All the officials were given seats according to their ranks. Each rose and proposed a toast to the emperor. Whoever failed to follow the new etiquette was asked to leave the hall. The whole ritual proceeded without a hitch. There was no shouting or fighting.

Liu rose to offer a toast to his father.

"Father," he said, "you used to say that I was useless. I couldn't manage family property for you and I was not half as hardworking as my brother. Now you see who is doing better."

All the officials laughed and wished long life to the emperor.

At the end of all this, Liu Bang said: "For the first time in my life, I realize what it is like to be an emperor."

He awarded Shu Suntong five thousand ounces of gold and put him in charge of all the protocol of the Han court. Shu took the opportunity to ask Liu to employ all his students who had assisted him in making the ceremony a success.

Liu called on his father every five days. When he bowed to his father like a son to a father, his father stopped him.

"You are the emperor now. Even though you are my son, I am your subject. You should not bow to me. Otherwise you lose your dignity."

The next time when Liu came to visit his father, he found the elderly man was sweeping the path respectfully with a broom. Liu was startled. He quickly got down from the carriage and ran to his father.

"You are the ruler of the people," his father said. "Don't break the rule because of me."

Liu gave his father the title of Grand Superior Emperor and awarded the steward who advised his father on etiquette five thousand ounces of gold.

Another scholar named Lu Jia constantly talked about Confucian classics to Liu Bang until one day Liu had had enough and told him to shut up.

"I conquered the world on horseback. Why should I be bothered about those classics?"

"True, Your Majesty have won it on horseback, but can you rule it on horseback, too? To make your rule last, you have to attend to both military and civil matters. Qin lost its empire just because it only ruled with brutal force and draconian laws. If the First Emperor had practiced the virtuous rule that Confucius preached, would Your Majesty ever have had a chance?"

Liu saw his point and asked Lu Jia to write an analysis on Qin's fall and on such key factors as had contributed to his own success. Lu wrote a book of twelve chapters on the rise and fall of all the past dynasties. Whenever he finished one chapter, he read it to Liu, Liu warmly praised his work and named his book New Discourse.

FALL FROM GRACE

Han Xin was transferred from Qi to Chu. As he was a Chu native, Liu Bang renamed him the king of Chu to rule in his native place, Huaiyin, a city in modern Jiangsu, but stripped him of his military rank.

When he returned home, the first thing Han Xin did was to find the old woman who had once fed him by the river and gave her ten thousand ounces of gold. He also located the village head who had helped him for quite some time and rewarded him a hundred ounces of gold, saying: "You made a good start in helping me, but what a pity you didn't follow it through."

Then he found the man who forced him to crawl between his legs and made him police officer.

"He is, after all, a brave man," Han Xin told his associates. "When he humiliated me, I could have killed him, of course. But killing him would not do any good for me. So I put up with it and finally got where I am now."

One of Xiang Yu's senior generals was a friend of Han Xin. After the death of Xiang, he came to seek shelter with Han Xin. Although Liu Bang ordered his arrest, Han Xin refused to turn him in. Liu felt uneasy about this. He also received reports that wherever Han Xin went, he was always accompanied by a large number of armed guards. Liu began to suspect that Han Xin was plotting against him in collaboration with the fugitive enemy general.

At the suggestion of Chen Ping, Liu announced he was going to inspect the Lake Yunmeng area (in modern Hubei). On his way, he would like to meet various lords and generals in the vicinity. Han Xin felt a bit odd about this meeting. He was not sure of Liu Bang's real intention, but believed Liu had nothing to incriminate him.

Someone suggested to Han Xin that he execute his friend, the fugitive general of Xiang Yu, to please Liu Bang.

Han Xin discussed the matter with the general.

"The only reason that Liu Bang did not attack you is because I am here," said the former general of Xiang Yu. "If you kill me in order to please him, you'll be the next one to be killed."

Seeing that Han Xin was still wavering, he raised his sword and killed himself.

Han Xin went to pay his respect to the emperor. But the moment he arrived, Liu Bang ordered his arrest.

Han Xin protested: "I have long heard when wild beasts are killed, it is the hunting dogs' turn to die. When the enemy is wiped out, it is time that meritorious generals be put to death. Should this really be my fate?"

"I received information that you are plotting against me," Liu said.

Han Xin denied vehemently. In the end Liu set him free, demoted him to the rank of marquis, and took him to the capital where he could be watched. Han was depressed. Knowing that the emperor was afraid of his abilities, he gave a wide berth to the emperor by pretending illness.

On one occasion Liu Bang had a chat with Han Xin.

"In your opinion, how many troops can I command?" Liu asked.

"At most ten thousand men."

"What about yourself?"

"The more the merrier."

"If that's the case, why were you captured by me?"

"Because although you are not a good general, you are good at managing generals. You are born with such talent. It is rare gift, something no one can imitate."

The emperor was pleased.

When General Chen Xi was appointed governor of Julu (in modern Hebei). He went to say good-bye to Han Xin before departure. Han dismissed all the attendants and saw him to the courtyard.

"Can we talk?" said Han Xin. "I have some confidential matters to discuss with you."

"Please do," Chen replied. "You can trust me." He always had deep respect for Han Xin.

"The place you are going to has the best troops in the country. And you have the emperor's trust. If we cooperate, with your forces outside the capital and my support inside, we stand a good chance to take over the country."

"I'll keep it in mind."

Five years later, General Chen Xi did rebel. Liu Bang personally led an army to suppress the insurrection. Han Xin did not go with him on pretext of illness. He forged an imperial decree to release all the prisoners with the intention to use them to attack the palace. Everything was ready for a coup d'etat as soon as he heard from Chen Xi.

But the plot was made known to Empress Lü. It just happened that when Han Xin announced his intention to execute one of his subordinates who had, in some way, offended him, the man's brother ran to the empress to report on his hidden scheme. The empress was alarmed. She quickly summoned Xiao He, the prime minister, for consultation.

Xiao had a man disguised as an envoy from Liu Bang with the news that Chen Xi had been killed and the insurrection put down. He then invited all the officials in the capital to the palace to offer their congratulations to Empress Lü. Xiao He made a personal call on Han Xin.

"I know you are not well," he said. "But this is a special occasion. You must go and make a gesture to the empress."

Han Xin let Xiao He accompany him to see the empress. As soon as he entered the palace, Empress Lü ordered the guards to seize him and have him summarily executed. All his family was executed, too.

Before his death, Han Xin shouted he regretted that he did not listen to Kuai Tong.

It was Xiao He who first brought Han on board. It was he, too, that ensnared and killed Han in the end.

Upon returning from a successful campaign to put down General Chen Xi, Liu Bang learnt of Han Xin's death with mixed feelings. He asked to know what Han's last words were. Kuai Tong's name was thus brought up. And Liu Bang ordered an immediate arrest of Kuai Tong.

"Did you instigate Han Xin to oppose me?" Liu questioned him.

"Yes, I did," Kuai Tong replied. "But he was a fool. He didn't listen to me. Now, look at what happened to him and his family. If he had listened to me, how could you possibly have destroyed him?"

"Kill the man," the emperor was angry.

"This is no justice," Kuai Tong said.

"You deserve to die because you tried to persuade Han Xin to revolt, didn't you?"

"When the Qin empire was crumbling, ambitious men rose everywhere in the country in pursuit of power. In the end the swiftest got the throne. A dog barks at anyone but his master. At that time I only knew Han Xin; I didn't know Your Majesty. Am I to blame for that? There are so many people who would like to do what you did, but they are not up to the job. Do you think you can kill them all?"

"All right. I'll let you go." Liu released Kuai Tong.

RETURN OF THE NATIVE

Later that year, Liu eliminated another general who rebelled against him. On his way back to the capital, Chang'an, he passed through his native town of Pei. It was a grand occasion. Liu's old friends, townfathers, village elders and others all came. Liu picked out some one hundred and twenty children and taught them a song he had composed himself.

A great wind is sweeping into the sky,
Sending the clouds flying up on high.
I'm home again, a ruler of the four seas,
O homeland, sweet homeland,
Where can I find brave men to safeguard thee?

The emperor struck the lute and sang the song. The children's choir joined him. Then the emperor rose to dance, tears of nostalgia mingled with happiness flowing down his face.

"Although I made Chang'an my capital, I will always miss my hometown," the emperor declared. "When I am dead and gone, my spirit will come back to my birthplace. It is here in this very place that I started as governor of Pei, and now I have conquered the world. I want to exempt all taxes for my hometown people, forever."

The people of Pei were overjoyed. For more than ten days, the emperor stayed in Pei. Men and women, old and young, all came to talk with him amidst drinks and cheers. He wanted to leave, but all the people there begged him to stay for a few more days.

"No, thank you. I have too large an entourage. I should not give you any more burden."

The entire town came out to see him off.

Half a year later, Liu Bang died. He was fifty-two then.

Comment: The Han Dynasty Liu Bang founded was one of the longest and greatest dynasties in Chinese history. It made such an indelible imprint on the collective consciousness of the Chinese that till this day the majority of the Chinese refer to themselves as the people of Han, whereas the name "China" was mainly used by the rest of the world.

It is in the Han Dynasty that the thought of Confucius was officially sanctioned as the orthodox philosophy of China. This is a most significant development in the history of the Chinese civilization.

Curiously in a way, the fate of the country was determined in one of the most momentous discussions between Liu and his advisors.

After overthrowing the rule of Qin, Xiang Yu did not restore the six former states wiped out by Qin but divided China into nineteen smaller kingdoms. He awarded, rather arbitrarily, the divided land to various generals who fought in the anti-Qin revolution.

When Liu Bang was under siege in Yingyang, a scholar suggested that he agree to restore the six former states in order to win over more support. Liu was tempted and was almost on the point of sending off seals to the descendants of the former royal families of these countries to authorized such a restoration. But he was stopped by Zhang Liang.

Zhang pointed out that such a move amounted to self-destruction. Because once the six states were restored, all those men of talent, who gathered under the leadership of Liu Bang in the hope of getting some reward for themselves, would go back to serve their own countries. Nobody would be left to fight with him and he would probably never be able to defeat Xiang Yu.

Liu was so shaken that he immediately stopped eating, spat out the food in his mouth, and ordered all the seals be destroyed.

Thus the talk about dividing China into feudal states was forever put to rest. For most part of the next two thousand years, China has been under the rule of a central government.

38. THE ART OF FLATTERY

> Gradually increase what you give to people, and they will always be grateful. But if you gradually reduce what you give to them, they tend to forget your favor. Gradually relax discipline and restriction placed on them, and they will feel more and more comfortable and satisfied. But if you gradually strengthen discipline and restriction on them, they will be resentful.
>
> —*Vegetable Roots*

THREE ARTISTS

There was a king whose right eye was blind and right leg crippled. One day he had an artist draw a portrait for him.

The artist portrayed the king as a mighty warrior. His eyes were bright and piercing and his legs muscular like an athlete's. The king was not happy about it.

"You are just a sycophant. This is not me." He ordered the guards to take the artist away and throw him into prison.

A second artist was summoned. Upon learning what had happened before, the artist drew a picture of the king exactly the way he looked. The king was not pleased at all.

"What art is it?" he questioned the artist angrily and had him imprisoned, too.

The third artist came and looked carefully at the king. The king appeared in a hunting outfit in the portrait. He was shooting from a kneeling position with the right leg bent and the left leg supporting the butt of the rifle that he was holding. Only his left eye was open as he was taking aim at a fox in the distance.

The king was very glad. He awarded the artist a bag of gold and praised him as the number one artist in the country.

ONE HUNDRED HONEYED PHRASES

After passing the imperial examinations in Beijing, a young man was appointed as a government official in a provincial city. He went to bid

good-bye to his mentor, a senior government minister.

"It's not going to be easy working in those provincial places. You need to be prudent."

"Yes, sir. Thank you for your advice," the young man said. "Please don't worry. I have prepared a hundred honeyed phrases in mind. When I meet an official there, I will use one. He will surely be pleased."

"How can you do that?" his mentor was not too happy. "We are gentlemen. We have our principles. We should not stoop to flattery."

"The truth is, unfortunately, that most people like being flattered," said the student looking helpless. "Only very few true gentlemen like you do not like compliments."

"Maybe you are right," his mentor nodded with a smile.

Later the young man related the story to a friend of his.

"I've just used one item in my stock. Now I have ninety-nine honeyed sayings left."

HEAVENLY DESIGN

Three scholars were on their way to Beijing to sit for the imperial examinations. They passed by a scenic mountain on which there lived a fortune-teller.

They called on him to ask him to predict the results of the examinations. After inquiring about their respective days and hours of birth, the fortune-teller did not say anything: he only stuck out a forefinger. The three men pressed for an explanation for they could not understand what he meant.

"I am afraid that I am not in a position to reveal what Heaven has in store for you. Please forgive me."

The three men left disappointed.

"Master, what did you really mean by sticking out one finger at the three men?" his pupil asked the fortune-teller in the evening.

"Well, that is simple. There were three of them. If one passes the examinations, my finger will mean only one of them will pass; if two of them pass, my finger will mean only one of them will fail; if all three succeed, the meaning is all of them will pass together; if all of them fail, my finger can also mean all of them will fail."

LADIES OF JIN

Zhang Yi was staying in the state of Chu as an envoy of the state of Qin. The king of Chu gave him a cold reception. Zhang did not fulfil his mission, but his long stay caused him financial difficulties.

He went to see the king of Chu, telling him that he was leaving for the state of Jin in the north. The king nodded to him indifferently.

"What can I do for Your Majesty in Jin?" Zhang asked.

"Well, nothing really," the king said. "I've got everything here in Chu. Gold, ivory, gem, pearl, you name it. What can Jin offer?"

"Ah, that is because you haven't seen the women of Jin. They are the prettiest in the world. Those who don't know take them for angels."

"I have never seen any woman from Jin. If they are really as pretty as you said, I certainly know how to appreciate." The king was interested.

He gave Zhang Yi lots of jewelry and other gifts, asking him to bring back a few beauties from Jin.

When the two queens of the king heard of it, they were concerned. They sent a man to Zhang with the following message:

"We heard that you are leaving for Jin. Here are some 10,000 ounces of gold as your travelling expenses."

One of the queens gave Zhang an additional 5,000 ounces of gold. The import of the message and the gift was not lost upon Zhang Yi.

He went to bid the king good-bye. "It is going to be quite a while before I am back. I'd like to drink a toast to Your Majesty."

The king ordered that wine be served. After a few glasses, Zhang bowed and requested.

"There are no outsiders here. Could you ask your two queens to accompany us?"

"As you wish," the king agreed.

As the two queens were pouring wine, Zhang knelt before the king.

"I beg your pardon, Your Majesty. I have lied. I ought to be punished."

"What is it?"

"I have been to so many places but I have never seen any woman as beautiful as these two queens. Now I know that when I said that I would get Your Majesty some beautiful women from Jin, I really did not know what I was talking about."

"Never mind," the king laughed. "I've always thought that these two are the most beautiful in the world."

Zhang Yi was never asked to return what he had received from the king.

THE HANDSOME MAN

Zou Ji, the prime minister of Qi, was tall and handsome. One day as he was putting on his robe and cap before going to the royal court, he looked at himself in the mirror and said to his wife, "Who do you think is more handsome, me or Lord Xu?"

His wife replied, "You, of course. There is no question about it." But as Lord Xu was famous for his handsome look in the country, Zou Ji could not take his wife's words for granted. So he put the same question to his maid.

"Who is better-looking, me or Lord Xu?"

"Lord Xu cannot compare with you," the maid replied.

The next morning a guest came. While they were chatting, Zou Ji asked, "Between Lord Xu and I, who, do you think, is better looking?"

"Lord Xu is nowhere near so handsome as you," said the guest.

The following day Lord Xu himself came to visit Zou Ji, looking at Lord Xu closely, Zou Ji was convinced that the visitor was more handsome than he himself. He looked in the mirror again. Indeed, there was an obvious difference between them.

He thought to himself. "My wife says I am better looking because she loves me, my maid says I am better looking because she is afraid of me, and my guest says so because he is asking me for a favor."

Then he had an audience with the king.

"I am certainly not as handsome as Lord Xu," he said to the king. "And yet my wife, my maid, and a guest of mine all told me that I am better looking than Lord Xu. Now Qi is a large country with a hundred and twenty cities. No lady or courtier in the palace is not partial to Your Majesty. No government minister is not afraid of you. And everyone in the country hopes to get something from you. Think how serious the consequences can be if you are deluded by flattery."

"You are right," said the king.

He issued an instruction to the effect that any official or ordinary citizen who pointed out his faults to his face would be awarded first prize, anyone who did so by writing to him would be awarded second prize, and anyone who criticized the king in public would be given third prize.

When the instruction was issued, there were so many people who came forward with advice that the gate of the palace became as crowded as a market place. After several months, there were still people coming forward occasionally with suggestions to improve on the government. By the end of a year, no one could find anything more to criticize though people were still eager to win a prize.

Comment: Every one likes sincere appreciation and deserving compliments, but not flattery. But flattery is the one art of telling another man exactly what he thinks of himself. Flattery, in a sense, helps one to play safe. Flattery, like courtesy, even when overdone, will not hurt half as much as blind bluntness and rudeness. However, it should be used with discretion. And doing it subtly is essential to success.

PART IX
POLITICS: THE GOOD, THE BAD AND THE UGLY

39. THE DEVIL INSIDE

Great evil often lies in gentleness. The wise are watchful of needles hidden inside cotton. Deep hatred often has its root in affection. The wise are wary of the honey on the edge of a knife.
—*Vegetable Roots*

Looking through the annals of China's long history, I found that, compared with other periods, the transitional age from one dynasty to another offers a better focal point to examine the folly and wisdom of man. One of such periods, that from the Qin Dynasty to the Han Dynasty, has already been portrayed in the earlier chapters. In the next four chapters I will try to describe what happened in the turbulent years of the last emperor of the Ming Dynasty who lost to the rulers of the Qing Dynasty.

But the demise of the Ming Dynasty that had ruled China for 277 years, was not solely the fault of the last emperor, Chongzhen. As the saying goes, coming events cast their shadows before them. The seeds of decay were buried by Emperor Chongzhen's grandfather Wanli, half a century before Chongzhen came to power.

A STERN TUTOR

Emperor Wanli was the fourteenth emperor of the Ming Dynasty. He was one of the longest reigning monarchs in history, having ruled China for forty-eight years. It was during his reign that Christianity was introduced to China by European missionaries, that Portuguese merchants began to settle down in Macao, that peanuts and sweet potatoes were introduced from America, that China sent troops to Korea and helped the Koreans to have repelled Japanese invasion.

All these are events known to the world. What is not known is Emperor Wanli himself as an individual. And what he did had far-reaching impact on the course of China's history.

Wanli came to the throne in 1572 at the age of nine. Zhang Juzheng, one of the greatest politicians in Chinese history, was appointed as his tutor and the prime minister.

It was a time when the Ming Dynasty had already ruled China for two hundred years, when law and regulations became lax, when the government was no longer efficient and bureaucratic formality had replaced good administration. Zhang Juzheng started an overhaul of the system. He enforced a general appraisal of the performances of all the officials and a curtailment of some of their undeserved privileges, such as the free use of government postal system and transportation facilities.

A population census and a nation-wide land survey he conducted revealed that many of the rich and powerful had evaded tax by concealing their holdings and giving false account of the number of people working in their households. His efforts to stamp out tax evasion met with resistance from the relatives of the emperor and various interest groups. But the Prime Minister did not budge an inch.

At the same time, he cultivated good relationship with two most powerful persons behind the scene: the emperor's mother and the chief eunuch. Both stood firmly by the prime minister who bore down all those who opposed to his reform. Under Zhang Juzheng's administration, corrupt and incompetent officials were replaced, border defense strengthened, tax revenue and grain reserve increased. The country became prosperous and peaceful.

Another important task of the prime minister was the education of the emperor whom he spared no pains to coach. An illustrated textbook was prepared depicting eighty-one good examples and thirty-six bad examples of past emperors for Wanli to study. Zhang was a strict teacher. The young emperor was a good student, very bright and very fond of books. He studied hard, asked intelligent questions, and listened to his tutor attentively. He loved his tutor dearly and, to express his appreciation for his tutor whose devotion and loyalty touched him deeply, he showered gifts on him and his family.

Beneath the veneer of an ideal young emperor, however, there was a troubling side of the picture, his alcoholism and his love of money. Drinking started when he was only fourteen. But Zhang Juzheng managed to restrain him. When he was only twelve, Wanli asked the treasury to lend him 130,000 ounces of silver to supplement his private purse. Because he had no valid reason for such a borrowing, his request was turned down. But he insisted, saying this was a one-time-only loan, and got the money. When he was fourteen, he wanted to borrow

270,000 ounces of silver as pocket money. Even Zhang Juzheng could not dissuade him. The following year, the teenage monarch again requested a loan of 270,000 ounces of silver. Of course none of these loans were ever paid back.

Zhang Juzheng died when Wanli was nineteen. Now there was no one to keep him under control. He drank at every meal. Every time he drank, he got drunk. Every time he got drunk, he became irascible. He would beat his attendants to death at the slightest offense.

In carrying out the policy he deemed good for the country, Zhang Juzheng had incurred, in his life time, the enmity of many high-ranking officials. Shortly after his death, his opponents gathered force and accused him of various wrong-doings. Wanli's view of his beloved tutor and prime minister underwent a complete change. He denounced him for betraying his trust and for taking too much power into his own hands. Zhang's posthumous honors were all nullified. His house was searched for evidences of alleged embezzlement. His eldest son, unable to stand severe torture, committed suicide after making a false confession of the family's hidden wealth. During the search, the whole family was locked up for two weeks without food or water. A dozen of Zhang's family members were starved to death.

Not even in the wildest dream could Zhang Juzheng ever have imagined that the betrayal of his good pupil would be so thorough and so savage.

A PROFLIGATE RULER

Wanli began to handle all the government affairs. He loved power, but he found running a government too strenuous for him. Yet he was not willing to delegate authorities to his ministers.

Gradually he turned negligent. A few years later, he ceased meeting with his ministers any more. Imperial decisions were conveyed by eunuchs shuttling in and out of the palace. They became the intermediaries between the emperor and his ministers. He complained about dizziness, back pain and sore feet. However, this did not stop loyal ministers to wait outside his palace from morning till night to ask for an audience.

Irritated, Wanli then adopted different tactics to deal with those persistent officials. On every memo submitted in, he would write two words: "I know." In fact, he never bothered to read the memos and never responded.

As a result, ministerial positions were left vacant for years, for the emperor was the only one who could make the appointments. The Ministry of Personnel was left without a head for six years. Personnel matters such as transfers, retirement, leaves, promotion were all suspended. One of his prime ministers only met him twice in twelve years. The government was left without a defense minister for fifteen years, without a minister of public works for sixteen years, without a minister of justice for six years. Hundreds of prisoners were languishing in prison because their cases were suspended for want of trial judges. Jails became overcrowded.

While one government minister had to do several persons' work, some died from exhaustion. Thousands of people who came to Beijing to apply for government jobs could not get an interview for years. Many officials resigned. But Wanli did not even bother to look at the resignation letters they handed in. Some stayed on. Some left on their own after submitting their resignation a number of times. Wanli did not seem to care whether they stayed or quit. Since all major decisions had to be made by the emperor, his total negligence pushed the administration to the brink of paralysis. Such situation lasted some thirty years.

However, when it came to money, Wanli was never indifferent.

He was one of the most extravagant rulers in Chinese history. He received annually nearly 1.6 million ounces of silver from the government in addition to the income from his own estates. He occupied about 340,000 acres of land in and around Beijing. His mistresses and court ladies spent about 400,000 ounces of silver's worth on cosmetics each year. The royal kitchen had a staff of three thousand. Lavish dinners were an every-day affair. The entire annual budget of the government was only a little under 19 million ounces of silver and 1.6 million metric tons of grain.

The construction of his tomb, the famous Ming Tomb outside Beijing, took six years and over 10 million ounces of silver to complete. Most of the laborers were farmers who had to abandon the field in order to perform the corvee duty.

Meanwhile his greed for money knew no bounds. As he kept

"borrowing" from the treasury, his debt amounted to some six million ounces of silver which he never paid back. He sent inflated bills to the treasury. For instance, the wedding of some of his children cost about five million ounces of silver. But Wanli's claim was forty-seven million.

He always complained that he was in want of money especially after the war with the Japanese invaders in Korea in 1592 when Korea appealed to China for help. The war which lasted seven years cost China nearly ten million ounces of silver. However, this was still considered to be one bright spot on Wanli's record. Ironically the war had been used by the emperor as a pretext to launch an unprecedented "silver rush" all over the country. For a while silver mining became Wanli's obsession. Hundreds of silver mines were opened up all over the country. No matter whether any silver was found at all, taxes on a proposed silver mine were fixed and extorted from the populace.

Wanli was nothing short of a fanatic in so far as money was concerned. The way he plundered his own country was unprecedented. It went against the very essence of his earlier education. Not that he did not know what he did was wrong, but he acted deliberately as though he wanted to be a bad emperor.

This was borne out by what happened in November 1602 when Wanli was very sick and thought he was dying. He repented on his death bed, and ordered, as his last will, all the silver mining and the extraordinary taxes be stopped. Overnight government ministers spread the imperial order all over the country. However, Wanli unexpectedly recovered. He immediately regretted his death-bed repentance and wanted to rescind his last order. His ministers stubbornly resisted. But in the end the emperor prevailed. After all, an emperor was an emperor.

Several of his ministers warned him of disastrous consequences if he continued his practices, but Wanli was deaf to all good counsels.

THE POWER OF EUNUCHS

Under Wanli, stealing by eunuchs from the imperial treasuries was an open secret. Curiously enough, the emperor never bothered to conduct an effective audit of the treasuries.

Eunuchs were a queer group of people. The majority of them were boys who had been castrated by their parents when they were small.

Some adults had themselves emasculated voluntarily. All were for the purpose of obtaining a secure and lucrative position in the imperial palace.

The operation to remove the sexual organ was often crude. Many were said to have suffered from chronic incontinence of the bladder. They were fat and soft, had no beard and moustache, and spoke with a high pitch falsetto. They were employed as palace attendants to guard the palace and to wait upon the emperor's mistresses and court ladies.

Originally eunuchs were employed by a jealous emperor who wanted to make sure that there would be none but he himself who had the privilege to enjoy beautiful women recruited to the palace. The impotency of the eunuchs made the emperor feel safe.

Thus the eunuchs were closer to the emperor than government ministers. They were well informed about the preferences and weaknesses of the emperor and knew how to gratify his whims, how to play upon his prejudices and, therefore, how to pull the strings and gain advantages for themselves.

Perhaps bound by a sense of physical inferiority, eunuchs tended to band together, helping each other against the outside world. They were sensitive, moody, suspicious, and easily offended. They were conscious of their status as pariahs of the normal world. They were usually greedy, because, knowing what price they had paid for securing their occupation, they wanted to make sure that their disability was amply compensated, even if it meant theft.

To gain favor with the emperor, some eunuchs suggested that, on top of regular taxes, extraordinary taxes be levied on tea, on salt, on shops, on boats, on pigs and chickens, and on almost everything. Their suggestions met with Wanli's hearty approval.

In the Ming Dynasty, the state budget and the imperial budget were managed separately. As a rule, regular taxes were collected by the government tax authorities. Now eunuchs were sent out to various provinces to collect extraordinary taxes. They frequently extorted money from well-to-do families and the local civil service. Some local governments were forced to pay the extraordinary taxes with the money earmarked for defense purposes. Many businesses were closed because their owners could not afford to pay the taxes.

Government ministers, unanimous in their opposition against such abuses, bombarded the emperor with protests. Some government officials even submitted memorandums with illustrations depicting how people sold their children in order to pay taxes and how people died or got maimed working in silver mines. But Wanli was callous to their suffering.

The abuse of power by the eunuchs provoked numerous popular revolts. On one occasion, for example, over thirty eunuch tax commissioners were murdered in Shandong Province. On another occasion, a eunuch and his henchmen, about two hundred in number, were killed in Yunnan Province.

But the activities of the eunuchs only increased the imperial treasuries slightly. Most of the money collected went to the private pockets of the eunuchs. They took much more than they gave to the emperor.

ASSASSINATION PLOT

The succession issue was also a focus of major contention during Wanli's reign.

Wanli was married at sixteen. After three years he still had no child. Then something happened when he was eighteen. One day he called on his mother, but she was not at home. Wanli found an attractive maid in his mother's residence and made love with her. She became pregnant. Normally Wanli should be happy about it. But this pregnancy was not what he intended. Almost at the same time, a nation-wide beauty search was conducted to select secondary wives for him. From among those finally recruited into the palace, Wanli picked up nine girls. One of them, a very pretty, young girl, became Wanli's favorite. She was soon given the title Lady Zheng.

When his mother saw her maid pregnant, she confronted Wanli with the matter. Wanli first tried to deny, but his mother showed him the diary kept by the eunuchs in her palace. The emperor was forced to admit and a royal title was conferred on the maid. She was to be called Lady Gong. In time, Lady Gong gave birth to a boy. The boy was named Zhu Changluo, Zhu being the family name. As he was the emperor's eldest son, he was automatically the heir apparent, according to the imperial tradition. The emperor, however, wanted to make Lady Zheng's son the heir apparent. But he was opposed by most government ministers as well as his own mother.

"Why didn't you make Changluo the heir apparent?" his mother once asked him.

"He was born by a maid," Wanli replied.

"But you too were born by a former maid," his mother angrily reminded him that she had been a maid too. Indeed Wanli was born as a result of casual sex between his father and a maid, his mother.

It was not until after fifteen years' petition by more than a hundred government officials that Wanli declared his eldest son to be his successor. This happened in 1601 when Changluo was already nineteen.

Wanli did not like Changluo at all. He made his son's life miserable. Changluo began studying in preparation for his role in the future. No summer vacation was allowed. No heating was provided in winter. No leave for sick days was permitted even if Changluo had a fever.

On an evening of early June 1615, a suspicious man carrying a club forced his way into the quarters of the Crown Prince inside the Forbidden City. He ran into several eunuchs who tried to stop him, but he knocked them down. However, before he got any further, he was subdued by other eunuchs who, alarmed by the noise, rushed out to catch him.

During the interrogation, the suspect, Zhang Chai, confessed that his target was the Crown Prince. He had, for three years, been on the payroll of two eunuchs who had promised him land and money if he succeeded in killing the Crown Prince. The two eunuchs were found to be in the service of Lady Zheng whose hostility against Changluo was well-known. So several senior government ministers were determined to get to the bottom of the case no matter who was behind the plot.

Wanli was disturbed at what had happened in the palace. But he had no intention to let Lady Zheng get implicated in the case. He thought the only way to protect her was for her to appeal directly to Changluo. So she went to Prince Changluo's palace to plead innocent. She knelt before her stepson, weeping and begging for mercy. Long hated and maltreated by Lady Zheng and Emperor Wanli, Changluo grew up a weak man. When he saw Lady Zheng throw herself at his feet, he was stupefied and quickly forgave her.

The case was closed without further investigation. The next day Zhang Chai, together with the two eunuchs, were sentenced to death.

Officials who had conducted the investigation of the case were dismissed from office. They knew too much for the comfort of the emperor.

When Wanli died in 1620 at the age of fifty-eight, Prince Changluo succeeded to the throne.

A WEAKLING

In his last will, Wanli ordered Changluo to raise Lady Zheng to the rank of empress. This time, however, Changluo refused to follow his father's behest, deeply hurting Lady Zheng. Changluo fell ill a few days after his ascension. He had only been the emperor for twenty-nine days when he died suddenly as a result of taking some mysterious red pills reported to have been prepared by a former associate of Lady Zheng, though no hard evidence was found to link the lady with his death.

Changluo was succeeded by his fifteen-year-old son Zhu Youjiao who became known as Emperor Xi Zong.

The young monarch was deeply attached to his nanny Lady Ke who had brought him up because his mother had died when he was yet an infant. Shortly after he came to the throne, Lady Ke and her husband, Wei Zhongxian, were given senior positions. Wei was a eunuch. According to the palace tradition, favored eunuchs were allowed to form a family with court ladies to keep each other company even though they had lost reproductive capabilities.

Wei Zhongxian was an unscrupulous man. In order to escape gambling debts, he found shelter in the royal palace where he was accepted as a eunuch. Actually, his self-administered castration left his sexual capability largely intact. He first ingratiated himself with Lady Ke's first husband Wei Chao, who naively introduced him to Lady Ke.

Wei Zhongxian was young and handsome. Lady Ke soon took a fancy to him and the two became lovers. One night Wei Chao caught Wei Zhongxian in Lady Ke's bedroom, and a fist fight followed between the two men. The noise awoke Xi Zong who, after hearing the three of them, decided to let Lady Ke have her choice. Naturally, Wei Zhongxian was the victor. Wei Chao was ousted and later forced to hang himself.

The boy emperor was a weak, fatuous and self-indulgent person. He was not interested in work. He made carpentry and acting his hobbies. He found government affairs tedious and preferred to spend much of his time making fine pieces of furniture, putting on theatrical performances, watching cock-fighting, hunting birds, or playing games.

Wei Zhongxian would not submit government documents or ministerial memorandums to the emperor until the latter was so engrossed in his favorite hobbies that he would certainly ask Wei to make a decision on his behalf. Thus, the effective decision-making authority fell into Wei's hand.

The power of the eunuchs reached an apex during the reign of Emperor Xi Zong. Wei interfered with the running of the government as well as national defense. He was also in charge of the country's secret police. Lady Ke, for her part, frequently meddled with Xi Zong's meetings with government ministers.

Wei and Ke were detested by court ladies, government ministers and army generals at large. On the advice of several senior ministers, Xi Zong did expel Lady Ke and Wei Zhongxian out of the palace. However, he missed Lady Ke's cooking so much that she was recalled after a few days.

Bad luck awaited those who dared to run afoul of them. Dozens who opposed to them were imprisoned, tortured, murdered or forced to commit suicide. It was a reign of terror.

Xi Zong's wife, Empress Zhang, was no friend of Ke and Wei. She frequently warned the emperor of the danger of the excessive power in the hands of the eunuchs by comparing Wei Zhongxian to Zhao Gao, the chief eunuch of the Qin Dynasty who had murdered the Second Emperor of Qin. But she could not outstrip Lady Ke in influencing the emperor.

For their part, Ke and Wei tried but failed to vilify the empress. When Lady Ke learnt what the empress was expecting, she was afraid that once the empress became a mother, her own influence might be weakened. She set about replacing those who waited on Empress Zhang with her own maids. As the empress often needed massage to soothe her back pain, Lady Ke bribed one of the maids and instructed her to massage the empress in such a way as to induce an abortion. Her scheme succeeded. Empress Zhang's baby was still-born.

When Empress Zhang realized what had happened, she reported the matter to Xi Zong, but the inane emperor appointed none other than Wei Zhongxian to look into the matter. Lady Ke killed the maid who administered the massage, for a dead person could tell no tales.

Saddened but undaunted, Empress Zhang was resolved to fight it out with Ke and Wei to the bitter end. Lady Ke often took young maids out of the palace to get them pregnant and then tried to persuade the emperor to sleep with them in the hope that once the child was born, he would be the heir apparent, and so she herself would always be in control and continue to enjoy her privileges. But her scheme failed. The emperor's affection for the empress was unabated.

Always in poor health and frequently struck by illnesses, Emperor Xi Zong died in 1627 at the age of twenty-three after ruling China for seven years. Strongly urged by Empress Zhang, he appointed his seventeen-year-old brother Chongzhen as his successor shortly before his death.

Encouraged by Empress Zhang and other ministers, the first action Chongzhen took was to execute Lady Ke and sent Wei Zhongxian into exile. A few days later, a warrant was issued to arrest Wei. Knowing he was doomed, Wei committed suicide on his way to the place of exile.

By that time, the Ming empire was already in deep trouble. Little did Chongzhen know that he was to be the last emperor of the Ming Dynasty.

Comment: Wanli was like an agent of destruction. During his rule, China went from stability and prosperity to the brink of collapse. The whole process took just a little less than fifty years. Wanli's pathological indolence and compulsive extravagance eventually cost him the Ming Dynasty.

The behavior of Emperor Wanli presented an inexplicable picture. Why did he suddenly turn to hate his departed tutor whom he had so loved and whose illness had caused him to weep so feelingly only a few months ago? What made him throw away all that he had learnt? Why did he fail to honor his promise to follow good examples set by wise and virtuous kings and emperors in history? Was it caused by alcoholism? Was he overly suppressed in his formative years by his mother and the prime minister? Was there some mysterious chemical imbalance in his brain? In any case, his twisted personality makes an interesting study in psychiatry.

As for Wei Zhongxian and Lady Ke, both having done so much harm to the country, their end was only what it ought to have been. This seemed to have vindicated a generally held belief among the Chinese about the cause and effect of one's action: Good deeds bring good rewards, wrong-doings beget punishment. Not that there is no justice, but retribution has its own timing.

40. THE SEDUCTION OF A MING GENERAL

I like fish and I also like bear's paw. If I cannot have both, I prefer bear's paw to fish. I love life and I also care about fulfilling my moral duty. If I cannot have both, I choose to honor my duty. I love life, but there are things I care about more than life. Therefore I will not seek life improperly. I hate death, but there are things I hate more than death. Therefore I will not try to escape when I am called on by my duty.

—*Mencius*

The last of China's fifteen dynasties was not a Chinese dynasty but a Manchu one. And the last Chinese emperor was not the last emperor of China in the sense that the former was a Chinese by origin whereas the latter was a man of Manchu stock.

The Manchus used to live in small tribes in Manchuria, a huge expanse of cold zone in present-day northeastern China near the border of Korea. In the course of time they were largely assimilated into Chinese life. Today Manchuria is part of China and the Manchus one of the fifty or so ethnic minority groups living in China, some Manchus still maintaining their distinctive customs and costumes that once prevailed in China under the Qing rule.

But in the Ming Dynasty, they had always been regarded as alien by the Chinese. For generations in history, they had been subjects to the Chinese court. They traded ginseng, sable, horses, and timber with the Chinese for oxen, cloth, salt and grain. With conflicting interests among themselves, these tribes did not live on amicable terms. To maintain stability in the border regions and to rule over them more effectively, the Ming government adopted a policy of power balance, sometimes playing off one tribe against another so as to prevent any one group from dominating over other groups. However, things were fated to change.

NURHACI VERSUS THE MING DYNASTY

In the late sixteenth and early seventeenth centuries, Nurhaci, one of the tribal chiefs, succeeded in subjugating all the rival tribes and emerged as the sole leader of the Manchu. From the start, he bore a grudge against the Ming court for having helped a rival chief kill his grandfather and his father.

An ambitious man, Nurhaci wanted to create an independent Manchu state. At the beginning of the seventeenth century, he founded what became known as the Eight Banner system to turn the entire population into a military organization. Each banner was made up of 25 companies, and each company consisted of 300 soldiers plus their families under the supervision of a hereditary captain. During peace time, the company worked as farmers or craftsmen. In war time, soldiers, equipped with provisions supplied by their own companies, were grouped to form a fighting unit of 7,500 under their respective banner. Thus the entire Manchu operated like a military machine. In 1616, Nurhaci announced the establishment of his own dynasty in rivalry with the Ming court.

The emergence of Nurhaci alarmed the Chinese. Knowing that the Manchus depended heavily on trading with China for their food, the Ming government decided to suspend trade along the border with the Manchu in order to exert pressure on Nurhaci. The embargo sharply provoked Nurhaci.

In 1618 Nurhaci declared war on Ming. He quickly overran three strongholds on the northern border. The following year the Ming government dispatched four armies totalling 90,000 in a bid to crush his forces. The Chinese strategy was to have the four armies converge from four directions at one point, Mukden (present-day Shenyang) at precisely the same moment to attack Nurhaci's forces. This plan would have worked if all the armies had arrived simultaneously for the concerted action. But none of them kept to the schedule.

Nurhaci had 60,000 soldiers. His strategy was no matter how many directions the Chinese took, he would concentrate his forces on fighting one Chinese army at a time. He did not wait for the Ming troops to join forces. Instead, he sought to attack the army nearest to him. He routed one Chinese army that arrived at Mukden one day ahead of schedule and then another the following day and yet another three days later. The fourth Chinese army was forced to retreat. China lost nearly 50,000 men in the battle. This was the first major defeat of the Chinese troops by the Manchu. The commander-in-chief of the Ming forces was held responsible and was subsequently executed for failing to coordinate the campaign.

Nurhaci's victory laid the foundation for Manchu's further expansion. During the next two years, Nurhaci brought the entire Liaodong Peninsula, a large area to the east of the River Liao in modern Liaoning Province, under control. Then he moved his capital to Mukden. Whereas Nurhaci's power was growing fast, the Ming court was debilitated by the inner power struggle and policy debate between the chief eunuch Wei Zhongxian and his opponents, mainly scholar-officials. The Ming Dynasty was unable to organize any effective defense until the appointment of General Yuan Chonghuan in early 1626.

THE DEATHTRAP

In January 1626, after a lull of four years, Nurhaci attacked Ningyuan, a city outside the strategic pass of Shanhaiguan. Shanhaiguan was the easternmost terminal of the Great Wall. It was a key military position in China's northern defense. Before anyone could make inroads to Beijing, they had to clear this pass. The Chinese troops, under General Yuan Chonghuan and with the help of their newly acquired European cannons introduced by Portuguese priests, inflicted heavy casualties on the enemy. Nurhaci was wounded. The defeat was totally unexpected. It was his first defeat in forty years since he took arms. Badly shaken, Nurhaci had never recovered. He died a few months later, and his son, Huangtaiji, succeeded to his position as the head of the Manchu regime.

Huangtaiji attacked Jinzhou, another key military position outside Shanhaiguan. Severely defeated by General Yuan, he nearly lost his life in the battle.

The new Ming emperor, Emperor Chongzhen, was different from his grandfather Wanli and his brother, Xi Zong. He was dedicated, energetic, hardworking, and had a sense of mission.

In an individual audience given to him by Chongzhen as a special honor in recognition of his success, General Yuan Chonghuan laid out his plan for the defense on the northern border: Using the people of Liao to defend the land of Liao, and using the land of Liao to provide for the people. He promised that the lost territories would be recovered in five years if he had a free hand. He especially asked the emperor to trust him completely and not to be swayed by possible slanders of his opponents in the court. The eighteen-year-old emperor gave him full authority to direct the border defense.

Unwilling to accept defeat, Huangtaiji decided to change the direction of his attack. In 1629 he secretly diverted his troops to stage a surprise raid on Beijing by way of friendly territories in Mongolia. Yuan was caught unawares. His army raced back to the defense of the capital. A fierce battle was fought in the suburbs of Beijing and the Manchus were driven back. But the fact that the enemy was able to penetrate so close to the capital stunned the emperor, and General Yuan's credibility suffered.

To exploit the situation, Huangtaiji acted on a ruse proposed by his Chinese advisor Fan Wencheng. He wrote two letters to General Yuan about a non-existent peace talk. The correspondence was delivered in Beijing to be deliberately intercepted by eunuchs who reported it to Chongzhen. Alarmed by this secret deal behind his back between his trusted general and Huangtaiji, the head of the Manchu government, Chongzhen sent two eunuchs to look into the matter.

On their way to General Yuan's garrison, they were captured by Huangtaiji's men who had anticipated their mission. Huangtaiji then arranged for the two captive eunuchs to overhear a conversation among his officials concerning General Yuan's secret dealings with himself regarding a truce. The conversation revealed that Yuan agreed to have peace talks with the Manchu and as a good-will gesture, the Qing army would retreat a few miles the following morning. Indeed, Huangtaiji ordered such a retreat the next day. Subsequently he created a chance for the two Chinese eunuchs to escape. When they fled back to Beijing, they briefed the emperor on what they had overheard. As Yuan was never a friend of the eunuchs, they falsely suggested that it was General Yuan who had allowed Huangtaiji's troops to launch that surprise raid on the capital just to emphasize how indispensable he was to the emperor.

While Emperor Chongzhen was devoted to his duties, he was inexperienced, impetuous, self-willed and suspicious. He felt betrayed. General Yuan was quickly summoned back and summarily executed for high treason without a fair hearing.

The death of Yuan Chonghuan removed the main obstacle to the realization of Huangtaiji's plan and plunged the northern defense of

China into disarray.

SINICIZATION

In the meantime, Huangtaiji made a conscious effort to woo the Chinese officials and scholars in the occupied Liao Peninsula. He set up, after the Ming Dynasty's fashion, civil service examinations to recruit the Chinese for government work. He also promoted quite a few Chinese officials to senior offices. To honor the Chinese concept of family relationships, he repealed the Manchu law that required people to report the misconduct of family members. He decreed that there should be no discrimination against the Chinese. When his forces captured a Chinese city, he ordered them to behave themselves and invited surrendered Chinese officials to wine and dine with him in his tent. He organized Chinese soldiers into a separate Chinese Legion under a trusted Chinese collaborator to fight side by side with the Manchu troops.

Huangtaiji lost his temper one time when a captured Chinese army commander refused to bow to him. He was on the point of killing him when his brother intervened.

"Why kill him?" demanded his brother. "If the Chinese wants to die a martyr's death and if we kill him, we will be as good as yielding to his wish. And our policy has always been to treat our prisoners well. So, let him live is my advice."

Huangtaiji calmed down. He had food sent to the officer that evening. But the Chinese commander refused to eat, saying he preferred death to surrender. On the third day, Huangtaiji personally went to see him and served food to him. The officer was so moved that he changed his mind and surrendered to the Manchus.

In 1631, The Qing army surrounded the strategic stronghold of Dalinghe, a city to the east of the Liao River. They dug a trench eleven feet deep and eleven feet wide around the city, built a high wall to form a second ring and then another trench of five feet in width and eight feet in depth. After a siege that lasted two and half months, the Qing army, under the personal direction of Huangtaiji, attacked the city with advanced European-type artillery built with the help of captured Chinese technicians. The Chinese surrendered at last. This battle, called the battle of Dalinghe, marked a turning point in the Sino-Manchu conflict, for from then on, the Ming forces were put on the defensive, unable to launch a counterattack any more.

Having consolidated his victories, Huangtaiji proclaimed himself emperor and formally adopted Qing as the name of his dynasty in 1636. Huangtaiji was in favor of Confucian education and loved Chinese classics. But he feared the sinicization may cause the Manchus to lose their martial values and fighting spirit which had been fostered by hunting and archery. So he prohibited his people from wearing Chinese clothes or adopting the Chinese habit of drinking and sexual indulgence.

During the next few years, he invaded and conquered Korea and Mongolia, and repeatedly invaded and pillaged Chinese cities.

GENTLE PERSUASION

In 1639, Emperor Chongzhen appointed General Hong Chengchou, a former Defense Minister and reportedly the best strategist among Ming generals, as the commander-in-chief of the 130,000 Ming troops stationed in Liaodong, to check the Manchu's invasion.

General Hong based his headquarters in Songshan, an important outpost outside Shanhaiguan. In early 1641, the Qing army laid siege to Jinzhou, a key stronghold nearby. Hong's original strategy was to strengthen the overall Chinese defense which had deteriorated since the downfall of General Yuan Chonghuan and to store supplies sufficient for a year before launching any offensive. But Hong did not have full power over his army. Other officials, such as imperial supervisors and eunuchs stationed in the army, were also involved in decision making because Emperor Chongzhen never fully trusted any of his subordinates and never gave them, not excepting General Hong Chengchou, full authorities to carry out their duties even in a time of dire crises.

As the emperor was impatient, too, Hong was forced to attack the Qing army earlier than he had wanted. In a series of losing battles, the Chinese suffered heavy casualties, and Hong had to turn back to Songshan, only to find his supplies already cut off.

In September 1641, Huangtaiji launched a large scale offensive against Songshan. He surrounded the city for nearly half a year and repelled all the reinforcements sent by the Ming government.

Inside Songshan, the Chinese were forced to kill war horses to feed themselves. The morale of the troops was low, but General Hong Chengchou refused to surrender in spite of the peace overtures made to him by Huangtaiji. On a March night in 1642, one of Hong's aides defected, and helped the Manchus to climb over the part of the city wall under his control. The Manchus took over the city by surprise, and Hong was captured alive.

General Hong was the most senior Ming officer ever taken captive by Qing. Huangtaiji knew if he could persuade Hong to surrender, it would be of tremendous value to his cause. As an eminent scholar, Hong had been mentor to many Ming generals and officials. His defection would conceivably have a great impact on the Ming government.

Hong was put up in a comfortable house and treated well. Huangtaiji came to greet him personally. Pretty maids were sent to wait upon him. But the Ming general was defiant. He refused to eat. Frustrated, Huangtaiji turned to his Chinese advisor Fan Wencheng for help. Fan visited General Hong in an effort to win him over. But he failed, too. However, when they were chatting, a draft blew down some dust from the ceiling, and Fan noticed how Hong quickly flipped it off his clothes.

When Fan told Huangtaiji that he had failed to persuade Hong, the Qing emperor was ready to give up.

"It seems he is really bent on dying for his country," said the emperor. "Let's grant his wish and put him to death."

"No, I don't think Hong is ready to die yet," Fan said.

"Why?"

"He cares a lot for his clothes. I'm sure he cares more for his life."

At that time Empress Borjigit, wife of Huangtaiji, suggested that she might be able to persuade him.

Borjigit was the greatest beauty of Manchuria. She was formerly a Mongolian princess and a descendant of Genghis Khan. She rode, swam and hunted like a man. She was then twenty-nine.

"But you are the First Lady of Qing," Huangtaiji said.

"For the sake of the dynasty, I will not spare myself any risk. But I'll be discreet."

Hong was weak after starving for days. He was resting on a couch with his eyes closed. Suddenly he scented a whiff of fragrance. As he opened his eyes, he saw an extremely pretty woman with a fair complexion standing in front of him. Hong straightened himself up immediately.

"How are you today, General?" the woman made a deep bow and asked in a gentle voice, her eyes smiling sweetly at him.

"Who are you? Who sent you here? What do you want?" Hong demanded.

"I've come here to pay my respects to you, General. I admire your loyalty and talents. I know you will never surrender. Nor do I dare to hope so. But I want to offer you some help, General, in my small way."

"What do you mean? My mind is made up."

"Please do not mistake me. I know better than asking you to change your mind. But starving yourself to death is a slow and agonizing process. I am a Buddhist. I cannot bear to see my most respected and admired person suffer. I have secretly prepared some poison. It is effective. If you drink it, you will die very quickly and without pain."

General Hong was touched. Staring at this mysterious woman, he nodded. Borjigit gave him the cup that was said to contain the poison. Hong gulped it down. As he did it too fast, he choked, coughed, and inadvertently spat on the dress of the lady. He hastened to apologize. The lady just smiled and took out an embroidered handkerchief to wipe his mouth.

Borjigit asked Hong about his hometown, his old mother and his wife.

"Now you have drunk the poison. You have fulfilled your duty for Ming. But if I were you, I would not die so hastily. I would try to survive and wait for a chance to serve my country again. Do you have any last words for your family?"

Hong's eyes were moistened. Borjigit leaned over and wiped off the tears that were flowing from the corners of his eyes. Hong held her hand. Looking at this beautiful and elegant woman, he felt his own heart leaping with a yearning for her.

He was dying anyway. Whatever he did would not matter so much. Casting an knowing glance at him, Borjigit began to undress herself. Her shapely and voluptuous body radiated certain uninhibited sexiness not found in most Chinese women. General Hong could not control himself any more. He had had no woman for over a month.

The two threw their bodies together like a pair of passionate lovers.

Surprised by his own energy, Hong was wondering why the effects of the poison were so slow in coming. Finally the lady told him that it was ginseng tea, a most potent tonic that she had prepared for him specially. The general was dumbfounded. Borjigit urged him to reconsider his decision.

"How can I possibly surrender?"

"The Qing government is interested in negotiation with your government. We want you to stay here for the time being until a peace agreement is reached. You can write a letter to your emperor, saying you are working for the interest of Ming even when you are staying inside the Manchu."

"You've got a point. But I don't know how your emperor would feel about it."

"I guarantee it'll be all right."

The next morning Hong went to see Huangtaiji. As he raised his head, his eyes met those of Empress Borjigit who was seated by Huangtaiji's side. She gave him a knowing smile. Shocked by the identity of the beauty who slept with him the day before, he was overpowered and remained speechless for quite a while.

Huangtaiji held a sumptuous banquet in his palace to welcome Hong that evening. He gave Hong his own mink coat as a gift. He expressed abhorrence that the wives and children of the Chinese soldiers who were driven by circumstances to surrender should be killed or exiled by the Ming government. Hong was moved by his concern for his family.

After the dinner, some of the Manchu princes were upset that Huangtaiji treated a Chinese prisoner with such honor.

"We've been through so much hardship these years. What do we want?" Huangtaiji asked them.

"We want to conquer China."

"Let me give you an analogy. Suppose you agree that you and I are travelling like blind men, and I have found a guide to show us the way, shouldn't I be happy?"

A MOTHER'S RAGE

In the meantime, a false report of Hong's death reached Beijing. Emperor Chongzhen was moved to tears. He declared a three-day national mourning. A monument to Hong Chengchou's memory was erected in Beijing. The emperor personally conducted the memorial service at a shrine dedicated to Hong. Half way through the ceremony, a confidential correspondence from Hong reached the emperor saying that his surrender was a temporary expedient and that he would seek to serve His Majesty as soon as he had a chance. Chongzhen suspended the service but he did not punish Hong's family.

Later when Hong entered Beijing with the Manchus, he sent for his mother from his hometown in Fujian, a province in southern China.

"Shame on you!" his mother yelled as soon as she saw her son. Raising her stick, she hit at Hong. "You've betrayed your country. You are not my son. I want to beat you to death."

Hong had to dodge fast. Wrathfully his mother left him and rushed back to Fujian straight away.

Hong became a senior general in the Qing government, and helped Qing's cause without reservation.

On one occasion his troops arrested a young army officer of the Ming resistance movement by the name of Xia Wanchun. Xia was a child prodigy who could write poetry at the age of nine. He joined the anti-Qing movement at the age of fifteen.

Hong had heard of this young man's reputation and decided to talk to him personally.

"You are still young. If you join me, I'll make sure that you have a great career."

Knowing who was talking to him, Xia held his head high.

"I have heard of the great hero, General Hong Chengchou. He was a great patriot. He died a heroic death at the battle of Songshan. I am young but I am determined to follow his example to die for my country."

Thinking that Xia did not know whom he was speaking to, Hong's aide told Xia that he was speaking to the very general this very moment.

With a sneer, Xia said: "Everybody knows that General Hong has died for our country. The emperor personally mourned his death. How dare you discredit his name by alleging that he is still alive?!"

This was more than Hong had expected. Not knowing what to say, he dismissed the boy.

Soon enough, the boy was executed. He was seventeen then.

After the fall of Songshan, the only stronghold Ming had outside

Shanhaiguan was Ningyuan. The situation was desperate. Following consultation with his Defense Minister, the Ming emperor secretly sent an envoy to Qing to hold peace talks. The envoy returned with a letter from Huangtaiji to the effect that Qing was prepared to normalize relations with Ming on condition that Ming give up essentially all the territories outside Shanhaiguan and Qing will deal with Ming on equal footing. Emperor Chongzhen wrote a letter back. The defense minister inadvertently left the letters on his desk. His secretary took them, by mistake, to the official *Beijing Gazette*, which normally published official documents. The letters were published the next day. This caused an uproar and Emperor Chongzhen was greatly embarrassed. He tried to put all the blame on the indiscreet Defense Minister, who refused to accept any blame at all. In the end, the emperor had him executed. This was the last attempt of the Ming Dynasty for a negotiated settlement with Qing.

Comment: Among the numerous mistakes that Emperor Chongzhen made, the execution of General Yuan Chonghuan was the most fatal one. The official Qing records confirm that it was a plot on the part of Huangtaiji, who used to read such Chinese classics as the Chronicle of the Three Kingdoms *and* Sun Zi's Art of War *when he was young.*

As his mistrust of his own officials bordered on the paranoid, Emperor Chongzhen's personnel policy was nothing short of a disaster. He swapped many horses in midstream. In the sixteen years of his reign, he had changed his prime ministers seventeen times, leaving his government without a decisive leadership and without a coordinated strategy at a crucial time.

Failure to make use of the right person in the right way proved to be the biggest cause of his undoing. It makes me shudder to think that the fate of China rested on the shoulders of one young man in his teens and twenties during such a critical period.

41. THE LAST CHINESE EMPEROR

> Use brass as a mirror, one can straighten one's clothes; use history as a mirror, one can discern the causes for the rise and fall of a nation; and use other men as a mirror, one can understand one's own strengths and weaknesses.
>
> —*Tang Tai Zong (599-649)*

When Chongzhen came to the throne in 1627 at the age of seventeen, what he inherited was a most sorry legacy from his grandfather, Emperor Wanli, and his brother, Emperor Xi Zong. China was exhausted, the government demoralized and the people desperate.

From the very beginning, Chongzhen had to fight on two fronts simultaneously: the Manchu in the north and the rebel forces domestically. But unlike his brother, the young emperor had a sense of mission: to reverse the fate of the declining Ming empire against heavy odds. He fought his odds with grim determination and fortitude.

In the spring of 1628 there was a severe drought in Shaanxi, a province in northwestern China. The drought caused famine. The Ming government, being in financial difficulty, was unable to offer relief to the stricken area. The situation became desperate toward the end of the year. People were forced to eat grass, tree bark and earth. Children were abandoned; women were sold. Soldiers stationed there got no food ration and no pay.

Finally starving peasants rose in rebellion. At the beginning, the rebels were disorganized, and their activities, mainly raids on rich people's houses, were limited to local areas. Gradually they grew in strength and spread into areas between the Yellow River and the Yangtze River. Li Zicheng, a former post office courier in Shaanxi, emerged as the leader of the rebel forces. Li lost his job when the government reduced the postal service to cut expenditures. Then he served in the Ming army and joined his fellow soldiers in a mutiny against the local authorities who had failed to grant them necessary supplies. He moved quickly through the ranks of the rebels because of his bravery and personal skills.

The Ming government adopted a policy of combining appeasement with military strength towards the rebels. In 1634, the government troops, under the command of General Hong Chengchou, bottled up the rebel forces in a valley in southeastern Shaanxi. The siege lasted through the summer. The rebels were starving and the continuous rain rendered a large portion of their weapons useless. They were willing to surrender. Their leader Li Zicheng bound himself and appeared before the Ming army commander to beg for mercy. The staff of the army commander, having been heavily bribed by the rebels, persuaded the commander to accept the surrender. The rebels, totalling 36,000, were ordered to march back to their farms under the supervision of fifty guards. On their way home, however, they killed the guards and escaped.

When famine hit several neighboring provinces, the ranks of the rebels swelled to over a hundred thousand people. In 1635 the rebel forces raided the hometown of the emperor in Anhui. They burned the ancestral temples and tombs of the emperor. This victory had little military significance, but enhanced the morale of the rebels. The news shocked Beijing, and the emperor went into mourning.

On the northeastern frontier, in the meantime, the Manchu continued to make headway. In 1636, after four years in office, the Minister of Defense of the Ming government committed suicide, weighed down by accumulated failures on both fronts.

Under a new defense chief, the Ming troops scored a major victory against the rebels in late 1638. An important faction of the rebels surrendered to the government. Li Zicheng's wife and daughter were captured. Li escaped with eighteen followers. For a time, it looked as though the rebels had lost. Li was sick for half a year. His followers were contemplating giving up. All this so depressed him that he intended to commit suicide. But before ending his life this way, he asked his close associate Liu Zongmin to go to a temple to pray and then divine. He told Liu to kill him and surrender if the divination revealed bad luck. But three successive divinations gave favorable omens, and Li Zicheng was brought back from the verge of despair.

Those rebels who had earlier surrendered rose again when the attention of the government was diverted to the invasion of the Manchus on the northern border, and General Hong Chengchou, having been directing a successful campaign against the rebels, was transferred to confront the Manchus. Once more Li Zicheng built up his army. In 1641, the rebel forces struck back. They captured two important cities in Sichuan and Henan. Two Ming princes were captured and publicly executed, one of them being the son of Lady Zheng who had once contended for the position of the heir apparent with Prince Changluo as we described in the previous chapter. Unable to face the failure, the Defense Minister, like his predecessor, committed suicide after five years in office.

Years of squandering and corruption had depleted the government treasury. Chongzhen had to raise the tax four times successively to finance the war efforts, doubling the tax rate levied in the days of Emperor Wanli. He was ruling a country on the brink of economic breakdown, a country seething with popular discontent.

In the meantime, Li Zicheng's political advisors urged him to adopt a more moderate policy in order to increase his popularity. Li promised the people an exemption of all taxes for three years and equal distribution of land. Wherever he went, he strictly forbade his troops to harass the local residents. He declared: "If a man kills someone, I will feel as if he is killing my father. If a man rapes a woman, I will feel as if he is raping my mother." His words had a great appeal to a population stricken by famine, by ever-increasing taxes, and by the looting and violence of an increasingly demoralized Ming army. Many cities spontaneously opened their gates to welcome him and many former Ming officers turned to be his supporters.

In 1642 Li met with stiff resistance when he attempted to seize Kaifeng, an important city in Henan. For nine months, the former capital city of the Song Dynasty stood firm. Its citizens were starving, but they would not surrender. Li lost one eye in the fighting. Finally he gave an order to break the banks of the Yellow River to flood the city. Nearly 900,000 people were said to have lost their lives. It was a massive disaster for the Ming government and also a major failure for Li who had hoped to capture the city intact and take possession of its treasures.

Now Li's forces had expanded to a million, more than twice the size of the Ming army. Worse still, the latter had to fight on two fronts —against the rebels and against the Manchu invaders. In 1643 Chongzhen reappointed an experienced general, Sun Chuanting, to fight the rebels. Sun was in favor of a defensive strategy, but most officials in Beijing wanted him to attack Li Zicheng. Forced to take the offensive, he did win several victories initially. However, he was unable to sustain his success mainly because seven days of heavy rain hampered the transportation of supplies for his troops. He ordered a partial retreat. But under the attack of Li Zicheng, the retreat was soon turned into a rout. Half of his 90,000 elite troops lost their lives, and the general himself was also killed in action. Thus, the anti-rebel campaign ended in a fiasco.

Li Zicheng issued a formal statement to denounce the Ming regime. He promised to save the people from misery, saying that Chongzhen, although not an undutiful ruler, was a loner surrounded by corrupt, cruel and self-seeking officials and eunuchs who exploited the people by imposing exorbitant taxes on them and oppressed them by putting them in jail at will.

When Chongzhen obtained a copy of Li's statement, he seemed to feel regretful. The next day he issued a statement accepting responsibility for misgoverning the country. He blamed himself for failing to live up to the expectations of the people and promised to use honest and capable officials. He appealed to the people to rally around him and help overcome the rebels.

But all this was too late. Li Zicheng, after winning a series of victories, controlled the strategic mountainous region between northwestern China and Beijing. At the beginning of 1644, his forces were moving in the direction of the capital.

The Beijing garrison was manned by the old and the weak. And a plague in the previous year took the lives of half of the troops there. The remaining able-bodied ones were recruited by palace eunuchs as their personal bodyguards. Even the upkeep of the garrison was hard, for the treasury had almost run out of money. To raise fund, the emperor agreed to pardon prisoners in return for financial contributions to the defense of the city. There were also voluntary donations from business communities and private individuals. But all this amounted to a little more than a quarter of a million ounces of silver, far from what was required. By early 1644, the Beijing garrison had not received pay for a year. The defense of the city was hopeless.

One proposal was for the emperor to move to Nanjing, a major city on the southern bank of the Yangtze River and establish a southern Ming regime there. But his ministers were divided into the northerners' group and the southerners' group. They were often involved in factional wranglings and they tended to politicize military matters. Any strategy proposed by one side, even if it was a very sensible one, would be rejected by the other side.

For several months, those who were in favor of such a move and those opposed debated the pros and cons of the strategy. The majority was against abandoning Beijing, saying it was the sacred duty of the emperor to stay in the capital. Thus on April 10, 1644, Emperor Chongzhen made the fateful decision not to leave Beijing. That day, officials of the Observatory in Beijing reported that the pole star, the symbol of the emperor, had slipped from the sky. In the meantime, the rebel forces were approaching fast.

The only remaining fighting force of Ming that might stand up against the rebels was the elite troops stationed in Shanhaiguan under the command of General Wu Sangui. Along and outside the Great Wall, garrisons were placed to ward off invaders from the north. Shanhaiguan was at the most eastern end of the Great Wall. It was of utmost strategic importance. Up to that time, General Wu Sangui had successfully beaten back the Manchu troops despite their victories in other parts of northeastern China. Wu came from a distinguished family. His father was once commander-in-chief of Jinzhou in the northeast outside the Great Wall. The emperor now decided to recall these troops for the defense of the capital.

Inside the city the emperor appealed to all the residents to do whatever they could to defend the capital. Militia was organized. The emperor personally financed a private army led by a eunuch. The city walls were reinforced by additional soldiers armed with Portuguese guns. But all these last-minute measures were too weak and too late. Beijing was doomed to fall.

Li Zicheng was advancing toward Beijing. Except for a few isolated confrontations, what he met with was only token resistance. He also sent secret agents into Beijing to spread rumors and obtain intelligence.

On April 22 as the emperor was having a meeting with his ministers, a courier rushed into the meeting room with a document marked "to be opened by His Majesty only." The message was: Li Zicheng had overrun the vital strategic stronghold, Juyong Pass, 40 miles from the Forbidden City. The government forces had surrendered without putting up so much as a fight.

Chongzhen turned pale. General Wu Sangui's troops were apparently delayed. He rose and went into the inner palace. When he came back after a long time, he ordered all the officials to go home.

The next morning Emperor Chongzhen held his last audience. As he entered the hall, he was in tears. All the ministers present burst into tears, too. The emperor gave his permission for the ministers to commit suicide if they chose to.

Li Zicheng was ready to seize the capital. But he was somehow hesitant as to whether or not he should storm the city by force. So he decided to give the emperor a last chance to negotiate a peaceful settlement. He proposed that he himself be given an aristocratic title, one million ounces of silver and the area of Shaanxi and Shansi, and that, in return, he help the emperor to defeat other rebels and join the Ming army to fight the Manchus. The proposal was presented to the emperor by Li's representative, a former eunuch, the very person the emperor had entrusted to raise a private army for his own defense just three weeks before. Chongzhen was tempted to accept Li's proposal. But he also knew that if he accepted Li's proposal, he would probably forever be stigmatized in history for making expedient concessions to the bandits. Therefore before he could commit himself, he needed the support of his prime minister.

"What do you think of the proposal?" he asked the prime minister. "We are facing a crisis."

The prime minister chose not to respond.

"What do you think?" the emperor demanded again. The prime minister kept his silence. Apparently, he refused to share the burden of a historic decision.

Emperor Chongzhen was trembling with fury. He wanted to detain Li's envoy, the eunuch-courier, but was told that two Ming princes were held hostage to ensure the safe return of Li's envoy. He was forced to let go the eunuch. Unable to control his anger, the emperor suddenly struck out and knocked over the throne.

The next day, April 24, Li's men had broke through the south gate of the city. When the news came, Chongzhen burst into tears.

"The great enterprise is over," he said. As he and the empress wept, all those around wept, too. The emperor hastened to send the Crown Prince and his two brothers into hiding. After kissing farewell to her three sons, the empress dragged herself into her room and hanged herself. Chongzhen's other wife also tried to hang herself, but the cord broke, and she fell to the floor. The emperor struck her three times with his sword, but she survived, nevertheless.

Then he went into his daughters' chamber. The crown princess had just turned fifteen.

"Why were you born in such an unfortunate family?" the emperor lamented.

He was about to strike her with his sword, but he could not bring himself to do so. After a long while, he suddenly raised his sword and struck, covering his face with his left hand. Trying to ward off the blow with her hand, the princess had her right arm cut off. She fell to the floor unconscious. She miraculously survived, too. The emperor proceeded to kill another princess, who was six years old. He then ordered his own mother, the empress dowager, to kill herself.

Toward midnight, the emperor disguised himself as a eunuch and tried to flee the palace, only to be fired on by the guards who, not recognizing him, compelled him to return to the palace. Then he changed back to his royal robe, bit his finger and wrote his last words with his blood:

Seventeen years ago I ascended the throne. Now I have met with Heaven's punishment. My ministers have deceived me and the rebels are going to seize the capital. When I die, my soul will be too ashamed to face my ancestors. So let the rebels dismember my body and kill my officials, but I entreat them not to harm the people or pillage the imperial tombs.

It was in the early hours of April 25, 1644 that Emperor Chongzhen walked to the Coal Hill nearby and hanged himself on a pine tree. He was wearing a blue silk robe, his hair dishevelled. His right foot had a red shoe on it and the left foot was bare. A dynasty that had lasted 277 years thus came to an end. Emperor Chongzhen, the last Chinese emperor in history, was thirty-three then.

Comment: It may be said that at the beginning of his reign, Chongzhen had a chance to reach a peace accord with the Manchu whose aim then was not yet a wholesale conquest. Towards the rebels, his policy of appeasement, even when the government forces were on the point of crushing the rebels, was probably ill-advised or ill-implemented. It played into the hands of the rebels who used the appeasement policy to escape extinction, to gain time and to regroup.

If Emperor Chongzhen had moved to the southern capital of Nanjing, the Ming Dynasty could probably have lasted longer. In any case, it would not be too bad an idea to let Li Zicheng fight the Manchu when the latter invaded Beijing.

For thirty years, the country went from relative prosperity in the early years of Wanli to chaos and poverty at the time Chongzhen ascended the throne. It was tottering on the verge of economic collapse, military breakdown and bureaucratic paralysis when Emperor Chongzhen came to power. The writings had been on the wall long before then. His grim determination, his diligence and energy, his youth, ignorance, poor judgment and inadequacy made him all the more a tragic figure beset by external threat, internal revolt, natural disasters, and disloyal officials.

42. THE BEAUTY OR THE EMPIRE

It is easy to get rid of an enemy in the mountain; it is difficult to defeat an enemy in one's heart.
—Wang Yangming (1472-1528)

The Ming Dynasty had fallen. Li Zicheng carried the day. The history of China was at a turning point. A new dynasty was to be established by the rebels who, in time, would become legitimate rulers in the annals of history. Li's army was battle-hardened and powerful. Li's appeal was broad. Even if he had to deal with the looming menace of the Manchu, it might have been expected that he would carry on for some time. Yet he failed, and failed so precipitously that in a matter of six weeks, the regime in Beijing changed hands twice.

A few hours after Emperor Chongzhen had committed suicide, Li Zicheng entered Beijing. About three hundred officials led by the prime minister and the defense minister gathered at the city gate to welcome him. Li's troops were disciplined. At first the residents of Beijing were apprehensive, but when they saw looters executed on the spot, their anxiety was relieved. The Crown Prince was soon found and taken into custody.

Thirteen senior Ming officials took their own lives. About two hundred palace ladies drowned themselves in the moat or the wells in the Forbidden Palace. A sixteen-year-old pretty girl named Fei threw herself into a well but was rescued by rebel soldiers. She was about to be violated when she claimed that she was the emperor's daughter. The rebels were awed and took her to Li Zicheng. Li asked the eunuchs to identify her. When it was discovered she was not a royal princess, Li gave her to one of his generals as wife. On the wedding night, the girl made the rebel general dead drunk, stabbed him to death, and then cut her own throat. When Li heard of this, he ordered an honorable burial for the girl.

The body of Emperor Chongzhen was discovered three days after his death. Li Zicheng seemed shocked to see his remains.

"I came to enjoy the rivers and mountains with you," Li said to the corpse. "How could you have taken your own life?"

Later he met with the Crown Prince. He asked the boy how his father had managed to lose the empire.

"Because we made the mistake of appointing treacherous ministers."

"Ah, now you understand," Li agreed with the boy. "Most of the ministers and officers in your father's court are disloyal to your father. But it's not your fault. You won't be harmed."

On the one hand, Li needed the cooperation of former Ming bureaucrats to run the government. On the other hand, he had only contempt for them, believing that it was their corruption, disloyalty and selfishness that had brought down the Ming Dynasty.

He issued an order for all the former Ming officials to register with the new regime. On April 29, several thousand of them gathered in a compound outside the palace, supposedly to wait for appointments with the new government. They waited from morning till sunset without food to eat or water to drink, and Li's soldiers kicked, pushed and cursed them.

Looking at the crowd, Li remarked, "How could the empire not be ruined with such a group of unscrupulous officials in charge?"

As each name was called and the person responded, Li's secretary cited the person's wrongdoings. The atmosphere was like that of a public trial. Nevertheless new positions were given to nearly a hundred of them. The remaining ones were marched at sword point to the army camps of Li's generals to be punished. For Li believed those who did not die loyally for their dynasty could not be trusted to serve the new regime with loyalty, either.

Li was disappointed to have found that there were only 170,000 ounces of gold and 130,000 ounces of silver left behind by the former regime. This was not enough for him to reward his men with.

A scheme to exact funds from former Ming officials was proposed. The most corrupt ones would be tortured until they turned over their assets. Those who refused to work for the new regime would have their property confiscated. All others were asked to make voluntary contributions.

However, this form of extortion soon went out of hand. Li's troops looted the city. They searched civilian houses for money, jewelry and food. They raped women and beat pedestrians who happened to be in their way. Army camps were turned into torture chambers. The worst brutalities took place in the camp of Li's close associate General Liu Zongmin who even tortured businessmen for ransom. The city was terrorized.

Li tried to stop the spread of abuse. At a special meeting with his generals, he asked them, "Why can't you help me to be a good ruler?"

"You have the authority to rule the empire, but we have the power to plunder. There is no need to say any more about this." His generals snapped back.

Among those captured by the rebel general Liu Zongmin was a twenty-two-year-old girl called Chen Yuanyuan. She was the girlfriend of General Wu Sangui, who was in charge of China's northern defense against the Manchu at the strategic pass of Shanhaiguan.

Chen was a fabulously beautiful and talented singing girl from the south. Two years earlier she was taken to Beijing to be presented to Emperor Chongzhen. But, at a time when the national crisis was so threatening, the emperor was too busy to take any interest in a pretty girl. Chen Yuanyuan was taken to the mansion of Lord Tian Hongyu who was the emperor's father-in-law.

General Wu Sangui first met her when he came to Beijing to discuss military matters with the emperor. He fell in love with her the moment he saw her. Chen Yuanyuan was also drawn toward him, knowing he was a great soldier.

In early 1644 Wu was invited to a sumptuous dinner in his honor at the residence of Lord Tian Hongyu, who wanted General Wu to protect his family as the defense in Beijing was deteriorating. There he met Chen Yuanyuan again.

Wu arrived in full military uniform. Chen Yuanyuan was dressed herself simply but tastefully. One glance at her, and his heart leapt. When Tian asked the girl to sing for him and to pour wine for him, he became so high-spirited that he kept laughing and chatting with her as though there were no one else at the banquet.

It was time for Wu to leave when Tian Hongyu raised the important issue—the protection of his household.

"Do you feel safe to keep such a beauty at home?" Wu asked his host.

Tian took the hint.

"If I could have Yuanyuan," the general continued, "I'll do my level best to protect your family."

Tian Hongyu was compelled to let go his favorite girl, realizing he was not in a bargaining position at all. Wu led the girl away, elated. He wanted to marry Yuanyuan right away, but his father thought it was not appropriate for him to take her to his military post at this critical moment. So Chen Yuanyuan stayed in Beijing at Wu's father's home for the time being.

When the rebels entered the city, Wu's father hid Chen away. However, General Liu Zongmin, tipped by a former eunuch about the existence of such a beauty in Beijing, arrested the old man and forced him to yield Chen Yuanyuan.

While all this was happening in Beijing, General Wu Sangui's elite troops were marching toward the capital. Since he received the order from Emperor Chongzhen in mid-April to come to the rescue of Beijing, he had to evacuate the civilians out of harm's way in case of Manchu invasion after his withdrawal from Shanhaiguan. This considerably slowed down his pace.

On April 26 when his troops reached a town about a hundred miles from Beijing, word came that the city had fallen into the rebels' hands and the emperor had died. Wu immediately turned back to Shanhaiguan. He dispatched a messenger to Beijing to inquire after his family there.

Wu's father replied that the family was safe. Wu wrote back, intimating that he was considering collaborating with Li Zicheng.

At the same time, Li also recognized the importance of securing the cooperation of Wu Sangui if his cause was to succeed. He sent a former Ming general to see Wu with 1,000 ounces of gold and 10,000 ounces of silver as gift. In his letter to Wu, Li offered him the same rank and title as Wu had under Emperor Chongzhen.

Wu held a meeting with his officers. "Li's forces are formidable," he said. "His envoy is here to meet us. Should I welcome him or not?"

His officers assured him that he would have their loyalty whatever he decided to do.

Just when Wu was ready to negotiate the terms of surrendering to Li, a servant and a concubine of his father arrived at his camp. They brought the news that his father had been taken away by the rebels and was tortured, and that Chen Yuanyuan had fallen into the hands of Liu Zongmin, a general under Li Zicheng.

Wu was furious.

"A man cannot be called a man if he can't protect his woman!" he shouted.

He pulled out his sword, cut off a corner of the desk in his office and swore to avenge himself and restore the Ming House.

When Li heard of Wu's declaration of war, he knew there was no more hope for collaboration. He decided to lead an army of 100,000 out of Beijing to attack Wu at Shanhaiguan.

Wu was confronted with two hostile forces: outside Shanhaiguan, the Manchus; inside, Li's troops. To him, the Manchus seemed the lesser of the two evils. He decided to seek alliance with them in order to defeat Li.

In the Manchu, the Qing Emperor Huangtaiji died of a heart attack in 1643. His eldest son did not succeed to the throne because of strong opposition from his uncles. Instead, Huangtaiji's younger son was enthroned, but he was only six years old. The de facto control of the Qing government was in the hands of prince regent Dorgon who was Huangtaiji's brother. Dorgon had a distinguished military record coupled with outstanding political and diplomatic skills.

Wu wrote to the Qing emperor suggesting military cooperation against Li Zicheng. He promised to cede to Qing a greater portion of the territories in the north of the Great Wall to Qing and to give Qing part of the booty and the slaves captured after a joint victory over Li Zicheng.

Dorgon was overjoyed. In fact, he had already got the news of the bloody overthrow of the Ming regime and the subsequent rampage of Li Zicheng's troops in Beijing. He believed that time had come to realize the long cherished ambition of his father Nurhaci to take over China. He ordered the army to be ready to advance toward Shanhaiguan. Wu's offer could not have come at a better time. It meant that the Manchu could enter Shanhaiguan without a fight.

Wu Sangui had been his formidable adversary for a long time, but Dorgon was only too willing to forget the past. He tried to persuade Wu to join the service of Qing. But Wu would only go so far as to join forces with Dorgon to crush Li Zicheng. Dorgon did not press further.

He promised to help.

Upon the advice of Hong Chengchou, the ranking Chinese general who surrendered to Qing two years ago, Dorgon told his troops to give up their former hit-loot-and-run strategy because this time they were to stay in China. There should be no more looting, burning or needless killing. Whoever should disobey would be severely punished.

On May 26, 1644 a decisive battle was fought near Shanhaiguan between Li's 100,000 men on the one side and the combined forces of 50,000 elite troops of Wu and 140,000 troops of Qing on the other. Li was defeated amid a blinding sandstorm.

As Li retreated to Beijing, he was relentlessly pursued by Wu.

Li tried to stop Wu's pursuit by displaying Wu's family on the city wall and threatening to kill them, but Wu ordered his soldiers to shoot arrows at Li. Outraged, Li had the entire family of Wu, thirty-eight in all, executed. As Wu saw his father's head hanging on the city wall, he fell from his horse in a swoon.

When it came to Chen Yuanyuan's turn to be killed, she said to Li, "I would like to have a few words with you before I die."

Li agreed.

"I understand that I was the cause of all this. General Wu was ready to cooperate. He broke off the negotiation only because I was taken away. If you kill me now, he will pursue you to the end of the earth. But if you let me go, I will try my best to ask him not to run after you."

As Li planned to retreat, he felt he should take the chance. Chen Yuanyuan was thus released.

Curiously enough, it was at that moment that Li decided to formally announce himself the emperor of a new dynasty, the Shun Dynasty. The next day, June 4, 1644, he set the palace on fire, ordered the execution of large numbers of Ming officials at the city gate, and then fled the city.

His regime in Beijing lasted for only six weeks. The entire city cheered at his retreat. Those rebel soldiers who remained in the capital became targets of popular revenge.

On the morning of June 5, the city fathers and government officials, clothed in Ming official uniforms, lined up outside the city to welcome the victorious army of General Wu Sangui. But Wu was nowhere to be seen. He was pursuing Li all the way to the west. Standing on the chariot and heading the procession was Dorgon.

"The Manchus are coming!" All the residents in Beijing were in consternation, their euphoria evaporated.

"I am the prince regent," Dorgon announced. "The crown prince of Ming has appointed me to be your ruler."

The crowd stood there, aghast.

Dorgon ordered a national mourning the following day for the deceased Ming emperor. Chongzhen was reburied according to the Chinese imperial tradition.

Then Dorgon ordered all the Chinese to shave their heads like the Manchus. He moved the capital of Qing to Beijing from Mukden.

When Li Zicheng fled to Shaanxi, Wu turned back to Beijing. The city was already under the control of Dorgon. Seeing those who came to greet him have their heads half shaven after the Manchu fashion, he started to weep. Addressing the welcoming crowd, he said:

"The Qing people did not treat the Chinese with respect. When they took over Korea and wanted the Koreans to cut their hair, the Koreans would rather lose their heads than their hair. The Qing people did not dare to press them. We are subjects of the Ming Dynasty. How can we put up with such an insult? I came here too late. I am so sorry I failed you."

Later Dorgon rescinded the order about hair-cutting.

Wu was reunited with Chen Yuanyuan. He captured Liu Zongmin, the rebel general, and hanged him.

The remnant forces of Ming fled to Nanjing in the south. In his letter to a Ming general who was heading the resistance movement there, Dorgon wrote:

"It was not our army that toppled the Ming Dynasty. It was the arch rebel Li Zicheng who caused the downfall of the Ming empire."

Li's remaining forces were crushed in early 1645. The death of Li was a mystery: One story said he was killed in Hubei by guards of landlords; another suggested that he died thirty years later in a Buddhist temple where he took refuge after his defeat.

The Qing army moved south. This time they did not act with restraint as they showed in Beijing. They proved capable of the worst atrocities. The most notorious was the ten-day killing spree that followed the fall of Yangzhou, a city in modern Jiangsu, during which 800,000 people were massacred. Another carnage took place in Jiading, a town near Shanghai, where 200,000 people were slaughtered. At the end of 1645, the rule of Qing was firmly established in China.

Dorgon re-ordered all Chinese to show their loyalty by plaiting their hair in a queue as was the custom of the Manchus.

Thirty years after his surrender, Wu Sangui raised his own flag against Qing in 1674. His rebellion lasted eight years before it was finally put down by Emperor Kangxi in 1681.

The rule of the Manchu came to an end in 1911 with the revolution led by Dr. Sun Yat-sen, the father of modern China.

Comment: To many Chinese, General Wu Sangui was a traitor who set a higher value on a woman than on his country. His action of switching allegiance to Qing seems to have borne out an ancient Chinese saying: a beautiful woman can ruin an empire.

China was seriously weakened during the rule of the Qing Dynasty. It suffered humiliating losses for being unable to cope with the invasion of the Western powers and Japan. Its economic power and international stature had deteriorated. The Manchus, an alien minority who had been sinicized to a certain degree, ruled China like conquerors and ruled with the care and abandon due an alien conqueror.

But the decline of China did not start in Qing, or with the notorious Empress Dowager in the late nineteenth century, who certainly played an ignominious role. The seeds of decline were sowed far back in late Ming, during the years of Emperor Wanli. Up to the conquest of the Manchu, China had never recovered from the crises that Wanli's misrule had caused. In a certain sense, it was Emperor Wanli who paved the way for the eventual success of the Manchu whose rule, in turn, made China what it was at the beginning of the twentieth century.

History is a mirror. If we can read its reflection correctly, then it becomes a crystal ball for us to see what future has in store for us.

To the extent that history consists largely of human actions, there is no a prior reason that it will not be repeated if we choose not to heed its lessons or think we can outsmart its inexorable logic.

PART X
THE WAY TO PEACE

43. THE ART OF LIVING

When the desires of men are curbed, there will be peace in mind. When there is peace in mind, there will be peace in the world.
—Lao Tzu

In a world of chaos, of competition, of conflicts, of the rat race for survival and success, the voice of Lao Tzu is a voice with a difference. It is like a cool breeze on a summer evening after a long hectic day of work and struggle in our short life. Lao Tzu suggests to us that there are other ways of living, that there are more important things in life than fame and fortune. His way is the way of peace, with others as well as with oneself.

A contemporary of Confucius, Lao Tzu lived about two thousand and five hundred years ago. He is the founder of Taoism. We know practically nothing about his life except that he had been the curator of the National Library in Luoyang, the capital of the Zhou Dynasty and lived to the age of one hundred and sixty.

Lao Tzu said his teachings were easy to understand and easy to practice. Yet, just as he himself pointed out, few people seem to really understand or practice them. This made Lao Tzu feel as though he were hiding a crown jewel inside his coarse clothes, but nobody recognized him. Perhaps the common people's failure to understand the thought of Lao Tzu can be attributed to his ambiguous language which is frequently paradoxical and even mystical. Just as one fails to see clearly the real face of a great mountain when there are too many clouds around it, so does one fail to understand the doctrine of Lao Tzu when there are so many interpretations over the years that they threaten to crowd out the true meaning of Lao Tzu's thought.

The following is based on his famous book The Way.

BE HUMBLE

Nothing is softer than water. Yet nothing surpasses it in overcoming the hard. The weak overwhelms the strong. The gentle conquers the firm. Everyone knows that, but no one can practice it.

A good man is like water. Water benefits all things but it does not compete with them for a higher ground. It dwells in low places that nobody admires. Similarly, a good man stays in a humble place. He does not force his way ahead. Nor does he struggle for accomplishment. He is serene, sincere, faithful, diligent and compassionate. He accomplishes because he knows how to grasp the opportune moment and achieve his goal in a natural way.

Recede first if you want to proceed. Give first if you want to take. Humble yourself and place yourself below others first if you want to be above them. If you want to be the leader of men, you have to put their interest before your own, so that they will support you without feeling your weight on their backs.

The great oceans are kings of all streams and rivers because they take a low position.

BE GENTLE AND COMPASSIONATE

I have three treasures. Hold and cherish them: the first is compassion; the second, frugality; the third, shunning to be the first in the world.

Compassion for human beings gives one courage in safeguarding life.

Frugality means one's resources will not be exhausted.

And if one does not contend for the first place, he will find himself in the first place.

He will be doomed who abandons compassion to display valor, or gives up frugality in favor of wasteful spending, or throws off humility while contending for the first place.

When a man is alive, his body is soft and pliable. When he is dead, his body becomes stiff and hard. When a plant is alive, it is weak and tender. When it is dead, it becomes dry and brittle.

Therefore, hard and stiff is the way of death. And soft and pliable is the way of life.

A strong army can be the cause of destruction. A strong man often dies an unnatural death. A big tree may be hewed down for its timber.

If one dares to be daring, he will get killed. If one dares to be cautious, he will survive.

Bend in order to be straight. Be hollow in order to be full. Yield in order to be completely preserved.

Weapons are intrinsically ominous instruments. A good general uses war only as the last resort. He stops as soon as he has attained his goal. He takes no pride in what he does. Even if he wins the war, he does not enjoy the victory. For he who enjoys victory enjoys killing. He who takes delight in killing will never make his way in the world.

DO NOT HAVE TOO MANY DESIRES

Lights and colors blind the eyes. Sound and fury deafen the ears. Flavors and spices numb the tongue. The pursuit of pleasure drives a man out of his mind. The possession of rarities gets in the way of their owner.

Those who are violent often die a violent death. Those who indulge in their desires without restraint head for destruction. Those who are too strong quicken the process of aging. Whoever tampers with the way of nature will perish soon.

Take less, and you will have more. Desire more, and you will be overly obsessed. No disaster is greater than insatiable desires. No vice is worse than limitless greed. He who is content is always sufficient.

The Way of Heaven is like drawing a bow. If the bowstring is too high, it will be pushed down; if it is too low, it will be pulled up. If it is too long, it will be shortened; if it is too short, it will be lengthened. The Way of Heaven is the same: Surplus will be cut down; deficiency will be made up.

The way of man is the opposite. He takes where there is want and gives where there is surplus. Only a wise man acts according to the Way of Heaven.

Cherish simple life and plain honesty. Have fewer desires and be less selfish. The essence of achieving peace of mind is to be free of desires. And peace of mind will lead to peace in the world.

DO NOT BE TOO SELFISH

Honor and disgrace can both make you anxious if you attach undue importance to them. Remember those are only external things.

Self is a bad guide to happiness. If you are too conscious of your ego, you may cause yourself to worry too much. But if you can forget yourself, you have nothing to fear.

He who stands on tiptoes cannot stand firm. He who strides cannot go far. He who shows off does not shine. He who proclaims self-righteousness will not be honored. He who applauds himself will lose merit.

If you put yourself behind others, you will find yourself to be the first. If you do not give thought to yourself, you will enjoy life more. If you stop being selfish, your self-interest will be realized. The more you do for others, the more you will have for yourself. The more you give, the richer you will be.

He who achieves without claiming credit for himself will attain everlasting glory. True greatness lies in not claiming to be great. And a selfless person can be entrusted with governing the world.

Heaven takes no part in competition, yet it conquers everything. Heaven does not speak, and yet it responds. Heaven does not summon, and yet all things come to it of their own accord. Heaven is unhurried, and yet it plans well. The net of Heaven is vast and loose but it embraces all things big and small without omission.

Heaven is eternal and earth is everlasting because they do not exist for themselves.

The Way of Heaven is to benefit, not to harm; to serve, not to compete.

DO NOT BE TOO SURE

In dealing with difficulties, tackle easier ones first. In attaining great goals, begin with small ones. A wise man does not regard himself great. For this reason, he accomplishes great things. A wise man does not make big promises for fear he may not be able to keep them. Nor does he make light of difficulties for fear he may not be able to overcome them. Precisely because he is prepared for difficulties he may have to overcome, he does not encounter any.

It is easy to hold something when it is stable. It is easy to make plans before anything happens. A big tree grows from a tiny sprout. A tall tower is built with a mound of earth. The journey of a thousand miles begins with a small step. Deal with things when they are still easy to handle. Take precautions against problems before they occur.

Things are prone to failure the closer they reach the stage of completion. But if you can be as careful then as you were at the beginning, failure can be avoided.

If you do not know, and you know you do not know, it is good. If you do not know, but you believe you know, it is bad. If you know others, you are smart. If you know yourself, you are enlightened. If you beat others, you prove that you are stronger than they are. But if you conquer yourself, then you have the real power. A wise man knows himself, but does not show off. He loves himself, but does not exalt himself.

Misfortune may be the harbinger of blessing. Blessing can contain seeds of disaster. Who knows what the final outcome will be? How can one be absolutely sure? Everything changes. Do not be deluded by its appearance.

The Way of Heaven is impartial. It has no favorites, but is always on the side of the good people.

WITHDRAW IN GOOD TIME

Sincere words are not flowery. Fine words may not be sincere. He who knows is not talkative. He who is talkative does not know. The world does not contend against anyone who does not contend.

A quiet mind and a patient disposition are the basis of sound living.

Better stop than fill the cup to overflowing. Never be too proud, or you will have nothing to be proud of. Never be too sharp, or you will lose your edge. A house full of gold is hard to safeguard. A person too boastful of his fortune invites disaster. Quit in good time when your work is done. Do not hang on.

Fame or life, which is more precious to you? Health or wealth, which is more important to you? Gain or loss, which is more desirable to you?

If you love fame too much, you will pay a dear price. If you hold onto too much wealth, you will lose heavily one day. If you do not know where to stop, you will put yourself in danger. But if you know how to be content, you will not suffer disgrace.

This is the Way of Heaven. If you adhere to it, you can long endure.

GOOD GOVERNMENT

Governing a big nation is like cooking a small fish. You should not stir it too often, or it will come apart.

The best government does not make its presence felt. The second best is the one praised by the people. The next is the one feared by the people. The worst is the one despised by the people.

The best way to govern a nation is to govern in accordance with the nature of things and be simple and sparing. A good government does not make many policies or issue many orders; it runs the country in such a way that when its work is done, people will say: "All this happened to us naturally." A good government does not disturb the people unnecessarily, nor is it engaged in many activities interfering with the life of the people.

Too much taxes starve the people; too many rules and regulations make the land ungovernable. The more prohibitions there are, the poorer the people will become. The more laws are passed, the more thieves there will be. The more skills people have, and the more novel things they make, the more avaricious they may become.

A wise man does not have any fixed opinions. He regards the wishes of the people as his own wishes. He approves of good people, and also of bad people. Thus all become good. He trusts faithful people, and also unfaithful people. Thus all become faithful. To the wise, there are no hopeless people, for he knows how to educate them; and there are no useless things, for he knows how to make use of them.

When a big country takes a humble position, it will win over small nations. When a small country takes a humble position, it will be embraced by big nations. But a big nation should be more humble, for a humble small nation preserves itself at best, whereas a humble big nation wins the heart of the whole world.

My Way is the secret of the universe. Its greatness is beyond comparison. The superior man cherishes it and practices it. The average man sometimes grasps it but sometimes loses it. The lower man scoffs at it and rejects it.

Comment: The Way of Lao Tzu contains more than one meaning. Different people may read different messages in it. We probably can only scratch the surface of the profundity of Lao Tzu. Even so, we will be greatly benefited.

Our life is a journey of constant strife and endless changes. Sometimes we seem to have lost our way. Sometimes we do not see the forest for the trees.

Reading Lao Tzu, even though we do not understand everything he says, serves to remind us, in the thick of our struggle for existence or a better life, to take a step back and adopt a more detached attitude toward life and toward ourselves.

Let things take their own courses. Do not try to force a solution to a problem if we do not have one at present. If we can extricate ourselves, for a moment, from our daily preoccupations to reexamine our outlooks and values, we probably will be able to put our goals and objectives in perspective and have a better idea of the priorities of our life. Sometimes less means more. Sometimes a step back is better than a step forward. Sometimes the best gain is to lose. And there is also a time simply to let go.

We may never be able to live the way Lao Tzu espouses. But if we know when and how to take a respite and enjoy a moment of inner peace, we may be able to renew our strength and regain our confidence to handle the pressure on us with buoyancy, poise and grace, and to confront the challenges of life more successfully.

44. E.T.

I dreamed I was a butterfly fluttering here and there following the fancy of a butterfly. Suddenly I woke up. There lay Chuang Tzu again.

I wonder whether it was Chuang Tzu who dreamed he was a butterfly just now or a butterfly dreamed it was Chuang Tzu.

—*Chuang Tzu (369-286 B.C.)*

THE WOMAN IN THE PICTURE

Zhao Yan, a scholar in the Tang Dynasty, had a painting which he cherished very much, a painting of a beautiful woman.

"A woman so beautiful can never be found in this world," he said to the artist. I want to marry her if she were a real person."

"She can be one," the artist said. "Her name is Zhen Zhen. She is a celestial beauty. Call her name day and night for a hundred days, and she will respond. Pour into her mouth some wine the moment she responds to your call, and she will assume human life."

Zhao Yan started to call "Zhen Zhen" the next day. He called her name day and night without stop for a hundred days. On the hundredth day the woman answered, "Yes."

Zhao hurriedly poured some wine into her mouth. Suddenly her body moved. She walked out of the painting and began to talk and smile.

"Thank you for bringing me here," she said. "I am willing to be your wife."

She ate and drank like an ordinary human being. A year later she bore him a son.

Two years went by when Zhao met an old friend in the street. "That woman must be a spirit," said the friend. "Sooner or later she will do you harm. Let me give you a magic sword with which you can kill her." That evening the friend had the sword sent to Zhao.

"I have to bid you farewell, my dear," said Zhen Zhen the moment Zhao entered her room, her tears rolling down her cheeks. "I am the goddess of Mount Heng in the south. The artist happened to paint my image in the picture and then you called my name. I married you because you wished to. Now that you have suspicions against me, I cannot live with you any longer."

Instantly she mounted into the painting with her son, spitting out the wine she had drunk earlier. The painting became the same as the original one, except that a boy was added in now.

THE THUNDER GOD

Yue Yunhe and Xia Pingzi were great friends since boyhood. They lived in the same village and studied in the same school. Being a bright boy, Xia made a name for himself at the age of ten. He helped and encouraged Yue with his studies. Yue became a scholar, too. But he failed the imperial examinations repeatedly.

A few years later Xia Pingzi died of an infectious disease, leaving his wife and a son behind. They were too poor to bury him properly. Yue offered to pay all the expenses. He also took care of the livelihood of Xia's widow and son, sharing with them everything he had. What he had done earned him admiration and respect from the local community.

But Yue had his own family to support. Soon he found it difficult to support two families.

"Alas!" he sighed. "If a talented man like Xia died without achieving success in life, what could I expect? If I work and worry like this all my life, I can end up dying like a dog in a ditch. It is time that I tried something else. I must make a fortune while I am still young."

Thus, he gave up studying and took to trading. In six months he was already much better off than before.

One day, while he was staying at an inn in Jinling, the present-day city of Nanjing, he came across a tall, muscular man. The man looked depressed.

"Would you like something to eat?" asked Yue.

The man did not reply. Yue pushed some dishes to him. The man grabbed the food with both hands and finished everything in no time. Yue then ordered more food for him. This, too, was quickly gobbled up. Seeing this, Yue asked the innkeeper to bring a whole ham and a pile of pancakes. Now the stranger seemed to have had his fill, after devouring what was enough for several people.

"Thank you so much," he said, turning to Yue. "This is the first time in three years that I have eaten my fill."

"You are a fine man," said Yue. "But why are you so desperate?"

"It is a punishment from God," said the man. "But I am not in a position to talk about it."

Yue asked him where his home was.

"I have no home on land, no boat on water," the man answered. "At dawn I walk in the village. At night I sleep under the city walls."

When Yue packed his things up and got on his journey again, the man silently followed him as though unwilling to leave Yue.

"Why are you following me?" Yue asked him.

"You'll be in great danger. I want to be with you."

This sounded odd, but Yue let the man accompany him, anyway. On the way, Yue invited him to have meals with him, but the man declined, saying that he needed only a few meals a year.

The next day, when they were crossing a river, a storm suddenly broke out. The ferry was overturned. Yue and the man were thrown into the water. When the storm passed off, the man emerged from the water, carrying Yue on his back. He put Yue on board a passenger boat and dived into the river. A moment later, he reappeared, bringing up Yue's boat with him. Then he placed Yue in his own boat, told him to take a rest and jumped into the water again. This time he came out with some of Yue's lost properties under his arms. He threw them into the boat and plunged into the river once more. He went on doing this until everything was recovered for Yue.

Yue thanked him repeatedly.

"It is kind enough of you to have saved my life," said Yue. "I did not expect you to salvage my boat and all my goods."

Yue was exceedingly happy to have found that all his things had been retrieved. He began to regard the stranger a supernatural man. He was now ready to sail back home, but the man wanted to take his leave. Yue tried very hard to ask him to travel with him. In the end, the man agreed.

As they were sailing, Yue said to him, "It was not bad at all. I lost only a golden hairpin."

At this, the man rose and was about to jump into the water again. Yue hastened to stop him, but the man disappeared. Soon he emerged from the water, smiling.

"I am delighted I have accomplished my mission," he said, handing Yue the golden hairpin. Everyone on the riverbank, seeing this, was astonished.

Yue returned home with his friend. The man only ate once every ten days or so, but then he would eat an enormous amount. One day he spoke of leaving again. Yue implored him to stay.

At that time heavy clouds were gathering in the sky. It threatened to rain. There was a loud crash of thunder.

"I always wonder what it is like above those clouds and what a thunder is like," Yue said. "I wish I could go up there to take a look."

"I bet you like to take a walk in the clouds?" the man said with a smile.

Soon Yue felt sleepy. He took a nap on a couch. As he awoke, instead of lying on the couch, he found himself walking in the air, enveloped on all sides by fleece-like clouds as it was all softness beneath his feet. He sprang up in great alarm, but he felt dizzy. It was as though he were standing in a rocking boat. Looking up, he saw a star right in front of his eyes.

"I must be dreaming," he wondered. Looking around closely, he saw all the stars were studded in the sky like lotus seeds in the cup of a lotus flower. He tried to shake them with his hand. The big ones were firmly planted whereas the smaller ones quivered. He plucked a small one and hid it inside his sleeve. Then he parted the clouds to look down. What he saw was a vast sea of clouds shimmering like silver. Cities looked no bigger than beans.

"What would happen if I lost my footing?" he thought to himself. Just at that moment he saw two dragons coming, pulling a chariot behind them. The swing of their tails snapped like the crack of a cowherd's whip. On the chariot was an enormous container filled with water. Around it a dozen of men were busy dipping out water and sprinkling it on the clouds. As they saw Yue, they were astonished. Yue recognized his friend among them.

"This is my friend," the man introduced him to his colleagues. Then he gave Yue a ladle to sprinkle the water like everybody else. There was a severe drought that year. Yue pushed aside the clouds and scooped out as much water as he could to where he thought his village was. After a few moments, the man came over to Yue.

"I am the thunder god just back from a three-year exile on earth. I was punished because I had neglected to send down rain. Now as I have served my term, I have to say good-bye to you here."

He took a very long rope which had been used as the rein on the dragon chariot. Giving one end of the rope to Yue, he told him to hold fast onto it so that he could be let down to earth. Yue was afraid at first, but his friend assured him that all was well. Yue did what he was told and began to slide down the rope. In the twinkling of an eye, he found himself standing on the ground near his village. The rope was gradually drawn up into the clouds and was soon out of sight.

Because of the long drought, there was barely enough rainfall to submerge a man's toe in the area except for Yue's village where all ditches and drains were full.

When he returned home, Yue took out the star and placed it on the table. It was dark and dull like an ordinary stone. But when night came, it shone so bright that the entire room was lit up. Yue carefully wrapped the treasure up and put it away. He only took it out when he had guests. The star sent out thousands of dazzling rays. Everyone looked at it in amazement.

One evening, Yue's wife was combing her hair. All at once the stone began to dim and flicker like a glowworm. She was startled, her mouth agape. She had scarcely uttered a word when suddenly the stone flew into her mouth. She tried to cough it out, but it ran down her throat. Panic-stricken, she hurried to tell her husband about it. Yue was stunned.

That night Yue had a dream. He saw his old friend Xia.

"I am a Leo star," Xia said. "I have never forgotten your kindness. Now that you have brought me back from the sky, it is obvious we are knit together in fate. I intend to repay my debt of gratitude by becoming your son."

Yue had no child then although he was already in his thirties. He was pleased at the dream message. Shortly afterwards his wife was pregnant. When she gave birth to a boy, the whole room radiated brilliant light like the star that she had swallowed.

The boy was therefore named Little Star. He was a brilliant child. At the age of sixteen he passed the highest imperial examination.

Comment: These two stories are among the most delicious ones in Chinese fairy tales. They are included here as dessert to round off our feast of wisdom in Chinese history.

EPILOGUE

My recent tour to China took me to Confucius's hometown in Shandong Province. There I visited the Temple of Confucius where a collection of stone monuments, dedicated to the Master by his followers, are exhibited in a dusty, narrow, dimly-lit gallery. To my astonishment, it is a store house of three thousand years' history. Each dynasty in Chinese history from Han to Qing is represented by at least one monument. A surrealistic feeling came over me when I was walking down the aisle: for one fleeting monument, I felt as though all my ancestors were collectively communicating with me, and through me, to all their descendants; I felt as though I caught a glimpse of eternity. Here, in this gallery, history asserts itself in a most amazing display of proof, attesting to the continuity of our civilization, with silent, awe-inspiring eloquence.

These monuments have survived intact because generations of people have taken pains to preserve them. In striking contrast to them, many huge ancient monuments erected on giant stone turtles, in the yard just outside the gallery, are in a state of ruin. Most of the words carved on their weather-beaten surface are barely legible. And no one knows how long they will remain there. Obviously for whatever reason, little effort has been made to keep them from wear and tear.

The fate of these monuments reminds me of the fate of classic wisdom in our history. Wisdom is the most precious asset our ancestors have left behind them. But it is something that cannot be genetically inherited. Unless we want it, unless we are wise enough and humble enough to make conscious effort to learn and to practice it, wisdom will not be ours to keep.

China's classic wisdom is about one people, one nation, one history. But it is more than that. Transcending time, space and race, it speaks to all peoples, all nations. If you have found something familiar beneath its strangeness, or you have recognized something universal in its uniqueness, it is only because the wisdom of China is part of our common heritage, the heritage of mankind.

Chinghua Tang
New York, N.Y.
December 1995

A NOTE ON PRONUNCIATION

The romanization of Chinese names presents some difficulty. Although the Wade Giles system of romanizing Chinese names has long been in use in the West, this book generally adopts the pinyin system as it is the official phonetic alphabet current in China. Some proper names such as Confucius, Lao Tzu and Yangtse are spelled in their traditional way because Western readers are already familiar with them.

Most of the letters in the pinyin system are pronounced more or less as what the English reader would expect, but there are a few baffling transcriptions:

c = ts as in "cuts"
q = ch as in "chin"
x = sh as in "she"
zh = j as in "Joe"

For those who are interested, we have prepared a chart to compare the pinyin system of romanization with the Wade system.

Pinyin	Wade	Pinyin	Wade
ba	pa	bu	pu
bai	bai	ca	tsa
ban	pan	cai	tsai
bang	pang	can	tsan
bao	pao	cang	tsang
bei	pei	cao	tsao
ben	pen	ce	tse
beng	peng	cen	tsen
bi	pi	ceng	tseng
bian	pien	chi	chih
biao	piao	chong	chung
bie	pieh	chuo	cho
bin	pin	ci	tzu, tsu
bing	ping	cong	tsung
bo	po	cou	tsou

cu	tsu	gou	kou
cuan	tsuan	gu	ku
cui	tsui	gua	kua
cun	tsun	guai	kuai
cuo	tso	guan	kuan
da	ta	guang	kuang
dai	tai	gui	kui
dan	tan	gun	kun
dang	tang	guo	kuo
dao	tao	he	he, ho
de	te	hong	hung
deng	teng	ji	chi
di	ti	jia	chia
dian	tien	jian	chien
diao	tiao	jiang	chiang
die	tieh	jiao	chiao
ding	ting	jie	chieh
diu	tiu	jin	chin
dong	tung	jing	ching
dou	tou	jiong	chiung
du	tu	jiu	chiu
duan	tuan	ju	chu
dui	tui	juan	chuan
dun	tun	jue	chueh, chuo
duo	to	jun	chun
e	eh	ke	ke, ko
er	erh	kong	kung
ga	ka	lie	lieh
gai	kai	long	lung
gan	kan	lue	lueh, luo, lio
gang	kang	mian	mien
gao	kao	mie	mieh
ge	ke, ko	nian	nien
gei	kei	nie	nieh
gen	ken	nong	nung
geng	keng	nue	nueh,nuo, nio
gong	kung	nuo	no

pian	pien	tong	tung
pie	pieh	tuo	to
qi	chi	xi	hsi
qia	chia	xia	hsia
qian	chien	xian	hsien
qiang	chiang	xiang	hsiang
qiao	chiao	xiao	hsiao
qie	chieh	xie	hsieh
qin	chin	xin	hsin
qing	ching	xing	hsing
qiong	chiung	xiong	hsiung
qiu	chiu	xiu	hsiu
qu	chu	xu	hsu
quan	chuan	xuan	hsuan
que	chueh, chuo	xue	hsueh, hsuo
qun	chun	xun	hsun
ran	jan	yan	yen
rang	jang	ye	yeh
rao	jao	yong	yung
re	je	you	yu
ren	jen	yuan	yuen
reng	jeng	yue	yueh
ri	jih	za	tsa
rong	rung	zai	tsai
rou	jou	zan	tsan
ru	ju	zang	tsang
ruan	juan	zao	tsao
rui	jui	ze	tse
run	jun	zei	tsei
ruo	jo	zen	tsen
shi	shih	zeng	tseng
shuo	sho	zha	cha
si	su, szu, ssu	zhai	chai
song	sung	zhan	chan
suo	so	zhang	chang
tian	tien	zhao	chao
tie	tieh	zhe	che

zhei	chei	zhui	chui
zhen	chen	zhun	chun
zheng	cheng	zhuo	cho
zhi	chih	zi	tzu, tsu
zhong	chung	zong	tsung
zhou	chou	zou	tsou
zhu	chu	zu	tsu
zhua	chua	zuan	tsuan
zhuai	chuai	zui	tsui
zhuan	chuan	zun	tsun
zhuang	chuang	zuo	tso

ACKNOWLEDGEMENTS

I am indebted to Professor Constance Yang for her careful reading of the entire manuscript. Her superb knowledge of English and her insightful interpretation of classical Chinese have brightened these pages.

Thanks are due also to Robert Day, Barry King, Alison Juram, Herbert Eisenberg and Audrey Sasaki who read my earlier drafts and provided excellent suggestions.

I greatly appreciate the warm support from Xu Mingqiang, editor-in-chief of the Foreign Languages Press of Beijing, China, and I am deeply grateful to Shen Jun, senior editor of the English Division of the Press, who graciously agreed to stay on to be my editor even though retired. I admire her youthful energy and plenteous enthusiasm. Her understanding, thoughtfulness, and hospitality are an author's dream.

I also wish to thank Wu Ying, deputy editor-in-chief of Shanghai Translation Publishing House, whose encouragement was of great value, as was the help from Mary Shao, Zhou Jiaji, and Zhou Zhonghui.

The Yenching Library of Harvard University, C.V. Starr East Asian Library of Columbia University, and the Chinese Information and Cultural Center Library in New York rendered invaluable assistance in the course of my writing.

The illustrations are the creations of the following prominent Chinese artists:

Dai Dunbang, Chinese portraitist and frequent award-winner who has illustrated well-known Chinese classics such as *A Dream of the Red Mansions*, *The Water Margin*, etc.;

Ding Cong, Chinese cartoonist whose satirical works were cited in the *Fortune* magazine in as early as 1945, and in the *New York Times* and the *Time* magazine in 1990;

Chen Huiguan, renowned Chinese illustrator whose works not only have won prizes domestically, but have been exhibited internationally, together with works by contemporary Italian masters;

Gao Yonghui, Chinese artist of the realistic school whose specialty lies in fine, delicate detail; and

Lan Renjie, Chinese wood engraving artist whose works have been placed in international wood print exhibitions.

The dynasty chart is the product of the deft software work of Polly F. Kimmit, a graphic artist whose talent matches her enthusiasm.

Above all, it is the loving memory of my grandfather and grandmother that inspired me to write the book, and the steadfast support of my parents, my sister, Tang Ruihua, and my brothers, Tang Duo and Tang Jian, proved essential in guiding it to completion.

图书在版编目(CIP)数据

中国古代才智故事:英文/(美)唐庆华编著.
—北京:外文出版社, 1996
ISBN 7-119-01860-4
ISBN 7-119-01861-2

Ⅰ.中… Ⅱ.唐… Ⅲ.①故事-中国-英文
②英语-语言读物 Ⅳ.H319.4

中国版本图书馆 CIP 数据核字 (96) 第 02992 号
中国版本图书馆 CIP 数据核字 (96) 第 03738 号

责任编辑 沈　峻
封面设计 蔡　荣
插图绘制 戴敦邦
陈惠冠
丁　聪
蓝人杰
高永慧

中国古代才智故事
唐庆华
*

外文出版社出版
(中国北京百万庄大街 24 号)
邮政编码 100037
北京外文印刷厂印刷
中国国际图书贸易总公司发行
(中国北京车公庄西路 35 号)
北京邮政信箱第 399 号　邮政编码 100044
1996 年(大 32 开)第 1 版
(英)
ISBN 7-119-01860-4 /I·419(外)
03980 (精)
ISBN 7-119-01861-2 /I·420(外)
02980 (平)
10-E-3090